The Shipping Revolution

The Shipping Revolution

The Modern Merchant Ship

Editor: Robert Gardiner

Consultant Editor: Alastair Couper MA, PhD, FRICS, FNI, FCIT, Master Mariner

Naval Institute Press

Series Consultant DR BASIL GREENHILL
CB, CMG, FSA, FRHistS

Series Editor ROBERT GARDINER

Consultant Editor PROFESSOR ALASTAIR COUPER, MA, PhD,
FRICS, FNI, FCIT, Master Mariner

Contributors PROFESSOR P ALDERTON
PROFESSOR HEE SEOK BANG
SHANNON BENTLEY
CAPTAIN LAWSON W BRIGHAM
DR A G CORBET
PROFESSOR A COUPER
CAPTAIN STEVEN CROSS
DR CHRIS DAVIES
PROFESSOR DOUGLAS FLEMING
CAPTAIN V R GIBSON
PROFESSOR SYDNEY GILMAN
DR DAVID HILLING
JIM KEARON
PROFESSOR JOHN KING
PROFESSOR JACQUES MARCADON
PROFESSOR BRUCE E MARTI
PROFESSOR CHARLES E MATHIEU
BARRY E PECK
DR HANCE SMITH
CAPTAIN JOHN STRANGE
DR A D TRAILL

Frontispiece: the world's largest dry cargo ship, the 364,767 dwt ore carrier Berge Stahl, *is part of the fleet owned by Bergesen dy AS, Norway, which in 1992 totalled 9,221,000 dwt in service or under construction. Built by Hyundai Heavy Industries, of South Korea, in 1986,* Berge Stahl *has a length of 343m and breadth of 63.5m. The ore cargo capacity is 199,324cu m. Long-term employment for the vessel is guaranteed as upon completion it commenced a 10-year charter carrying iron ore between Brazil and Rotterdam. Each year the vessel will convey about four million tons of ore destined for German steel works. Whilst there are a few ore carriers of over 300,000 dwt in service,* Berge Stahl *is by far the largest, the next being the same owner's 1992-built ore carrier* Bergeland *(320,000 dwt).* (Bergesen dy AS)

© Conway Maritime Press Ltd 1992

First published in Great Britain 1992 by
Conway Maritime Press Ltd
101 Fleet Street
London EC4Y 1DE

Published and distributed in the United States
of America and Canada by the Naval Institute
Press, Annapolis, Maryland 21402

Library of Congress Catalog Card No. 92–82833

ISBN 1–55750–765–1

Manufactured in Great Britain

Contents

Preface

THIS volume is the third of the *History of the Ship* series, an ambitious programme of twelve volumes intended to provide the first detailed and comprehensive account of a technology that has shaped human history. It has been conceived as a basic reference work, the essential first stop for anyone seeking information on any aspect of the subject, so it is more concerned to be complete than to be original. However, the series takes full account of all the latest research and in certain areas will be publishing entirely new material. In the matter of interpretation care has been taken to avoid the old myths and to present only the most widely accepted modern viewpoints.

To tell a coherent story, in a more readable form than is usual with encyclopaedias, each volume takes the form of independent chapters, all by recognised authorities in the field. Most chapters are devoted to a ship type, but others deal with topics like 'Shipbuilding' or 'Propulsion' that relate to many ship types, thus avoiding repetition and giving added depth to the reader's understanding of developments. Some degree of generalisation is inevitable when tackling a subject of this breadth, but wherever possible the specific details of ships and their characteristics have been included (a table of typical ships for each relevant chapter includes a convenient summary of data from which the reader can chart the evolution of the ship type concerned). Except for the earliest craft, the series is confined to sea-going vessels; to have included boats would have increased the scope of an already massive task.

The history of the ship is not a romanticised story of epic battles and heroic voyages but equally it is not simply a matter of technological advances. Ships were built to carry out particular tasks and their design was as much influenced by the experience of that employment – the lessons or war, or the conditions of trade, for example – as purely technical innovation. Throughout this series an attempt has been made to keep this clearly in view, to describe the *what* and *when* of developments without losing sight of the *why*.

The series is aimed at those with some knowledge of, and interest in, ships and the sea. It would have been impossible to make a contribution of any value to the subject if it had been pitched at the level of the complete novice, so while there is an extensive glossary, for example, it assumes an understanding of the most basic nautical terms. Similarly, the bibliography avoids very general works and concentrates on those which will broaden or deepen the reader's understanding beyond the level of the *History of the Ship*. The intention is not to inform genuine experts in their particular area of expertise, but to provide them with the best available single-volume summaries of less familiar fields.

Each volume is chronological in approach, with the periods covered getting shorter as the march of technology quickens, but organised around a dominant theme – represented by the title – that sums up the period in question. In this way each book is fully self-sufficient, although when completed the twelve titles will link up to form a coherent history, chronicling the progress of ship design from its earliest recorded forms to the present day.

Robert Gardiner
Series Editor

The Shipping Revolution

After centuries of slow change in ship technology the shift from wind to steam power during the nineteenth century was one of the greatest revolutions in the history of shipping. Apart from the growth in Blue-Riband and emigration passenger liners this was followed by almost a century of only gradual changes in cargo ship propulsion, instrumentation, and cargo handling equipment; and by incremental increases in the speed and size of ships. The next major revolution took place between about 1960 and the 1980s, and had almost as profound an effect as the transfer from sail to steam.

The late twentieth-century technological revolution brought with it a decline in both traditional tramp vessels and break bulk conventional cargo liners, and saw the virtual disappearance of the long distance passenger ship as the airlines took over. At the same time there was a tremendous increase in the size of many ships, the emergence of a range of specialised cargo carriers, new types of ferries and dedicated holiday cruise vessels, and the spread of the revolutionary technology of container and roro systems world-wide.

The principal chapters in this volume detail the results of the second shipping revolution in the design and functions of modern cargo and passenger merchant ships, as well as the new offshore industries support vessels, fishing craft and other non-cargo vessels that emerged at that time. The related developments in ship building, propulsion, navigation and equipment, and the ownership of vessels are discussed as separate short chapters. The appendices of the book provide a glossary of terms and a bibliography. We start with an overview of world shipping and the shipping revolution against the background of the changing operational environment in the period from the 1960s onward.

A D Couper
Consultant Editor

Introduction

MERCHANT ships have two main functions. They are the servants of trade, and relate in their designs and patterns of movement to the commodity supply and demand needs of the world. Merchant ships are also business ventures and reflect the financial decisions of owners and managers. The first objective influences the second but does not dictate it. Owners will order ships, accept cargoes and follow routes to the extent that these are profitable and safe. The background to their financial decisions is the operational environment. This has many uncertain variables, ranging from climatic conditions to politics, and is subject to sudden changes well beyond the control of individual managers. During the postwar shipping revolution the operational environment was particularly dynamic. Before referring to these influences on contemporary ships some basic facts on the size, ownership and trading tasks of the world's fleet as a whole are outlined.

Trends in the world fleet

The world fleet of merchant vessels grew from 36,311 (129.7 million grt) in 1960 to 78,336 (423.6 million grt) in 1990. The fleet comprises many hundreds of types of vessel (Appendix 1), but broadly there are nine main categories. The 1989 tonnage divisions of these are shown in Table 1.

Almost half of the world merchant fleet in 1989 was controlled by enterprises in five countries, namely Greece, Japan, the United States, Norway and the Soviet Union. Most of the rest of the fleet was divided between thirty other states, with the developing nations (excluding 'flag of convenience' countries) owning about 20 per cent of the total. Of this latter figure ten developing countries (primarily in Asia) owned over 90 per cent.

In order to establish the ownership of vessels by country, it is necessary to take into account ships registered under their national flags and ships of the country under foreign flags. This is illustrated in Table 2.

Non-national flags are used by shipowners to avoid national taxes, enable employment of lower cost non-national labour, and sometimes avoid national legislation and other restrictions. The main so called 'open registry', or 'flag of convenience' (FOC) states were in 1991: Liberia (93.6 million deadweight tonnes), Panama (72.1 million), Cyprus (36.5 million), Bahamas (28.8 million) and Bermuda (5.2 million). In addition some seventeen other states offer FOC facilities. In 1970 there was 41 million dwt (12.5 per cent of world fleet) in the open registry sector and in 1988 about 225 million dwt (35 per cent). A further development in these respects has been the 'offshore registries', whereby many of the advantages of FOC have been obtained while retaining national or quasi-national flags (see Chapter 13).

Trends in world seaborne trade

The function of the fleet of merchant ships is to provide spatial links in the world economy. More than 90 per cent of international trade by weight moves by sea transport. In 1956 seaborne trade equalled 900 million tons and in 1966 it was almost double that figure. Subsequent years are shown in Table 3.

The quantity of shipping required to carry out the trading functions is determined by both the tons of cargo to be carried and the distances over which it has to be carried (ton/miles). Any changes in one or both of these components will alter the demand for shipping. The ton/miles trends for principal types of cargo are shown in Table 4.

Table 2: Control of shipping by top four countries (1989)

| | Under national flag | | Under foreign flag | | Total owned | |
	No	dwt (m)	No	dwt (m)	No	dwt (m)
Greece	984	37.0	1312	43.1	2296	80.1
Japan	1212	35.8	1527	36.9	2739	72.8
United States	810	22.2	605	37.5	1415	59.8
Norway	679	24.6	498	21.8	1177	45.5

Source: UNCTAD 1990.

Table 1: World fleet of cargo and passenger vessels by deadweight (dwt) tonnage (millions) and percentage of total (1989)

Type	dwt	%
Oil tankers	248.3	38.0
Liquid gas carriers	10.3	1.6
Chemical carriers	5.8	0.9
Miscellaneous tankers	0.6	0.1
Bulk oil ships	37.8	5.8
Ore and bulk carriers	193.5	29.9
General cargo (including passenger/cargo)	104.1	16.1
Container ships	24.6	3.8
Ferries and passenger ships	2.9	0.5
All others	18.6	2.9

Source: UNCTAD 1990.

Table 3: World seaborne trade 1975–91 (millions tonnes)

Year	Crude oil	Oil products	Iron ore	Coal	Grain	Other cargo estimate	Total trade estimate
1975	1263	233	292	127	137	995	3047
1976	1410	260	294	127	146	1075	3312
1977	1451	273	276	132	147	1120	3399
1978	1432	270	278	127	169	1190	3466
1979	1497	279	327	159	182	1270	3714
1980	1320	276	314	188	198	1310	3606
1981	1170	267	303	210	206	1305	3461
1982	993	285	273	208	200	1240	3199
1983	930	282	257	197	199	1225	3090
1984	930	297	306	232	207	1320	3292
1985	871	288	321	272	181	1360	3293
1986	958	305	311	276	165	1370	3385
1987	970	313	319	283	186	1390	3461
1988	1042	325	348	304	196	1460	3675
1989	1120	340	362	321	192	1525	3860
1990	1190	336	347	342	192	1570	3977
1991 Est.	1200	323	352	360	180	1610	4025

Source: *Fearnley's Review*, 1991.

Table 4: World seaborne trade by types of cargo 1970–90 (billions tons/miles)

	Crude oil	Oil products	Iron ore	Coal	Grain	Other cargo	Total
1970	5597	890	1093	481	475	2118	10,654
1980	8385	1020	1613	952	1087	3720	16,797
1985	4007	1150	1675	1479	1004	3750	13,065
1990	6500	1500	1965	1905	1010	4510	17,390

Source: *Fearnley's Review*, 1991.

Factors in the shipping revolution

The changes which come about in the demand for various types of cargoes and their origins and destinations are major elements in the ship operational environment. It is the complex interactions of many underlying factors in this environment which have been the impetus behind management decisions leading to the

The multipurpose cargo vessel Saigonventure *epitomises the internationalism of shipping which has taken place during the shipping revolution. Beneficially owned by Danish company Baltimar ApS, Copenhagen, Saigonventure is registered with a Bahamas Company and flies that country's flag. Built in 1991 at Shanghai, by Zhonghua Shipyard, as Baltimar Zephyr, she was renamed for charter purposes operating between Singapore and Ho Chi Minh City, Vietnam.*

Baltimar embarked on a fleet expansion programme in 1986, and went to Republic of China shipyards for a long series of 'super coasters', which were delivered during 1987–92. Designed as multi-purpose carriers, with one hatch and one completely open hold, which is double-skinned and box shaped, the vessels can trade world-wide either as single decked bulk carriers, flush tweendeckers, or in a semi-container role. The flush tank top is also reinforced for grab handling, heavy and project cargoes, and containers (total capacity 256 TEUs). The majority of the vessels in this fleet are employed in the Far East and Australia. The vessels have a gross tonnage of 2850 and are equipped with three deck cranes each of 50 tonnes capacity and the majority operate in the Far East and Australasia.
(Baltimar ApS)

shipping revolution. For convenience, factors having a direct influence on shipping entrepreneurial decision-making are discussed under four headings. The bottom line always is, of course, economics.

Spatial relations

Under this heading it is useful to consider the spatial expression of the supply of and demand for commodities, that is the ways in which shifts in raw material sources, industrial processing and market locations in the world influence trade linkages and transport technology. These changes are superimposed on climatic and other geographic variables affecting agricultural production and domestic demand.

In the late 1950s a very important feature was the re-industrialisation of Japan. Subsequent Japanese rapid economic growth had an enormous impact on shipping. Japan has virtually no mineral resources, only 15 per cent or so of cultivatable land, a large population, and the country lies remote from supplies of oil and ores, as well as from the major markets in Europe and America. How Japan, under these circumstances and the devastation of the Second World War, managed to become one of the world's leading heavy industrial and high technology countries is a separate subject, but it did so very rapidly during the 1960s and '70s and in the process generated enormous demands for world-wide shipping services.

There were other marked spatial shifts within the world economy during this period. In North America much economic growth moved from the Great Lakes area and the eastern seaboard to the Pacific zone of California-Tacoma-Seattle-Vancouver. There emerged

also by the 1970s accelerated developments at the other side of the Pacific with the rise of the newly-industrialised countries (NICs) of Hong Kong, Taiwan, South Korea and Singapore, thereby generating additional cross-Pacific trade.

In Europe the relationships between the Netherlands, Belgium, France and Britain and their former overseas colonies had by then been drastically weakened, as had the demand in Britain for the output of Australasian agriculture. There was a redirection of agricultural and manufacturing trades on an intra-EEC basis. At the same time the demand for overseas minerals increased in Europe with the depletion of local resources. More ore and coal inputs were now drawn from Brazil, West Africa, North America and Australia. Other raw material source shifts came in the 1960s and '70s with the opening of new oilfields in the North Sea and the North America Arctic regions; although these did not reduce inputs from Middle East sources.

In this period some industrial locations and manufacturing processes were shifting. Technological improvements in the manufacture of steel and other metals meant that less raw material inputs were required per unit of output; and more semi-processing began taking place closer to raw material sources before exporting. There were further trends to the miniaturisation of electronic goods, as well as shifts in the location of assembly activities in manufacturing by multinationals to take advantage of cost differentials at widely separated locations – and especially in the process relations between Japanese industry and the lower labour cost countries of southeast Asia.

The period of the 1960s and '70s was thus

Shipping is still influenced by the physical restrictions of the world's principal waterways, and in particular the lock dimensions of the Panama and Suez Canals, which give rise to the descriptions 'Panamax' and 'Suezmax' for the largest designs that can be accommodated. Pictured here in the Panama Canal is the Panamax size (breadth 32.25m) third generation containership Selandia, *built in 1972 for East Asiatic Co of Denmark and with a capacity of 2512 TEUs. In 1984, together with the sister-ship* Jutlandia, *she was lengthened at the Hyundai Mipo Dockyard, Ulsan, and the addition of a new cargo section increased the capacity to 2774 TEUs. Gross tonnage was increased from 49,890 to 54,035.* (East Asiatic Co)

characterised by many complex geographical changes in the linkages between raw materials, industries and markets. The globalisation of manufacturing and the high inventory costs of many cargoes, meant greater emphasis was placed on the speed and predictability of delivery, and this affected the type as well as the volume of shipping demanded.

Strategic

Merchant shipping is inevitably affected by strategic factors, even when ships are from neutral states. The main impacts of wars, in addition to loss of life of merchant seamen, are on freight rates and the routeing of vessels. These often result in increased distances in world seaborne trade, creating a shortage of vessels, a consequent rise in freight rates and shipbuilding orders and prices, and a stimulus to new types of equipment and ships. Governments are also influenced by these events in the support they give to merchant fleets for military transportation requirements and continued guarantees of shipping supply during crises.

The major events in respect of the above have been in the Middle East – especially when the Suez Canal has been closed. This occurred during 1956–57, and between 1967 and 1973. The average distance from Europe to the oil ports of the Arabian/Persian Gulf is 6000 miles via the canal, and 11,000 miles by the Cape route. During the Middle East conflicts pipelines from the Gulf region oilfields to Mediterranean loading installations were also closed, leading again to longer voyages for crude oil.

Political and legal

Most ship-owning states have, in varying degrees, supported their merchant shipping. These have been political decisions based on economics (balance of payments and employment) and prestige, as well as strategic considerations.

There have also been international political dimensions to the attempts by countries to preserve their dominance in shipping, or to gain entry. The main arena for this has been the United Nations Conference on Trade and Development (UNCTAD). The shipping division at UNCTAD has, since 1964, concentrated many of its activities towards assisting developing countries achieve more control over the shipping services operating to and from their ports. This is in line with the general objective of UNCTAD to reduce the disparity between rich and poor countries. Outcomes have included the International Convention on the

Code of Conduct for Liner Conferences, which, amongst other things, provides for an equable sharing of liner conference cargoes between the ships of importing and exporting countries.

The International Labour Organization (ILO) has also been influential in shipping. ILO conventions include the International Convention Concerning the Minimum Standards in Merchant Ships (1978).

Of all the United Nations agencies, it is the International Maritime Organisation (IMO) which has exerted the greatest influence through international conventions on the design and equipment of merchant ships. These include the Load Line Convention (1968); Tonnage Measurement (1969); Safety of Life at Sea (SOLAS, 1980) and Prevention of Pollution from Ships (MARPOL 1973/78).

As well as conventions, IMO has introduced important codes which have influenced ship designs. There is the Code for the Construction and Equipment of Ships Carrying Dangerous Chemicals in Bulk (1971), and the Code for Mobile Drilling Rigs. Fishing vessels are covered by the Torremolinos Convention on Safety (1977).

All of the United Nations facilitated maritime conventions are multilateral and represent minimum standards. Occasionally, individual states legislate requirements on ship structures and equipment and apply these to foreign vessels calling at their ports or navigating in adjacent sea areas. Canada, for example, introduced a requirement in 1970 for special

The period since the 1960s has seen an increasing variety of specialist merchant ships developed, some of considerable sophistication. One such was the LPG (liquified petroleum gas) carrier Isocardia, *one of a pair built for Shell Tankers (UK) Ltd by Harland & Wolff, Belfast in 1982. Of 47,594 dwt, the ship was designed to transport liquified gas from the North Sea fields. The movement of hazardous or environmentally dangerous commodities has led to ever more rigorous international legal and political conventions.* (FotoFlite)

construction standards for vessels navigating in the Canadian Arctic. In the course of time this was incorporated into multilateral agreements (including the 1982 Convention on the Law of the Sea). On the other hand, the unilateral declaration by the United States (after the 1989 *Exxon Valdez* disaster) which required tankers calling at US ports to have double hulls, was initially regarded by many shipowners as departing too far from attempts to keep regulations unified on a world-wide basis by international conventions. On the other hand, such unilateral moves often result in subsequent multilateral conventions, and the US action brought such a response.

The role of classification societies

Many of the international conventions are of a general nature. These have to be further detailed for design and construction purposes. Important in this respect are the ship classification societies. The societies, most of which predate the international agencies, draw up safety rules for construction, and will act on behalf of owners and governments in carrying out surveys which will ensure ships are kept to these standards and 'in class'. During the shipping revolution new classification rules had to be continuously developed. Although classification is not a legal requirement over ninety per cent of the world fleet is classed. Amongst other things classification is very important for the insurance of ships and their cargoes.

The oldest and largest classification society is Lloyd's Register (1760). There are also Bureau Veritas (1828 France); American Bureau of Shipping (1862); Det Norske Veritas (1864); Germanischer Lloyd (1867); Registro Italiano Navale (1861) and Nippon Kaiji Kyokai (Japan 1899). There are also classification societies in the Commonwealth of Independent States (the former USSR Register of Shipping), South Korea (Korean Register of Shipping) and Poland (Polski Rijestr Statkow) which although formed in relatively recent times handle a very large number of vessels. With the increased concern for safety at sea and protection of the marine environment, the principal charterers and users of shipping expect ships to be kept up to standard through the societies.

Perceptions of market behaviour

Shipowners determine the numbers, types and designs of the ships they want partly in response to a combination of the factors outlined above. Of utmost importance are their perceptions of market behaviour. This involves assessing risks and uncertainties, especially when a ship's life has to extend for fifteen to twenty years.

The difficulties in predicting market behaviour may be appreciated from the major changes which have taken place in the recent past: in the 1960s there was steady growth of markets in the United States and Japan for raw materials and consumer goods. The 1970s saw regional wars and two oil crises, and in 1973 oil prices soared with decisions at OPEC (Organization of Petroleum Exporting Countries). During the 1980s there was a fall in oil prices until they rose again in 1986, then becoming unstable with wars in the Middle East.

In the mid 1950s a 35,000 dwt tanker was considered of 'super' size. The early 1960s saw 100,000-tonners and the crises in the early 1970s brought more decisions to build bigger vessels for the Cape route, although by then the 200,000-ton mark had been passed. The advantages of further economies of scale were then realised; new shipbuilding capacity emerged in Asia and tankers of 300,000 dwt and upwards to over 500,000 dwt came rapidly on to the shipping market.

The 1973 oil price increases led to a reduction in demand for petroleum and a decline in world commodity markets generally. The world fleet went on expanding, as previous shipbuilding orders were being fulfilled and governments of shipbuilding countries offered subsidies to ensure further work. This resulted in a massive over-supply of ships, allied to increased fuel costs and, in many cases, rising crew costs.

Shipowners responded to the events of the 1970s and '80s (which were accompanied by falling freight rates) by attempts at cost reductions. Several of these were reflected in new ship designs and equipment. These included more economies of scale in liners; retrofitting ships with more economic means of propulsion, introducing labour saving equipment, restructuring and reducing crews, as well as transferring ships to flags of convenience to facilitate cheaper crewing and tax avoidance. In the most capital intensive sector, container shipping, emphasis was put on the economies of scale and maximising the speed of turn round in port.

Apart from the unitised sector, shipbuilding orders slowed down and many shipyards went out of business, some of them long-established. In 1984, for example, only 2.5 million dwt of tankers was launched. By 1990 there was recovery with 23 million dwt launched. The total of all ships on order in that year reached 40 million dwt. However, building prices had more than doubled in the intervening years.

Some shipowners in 1990 were, judging by their ordering strategies, clearly looking ahead to a continued rise in world markets. In any event, most of the ships built during the late 1960s and early '70s boom were coming to the end of their economic life. A common perception was that the 1990s would be an era of ship replacement.

The question that really needed to be answered was, what types of ships would be required for the next two decades? There were a number of likely and postulated changes in the operational environment that would need to be taken into account in order to find some answers to this question.

New factors for the 1990s

The new political factors that were evident for the 1990s included East/West détente; EC Market integration; US/Canada free trade; and the relaxing of trade sanctions with South Africa. There was also speculation on the future of farm support subsidies (on the grain market), General Agreement on Tariffs and Trade (GATT) Rounds, and the future of the restructured economies of the former Soviet Union and eastern Europe.

On the major commodity markets, there were views that the United States, as the biggest consumer of petroleum, would increase its proportion of oil imports, due to exhaustion and conservation of national resources. Iron ore, the next major bulk commodity, was not expected to expand in seaborne trade partly because of technological advances in steel making which would continue to reduce raw material inputs per ton of output.

Concern for the environment was seen in 1990 as likely to have a significant effect on industry in the future, and consequently on the demand for shipping. Coal use seemed likely to be reduced in order to lessen acid rain and carbon dioxide emissions. On the other hand, natural gas would probably be favoured as a clean source of energy.

The assessments of political changes, commodity supply and demand, and all of the other factors which make up the inputs to forecasts do not, of course, take the place of the final decisions as to the type, dimensions, speed, consumption and other features of a merchant vessel. The final decision in that regard is made by managers, and is a matter of how they perceive the future and degrees of risk they are willing to take.

A number of trends could be discerned in the decisions of managers in the early 1990s. Ships were being designed for minimum crewing, several reefer vessels of 14,500 dwt, for example, were already built to be operated by a crew of six. Some small very fast vessels capable of carrying over 1000 tonnes of cargo at 50kts plus were under design in Japan. These would link processing and assembly plants in southeast Asia on the 'just-in-time' principle adopted for high value shipments. Increased emphasis was also being placed on more environmentally friendly innovations in the design of tankers and chemical carriers, including double hulls and other structural improvements. There was also experimentation going on regarding submarine cargo vessels constructed of concrete for Arctic transpolar routes below the ice.

The shipping revolution had slowed down by the 1990s, and its main elements were established, but it was not totally over. The chapters in this book detail the main events and implications of the revolution in the history of the ship.

A D Couper

1

Modern Tramp Ships, Bulk Carriers and Combination Carriers

ACENTURY ago the typical tramp steamship was a rather small coal-burner whose peregrinations and scruffy appearance conformed, in fact, to one's image of the homeless wanderer.[1] The impression of aimless wandering was quite misleading, however; there was always the purpose of providing a needed, reasonably-priced, shipping service for the movements of various foodstuffs and raw materials, often moving in bulk. Despite the impression of 'vagrancy', as the ships moved in and out of various trades, the selection of charter contracts and itineraries was really quite purposeful. The tramp owner was seeking profitable patterns of operation. As Sargent observed long ago, steamship lines were not worked for purposes of philanthropy but to pay dividends.[2]

Modern tramp ships must be defined primarily by the market they serve and the service they provide, for size and appearance mean very little.[3] A market-orientated classification scheme leads to a broad differentiation between liner vessels on fixed schedules in markets requiring a steady supply of shipping service and tramp ships irregularly serving sporadic needs. In this chapter there is a narrower distinction between the tramp vessel that competes in an open market to accommodate the spot demands of a shipper

for transporting a dry bulk commodity and the bulk carrier entering a more confidential market to serve the constant needs of a specific shipper for the steady movement of a dry bulk commodity on a specific route.[4] Tankers, dedicated to liquid bulk cargoes, serve another market and are discussed in Chapter 4.

In recent decades, many bulk trades have developed far beyond the sporadic tramp shipment phase into heavy volume, continuous cargo flows. Long ago, in observation of a vessel ready to load Welsh coal, the novelist William McFee seemed to capture the essence of the high-volume bulk trades:

> She was no longer a sentient thing in the sea, she had become but a line in the shipping news, a factor on the Exchange. There she had not even a name, she was simply a semi-hypothetical capacity, '8000 tons, Las Palmas, 8s.3d.', a bucket in the endless distribution chain that creeps across the world.[5]

In the modern era, bulk carrier service in the heavy volume bulk commodity trades is often synonymous with what is known as industrial carrier service.[6] Either by direct purchase or by long-term charters, large industrial corporations have acquired control of proprietary fleets of bulk carriers to serve their own ocean transport needs and, they hope, control their own transport costs.

In many respects ocean shipping has

1. L C Kendall, *The Business of Shipping* (Cornell Maritime Press, 1973; 5th edn, 1986), p12.

2. A J Sargent, *Seaways of the Empire* (A & C Black, 1918; 2nd edn, 1930), p15.

3. A D Couper, *The Geography of Sea Transport* (Hutchinson, 1972), p90.

4. B N Metaxas, *The Economics of Tramp Shipping* (Athlone Press, 1971), p4.

5. W McFee, *Casuals of the Sea* (Random House, 1931), p361.

6. S A Lawrence, *International Sea Transport: The Years Ahead* (Lexington Books, 1972), pp87–9.

Between 1945 and about 1970 the British merchant fleet included many tramp vessels which were often taken up on charter by liner companies. One example is the steamer Dunelmia, *owned by Metcalfe, Son & Co, West Hartlepool. Of 4907 grt, and with a slow 11kt service speed, she is here in service with Clan Line Steamers Ltd. Completed in June 1952 by Wm Gray & Co Ltd, Hartlepool, builders of hundreds of tramp vessels,* Dunelmia *carried around 8500 tons of general cargo, and was equipped with eleven derricks of 3 to 10 tons capacity. (R W Jordan)*

Burma Five Star Shipping Corp, Rangoon, was founded in 1960 and by 1964 owned a modest fleet of cargo liners trading to northwest Europe. Since then the fleet has been continually modernised and joining in 1983 was Pago, *a German-built cargo liner of 13,105 dwt. This vessel has four hatches and four holds served by six 25-tons cranes, and can carry 18,829cu m of general cargo or 383 TEUs including 24 refrigerated units. In 1989 Burma became Myanmar, the company became Myanmar Five Star Line, and Rangoon is now known as Yangon.* (FotoFlite)

accompanied other industries and services into the age of specialisation. Even so, multipurpose vessels of simple, standard design and comparatively modest size still form an essential core of some operators' fleets. These versatile ships can be moved from one type of service to another in response to shifts of market demand and the shipowners' various perceptions of 'good business'. Thus a tramp ship can sometimes be time-chartered into liner service or a liner vessel shifted temporarily to irregular tramp trading. A steel company's bulk carrier can be fixed on short term charter to accommodate a spot demand in another bulk commodity or tramp trade.

A typical general cargo tramp vessel of the 1960s was the 10,022 grt motor vessel Hopecrag, *owned by Hopemount Shipping Co Ltd, Newcastle, one-time home port of numerous vessels of this type. Apart from worldwide tramping,* Hopecrag *was occasionally involved in charter to liner companies, with a useful 13,965 dwt service speed of 16kts produced by a Barclay-Curle/ Sulzer diesel of 7500 bhp. She was built by Barclay, Curle & Co at Glasgow and completed in August 1963.* (R W Jordan)

Vessel types do not, therefore, match type of service in clear unambiguous fashion. Again, however, a market-orientated explanation of tramp and bulk carrier service helps one identify typical characteristics of vessel design, operating patterns, methods of pricing, systems of ownership and management philosophies.

Service characteristics

Tramp service

Tramp operators whose fortunes derive from spot movements of various dry cargoes find the

general-purpose or unspecialised vessel type quite suitable for many tramp trades.[7] The versatility and modest size of the 'Liberty' and 'Empire' type ships of the 1940s and the SD-14, 'Freedom' and 'Fortune' types of more recent vintage have been prized by tramp owners needing vessels with the flexibility to move in and out of a variety of transoceanic trades.

Long ago tramp vessels gravitated to the grain, coal and ore trades. In the modern era there has been a proliferation of other tramp cargo types – fertilisers, scrap, sugar, forest products, and the like – that often move in full-

7. A E Branch, *Elements of Shipping* (Chapman & Hall, 1964; 6th edn, 1989), pp45–7; Metaxas, *op cit*, p6; Kendall, *op cit*, pp20–1.

Since the early days of its independence from the Netherlands, the Republic of Indonesia has maintained an ocean-going merchant fleet, mainly in liner trades to Europe, North America and Japan. Joining Indonesia's modern fleet in 1982 was Ganda Bhakti *(10,179 grt), owned by PT Gesuri Lloyd. This vessel was one of two built in Italy by Italcantieri SpA, Monfalcone. With a capability to carry roro, bulk and container cargoes, and vegetable oil or latex in deep tanks, these were true multi-purpose vessels. A quarter stern door and ramp serves the roro facility, 600 TEUs are carried on deck, and the alternative bulk cargo is a maximum 27,419cu m. The vessel is well served by six cranes ranging from 15 to 35 tons.* (FotoFlite)

cargo lots. The typical tramp cargo is grain in bulk, with movements that fluctuate seasonally and from one year to another in accordance with harvest yields, food procurement needs, market prices, government edicts, import levies, embargoes and so forth. A variety of natural and human hazards effect this trade and give special significance to the concept of 'spot movement'.[8]

Grain and other favoured bulk cargoes for tramps share the characteristic of 'uni-directionality'. They are moving in one geographically specific direction and very often there is no direct return cargo lift, certainly not the same bulk commodity moving in the reverse direction. In contrast, two-way flows of liner cargoes, albeit sometimes directionally imbalanced in actual volume, are not un-common. The one-way cargo flows in the tramp trade strongly influence the geographical configurations of tramp shipping – that is, the tramp ship's itineraries and patterns of operation. After a voyage laden with revenue-paying cargo the tramp vessel must almost always proceed in ballast, sometimes very long distances, to the next one-directional tramp cargo trade. Tramps, as Sargent put it, tend to 'disappear' from a route since they are under no obligation to provide a regular or return service and they are in quest of new spot business.[9]

Typically, tramp service is very sensitive to market demand.[10] Typically, also, and in contrast to liner trades, it has been low-cost service, although the tramp operator is not shy about extracting a premium rate from a charterer when the operator has the only ship properly positioned for a particular voyage. The freight rate assigned to a tramp cargo movement is negotiated between ocean carrier and commodity shipper, that is between their respective commissioned chartering brokers, often at one of the three great chartering centres, namely, London, Tokyo, New York.

Here empty ships are continually match-ed with full cargoes at voyage charter rates that reflect the momentary needs for ship-ping space, the availability of ships and the general conditions of world markets, not to mention the idiosyncrasies of negotiators and their principals.[11] The theoretical model of perfect competition generally applies to these spot market dealings. There can be wide fluctuations in freight rates, an important feature of tramp service pricing and a function, especially, of the perpetual geographical variations of tramp shipping supply and demand.[12] On average, however, it is a low cost service since it does not have the regularity, frequency and certainty that shippers using liner service, in comparison, are willing to pay for.

An adventurous capitalist in Norway, for instance, or in Greece, has been able to enter the tramp shipping industry at modest initial investment – perhaps gaining a small percentage ownership of a single tramp vessel. One of the main sources of supply of tramp service has been the relatively small and independent shipping firm often with very low on-shore overheads. There is, however, a wide range in size of firms and their fleets. Some very large companies contain both liner and tramp divisions. On the whole tramp operators are profit seekers, and whether managing either one ship or several score, they are seeking remunerative cargoes, geographically efficient itineraries and profitable patterns of operation.

Because of the world-wide scope of the tramp trades and the constant tendency to move in and out of different trades the flavour of the tramp industry is truly international and often without the national 'flag-waving' of the liner trade. The tramp owner is usually seeking the most cost-efficient, convenient and tax-lenient places to finance, build, register, insure, crew, provision, fuel, repair and operate the

ships, although cost-shaving efforts need, of course, to be tempered by marketing considerations – that is, proper responses to customer needs.

The business careers of several of the fabled Greek and Norwegian shipping magnates began in tramp operations and reflected, in essence, an international quest for comparative advantages wherever they could be found. Eventually as their fleets grew and their long term shipping contracts developed, they graduated from tramp to bulk carrier service.[13] They were, by commercial affinities, truly international citizens.

Bulk carrier service

The revival and, then, spectacular growth of European, Asian and American industrial economies in postwar times greatly increased the need for a steady, low cost supply of shipping space, especially to accommodate the ores and mineral fuels that were essential industrial inputs. Independent shipping entrepreneurs, industrial corporations and government industries or agencies all responded to these needs, placing orders for specialised bulk carriers in Swedish, British and, by the 1950s, German, Japanese and other shipyards.[14] The astounding increase of this bulk carrier fleet, in numbers and in individual ship dimensions, has been monitored

8. D Morgan, *Merchants of Grain* (Viking Press, 1979), p28.

9. Sargent, *op cit*, pp18–19.

10. Kendall, *op cit*, p14.

11. D K Fleming, 'The Independent Transport Carrier in Ocean Tramp Trades', *Economic Geography* 44, No. 1 (Jan 1968), p23.

12. Metaxas, *op cit*, p18.

13. E D Naess, *Autobiography of a Shipping Man* (Seatrade, 1977).

14. Naess, *op cit*, pp137–41; Lawrence, *op cit.*, pp89–92.

A typical medium-size geared bulk carrier of the 1960s was Cape St Vincent *(20,022 dwt), owned by Lyle Shipping Co Ltd, Glasgow, and completed by John Brown & Co, Clydebank, in June 1966. Lyle Shipping Co, like many other owners involved in general cargo tramp shipping changed the make-up of their fleets to bulkers in the 1960s and '70s. Its five hatches were served by an 8-ton derrick (no 1), and twin 7.5-ton cranes (Nos 2–3, 4–5). The Brown/Sulzer 9600 bhp diesel engine gave a speed of 15.5kts. (R W Jordan collection)*

discussed also in Chapter 4 but their role in dry cargo movements is relevant here.

Since industrial carrier service is, by and large, an intracorporate phenomenon the establishment of a price for this service is a private corporate matter. In a sense the market has been completely closed, in extreme contrast to the tramp market. The company wants to control its own transportation function. One would expect an 'at-cost' operation, subject to variations of corporate book-keeping. 'Profits' in the shipping division are not the point, but voyage-cost

statistically by various shipping market analysts.[15]

The operating patterns of single purpose bulk carriers tend to be less complex than those of the general purpose tramp. The *raison d'être* of the large dry bulk carrier is to move large quantities of a bulk commodity over a regular route over regular time periods.[16] Industrial carrier service, a very important subset of bulk carrier service, implies that the commodity shipper is primarily attending to his own transportation needs. Sometimes this leads to spending half the vessel's steaming time in ballast, carrying Australian ore to Japan, for instance, and ballasting all the way back. The capture of very significant economies of scale, both in building and operating large bulk carriers, pays for a lot of ballasting, however.[17]

Sometimes the industrial carrier will move from its own regularly assigned route to accommodate some other shipper's demand for shipping space in an entirely different trade. In other words the voyage can be extended to incorporate a 'tramp segment',

thereby cutting down the percentage of total voyage time in ballast. If this incorporated segment is arranged by long term contract of affreightment with another commodity shipper that really signifies industrial carrier service too, only with another corporation controlling the shipping. To serve extended multiple-trade itineraries the multi-purpose bulk carriers, for example the ore/oil and ore/bulk/oil (OBO) vessel types, have proved useful.[18] These are

15. Fearnleys, *World Bulk Trades 1988* (Fearnleys); *Fearnleys Review 1989*; *World Bulk Carrier Fleet*, July 1988 (Fearnleys); H Clarkson & Co Ltd, *The World Tanker and Bulk Carrier Fleets* (Clarkson Research Studies Ltd, July 1988); Simpson, Spence & Young, *SS & Y Annual Shipping Review*.

16. Metaxas, *op cit*, p79.

17. G Manners, *The Changing World Market for Iron Ore 1950–1980* (Johns Hopkins University Press, 1971), pp180–1.

18. Lawrence, *op cit*, pp89–92.

The size of bulk carriers rapidly advanced in the 1960s and vessels of over 60,000 dwt were quite common. An example is Grischuna *(60,639 dwt), owned in Chur, Switzerland, under Liberian registration and managed from Lausanne. Employed exclusively in the grain trades,* Grischuna *was built in Japan in 1968 and was powered by a Uraga/Sulzer diesel of 17,600 bhp giving a speed of 16.25kts. (Suisse-Atlantique)*

minimisation and maximisation of the annual work capacity of the fleet are important objectives. Some of the giant single purpose bulk carriers built for heavy volume trades have the lowest ton-mile operating costs to be found in the shipping world today.[19]

To ensure an adequate supply of low-cost shipping space industrial corporations may have to supplement their fleet with vessels taken on long term time charter or consecutive voyage charter or contracts of affreightment specifying a certain amount of shipping space over a certain interval of time. These additional chartered ships, both single and multi-purpose bulk carriers, come from independent shipowners who still own a large portion of the world's bulk carrier fleet.[20] Although commissioned brokers are assigned to these negotiations there is usually very careful co-ordination, also, between major principals. The industrial corporation has externalised its transactions to deal with the independent shipowner. When there is close rapport between shipper and shipowner, there can be a sharing of expertise, to considerable mutual benefit. Then, in a real sense, bulk carrier service becomes a 'joint venture'.[21]

Through ingenious financing and ship-building programmes coupled with clever contractual strategies the storied shipping tycoons have built up large bulk carrier fleets. Some of these vessels have been operated as tramps on spot business but most of them, under charter contract, have been placed under the long term scheduling and routeing control of major industrial corporations or of government agencies involved in raw material procurement.

'Open registries', notably Liberian and Panamanian, have been widely used by the bulk carrier operators. The latter have shopped around internationally to find the desired balance of low cost and dependable quality. The issues of where to build, register, man and manage the ships are always on management's agenda.

The management philosophies behind tramp and bulk carrier service are not really alike. In simple terms the tramp operator looks for voyage profits in an open, ever-changing market, whereas the bulk carrier looks for reliability and cost-efficiencies in a steady, controlled market. In some of the most successful 'joint ventures' between in-dependent carriers and major bulk com-modity shippers the entrepreneurial ship-owner offers a 'tramp-like' imagination, flexibility, and sensitivity to market change while the commodity shipper contributes a sense of total logistics, continuity of flow and cost consciousness to the transportation function. The combination sometimes works beautifully if the mutual benefits are clearly perceived.

The Ships

The 'Liberty'

Over the past fifty years two standard tramp vessel types stand out as especially representative. The 'Liberty' ship was the universal, general-purpose tramp of the later 1940s and 1950s and the somewhat larger and faster SD-14 – the initial design for each was British – was one of its most popular replacements in the late 1960s and 1970s.

The Liberty ship was a wartime product. In 1940 Britain placed orders for sixty cargo vessels to be built in United States shipyards, and at around the same time the United States Government was contemplating an emergency construction programme of several hundred cargo ships of simple, standard design.[22] The particulars of a British 'Sunderland'-type, coal-burning tramp of roughly 10,000 dwt were studied by the United States Maritime Commission. Modifications were made, including fuel conversion from coal to oil and installation of 2500hp triple-expansion steam reciprocating engines, welded, simple to build and easily operated, but propelling the ship at a leisurely 10kts.[23] The design was quickly adapted to mass-production, assembly-line methods in shipyards on the Atlantic, Gulf and Pacific coasts and the first Liberty was delivered in December, 1941. In 1942, when wartime attrition of merchant fleets was most acute, 597 Liberty ships, including fifty-five for British account, were constructed. By 1944 shipyards had reduced the average time to build a Liberty ship, from keel-laying to delivery, to an astounding forty-two days. Altogether 2710 Liberty ships were built, the final vessel being delivered in October 1945.[24] Other United States dry cargo freighters built during this turbulent period included the various 'C' types and the 'Victory'. These types were faster with more tween-deck space than the Liberty, therefore somewhat more suitable for liner than tramp service, although they were used in all types of service after the war.

19. Manners, *op cit*, pp190–2.

20. Lawrence, *op cit*, p101.

21. Naess, *op cit*, p139.

22. Naess, *op cit*, p104.

23. C Rimington, *Merchant Fleets* (Dodd, Mead & Co, 1944), pp241–5.

24. W S, and E S Woytinsky, *World Commerce and Governments* (Twentieth Century Fund, 1955), p461; S E Morison, *The Battle of the Atlantic, September 1939–May 1943*; Vol 1 of *History of United States Naval Operations in World War II* (Little, Brown & Co, 1947), pp294–5.

The 'Liberty' ship was an emergency product of US shipyards, primarily for war use, and like other materials of war seen as expendable. Many were lost in war service. Although large numbers were laid up in the US Reserve Fleet following the war, several hundred were sold and put into successful commercial service. By mid-1967, 650 'Liberty' vessels were in the Reserve Fleet while about 600 still operated in the merchant fleets of many nations. From here on numbers diminished rapidly with the introduction of the so-called 'Liberty replacements'. With five hatches and five holds, useful derricks ranging from 6 to 50 tons and a deadweight of 10,414 tons, City of Colchester was in service with Ellerman Lines during 1947–59, and was broken up in 1968 when 25 years old. This vessel was one of twelve 'Liberty' ships in service with Ellerman Lines. (A Duncan)

Since the early 1970s the Lübeck shipowner Egon Oldendorff has been a frequent customer of shipbuilders in the UK. Eight of these orders have been for SD-14 type general cargo vessels, of which Globe Trader *is the latest.* Globe Trader *was completed by Austin & Pickersgill, Sunderland, in 1980 and is registered in the name of one of Oldendorff's associate companies, Westfalia Shipping Corp of Liberia. The SD-14 type designed by Austin & Pickersgill Ltd, Sunderland, and built by them and under licence outside the UK, is the most numerous and successful standardised cargo vessel built in peacetime, with over two hundred being constructed. There are variations in the vessels which conform to individual owners' requirements, and here* Globe Trader *has a 100-ton capacity derrick, in addition to those of 5–10 tons and 30 tons.* (Egon Oldendorff)

At war's end the United States merchant marine was the largest the world had ever seen.[25] Over 4000 vessels were government-owned and the largest component of this now-surplus fleet was Liberty ships. Domestic commercial operators purchased over eight hundred of the surplus vessels (and chartered others) and foreign lines took more than 1100, including hundreds of Liberties at bargain prices. Those not sold were relegated to the National Defense Reserve Fleet which, in 1950, reached its maximum size of 2277 ships.[26]

Although United States, Canadian and British shipyards had produced other merchant vessel types, some with quite similar cargo capacities, the Liberties simply outnumbered the others and became the backbone of the world tramp fleet in the late 1940s and 1950s. Metaxas estimated that the Liberty type constituted about forty per cent of the then world tramp fleet, even in the early 1960s.[27] This slow and somewhat clumsy vessel had a clean, functional design and a suitable cargo capacity and laden draught to make it the ideal tramp for its time. And, with its single tween-decks, it had the versatility to move into general cargo trades.

With five hatches and ample lower hold capacity the Liberty was suitable for full loads of a variety of dry bulk cargoes – coal, ores, phosphate rock, and average density grains, for example. Grain bagging requirements used to be a problem on the heaviest grains. At the other extreme the lightest grains would fill out cubic space before the Liberty ship reached her marks.[28] The cargo lifting capacity of about 10,000 long tons and a summer loadline draught in the 28ft range gave the vessel the flexibility to serve many of the smaller-volume trades in and out of the many ports around the world with harbour and berth depths of less than 30ft.[29] The one level of tween deck space could accommodate all types of packaged cargo. Full cargoes of lumber, including some on-deck, were feasible. The Liberty, in short, could perform in all sorts of trades that did not require fast transit.

Many Liberty ships found their way into British, Soviet Union, Netherlands, Norwegian, and, notably, Greek merchant fleets during and after the war. Hundreds of these were still trading satisfactorily more than fifteen years later.[30] If one adds to these the sizeable number of British and Canadian-built 10,000 tonners (eg 'Empire', 'Fort' and 'Park' types) one finds the nucleus of the postwar tramp fleet that gave the term 'Liberty-size cargo' its significance in the 1950s in London, New York and other chartering centres. Ten thousand ton cargo lots were the custom of many bulk cargo trades at this time.[31]

The SD-14

During the 1950s, new vessels built for general tramp shipping purposes were not a great deal larger than the Liberty, Empire, Park and Victory types: 12,000-tonners and, towards the end of the decade, 14,000-tonners were not uncommon. Ship operators were beginning to recognise the ton-mile economies of larger vessels but an owner ran the risk of a much larger vessel not being accepted by the trade.[32] In order to respond to spot demands in various dry cargo trades the tramp then required rather modest dimensions that gave the vessel operating flexibility. Even in the 1960s, according to the Maritime Research Inc 1964 *Chartering Annual*, the 10,000-ton Liberty-size lot of grain, coal, sugar, timber, and even iron ore was very popular in voyage charters. Voyage charters, of course, reflect mainly tramp fixtures.

Data on the average size of tramp vessels in the 1950s were still very much skewed by the predominance of the older vessel component. Some of the new buildings by the end of the decade had nearly half again as much deadweight capacity as the Liberty and this size had become acceptable in both the coal and the ore trades where bulk carriers were making inroads; however, some of the ports still required shallower-draught vessels.

By the early 1960s rising insurance rates on older ships presaged the end of the era of the Liberty and other 10,000-tonners of wartime vintage. By this time large new single-decked bulk carriers were invading the iron ore and coal trades, while converted tankers moved into grain trades.[33] In other words, tramp operators confronted new competition and needed competitive, adaptable vessel types. They needed also to watch the voyage charter market carefully to determine the appropriate specifications for a new tramp fleet and to discover new market niches as they were being edged out of old ones. In retrospect, Metaxas, Lawrence, Kendall, Naess and others who observed or took part in this era of shipping agree that the demand for tramp service was growing in the 1950s and 1960s, despite the inroads made by bulk carriers in some of the traditional trades.[34]

25. G R Jantscher, *Bread upon the Waters* (Brookings Institution, 1975), pp4–5.

26. US Department of Commerce, *US Ocean Policy in the 1970s: Status and Issues* (1978), V–35.

27. Metaxas, *op cit*, p203.

28. J Bes, *Chartering and Shipping Terms* (Barker & Howard, 1951; 9th edition, 1975), pp16, 43.

29. Lawrence, *op cit*, p278.

30. Naess, *op cit*, p109; Metaxas, *op cit*, p203.

31. Naess, *op cit*, p137.

32. *Ibid*.

33. Lawrence, *op cit*, p104.

34. Metaxas, *op cit*, p69; Lawrence, *op cit*, pp92–3; Kendall, *op cit*, p21; Naess, *op cit*, pp137–8.

In simple terms, there was room for a versatile general-purpose vessel with a carrying capacity half again that of the Liberty, a maximum draught permitting access to ports served by the old 10,000-tonners, and enough speed and tween-deck space so that the vessel would be functional also in liner service.

From many available designs in the 1960s only three standard types were eventually produced in sizeable numbers: the Canadian-designed, Japanese-built 'Freedom' type, the German designed and built 'Germany Liberty' type and the SD-14, designed and built at the Sunderland yard of Austin & Pickersgill and later built under licence in Greece and Brazil.[35]

The original SD-14, delivered in 1968, had a deadweight capacity of 15,250 tons on a laden draught of 28ft 6in with a service speed of about 14kts. There have been several new versions. The SD-14 Mark IV measures 15,000 dwt, attained a 15kt speed on a five-cylinder diesel engine consuming 25.5 tons of heavy oil daily, and has five holds and hatches, four tween-decks at one level and a mean draught of 28ft 9in.[36] This vessel is well suited to the carriage of full cargoes of heavy grain, ore, coal and timber and it fits easily into packaged or general cargo trades with its tween-decks, adequate speed, and ten cargo derricks.

Over two hundred SD-14s were built. They appealed especially to Greek shipowners whose fleets in the 1960s still contained many Liberty types nearing extinction. Two decades later there was still a place for vessels of this size, speed and configuration. The market for

The 'Freedom Mk II', is a development of the Japanese 'Freedom' standard type 'Liberty' replacement vessels of the 1960s and '70s. It has an overall length of 145.5m, breadth of 21m, and is equipped to carry 558 TEUs. The cargo handling equipment shown in this side elevation is the horizontal slewing type and consists of five sets of 25 tons capacity. As with other 'Liberty' replacement types variations existed to suit individual owners' requirements. (IHI)

second-hand SD-14s was still healthy in 1988.[37] There are still spot demands for shipping space in a multitude of dry cargo tramp trades and there are still liner operators who need conventional cargo ships rather than container ships on some of their routes.

Germany entered the tramp shipbuilding picture with the 'German Liberty' design and the Japanese with the 'Freedom' type. Both standard models had four cargo holds and ample tween-deck space, with superstructure and accommodation aft.[38] The Freedom type with a speed of 14kts, dwt capacity of 15,000 tons and mean draught of 29ft 3in had the same general capabilities in tramp and liner service as the SD-14. Later on the Japanese developed the 'Fortune' type, a multi-purpose ship of 20,000 dwt capacity, reflecting the realisation of scale economies of larger capacity tramp vessels but also the capabilities of more and more bulk commodity markets to accept larger lot sizes.[39]

Finally, in considering the evolution of tramp vessel types since the war, the definition of tramps by the service they perform should be remembered. By the 1980s most of the heavy volume bulk commodity trades were dominated by bulk carrier enterprises operated either by industrial corporations or by independent shipowners. Many tramp shipowners had acquired fleets of bulk carriers of various sizes and types. When these vessels were fixed on voyage charters, as they often were, this was tramp service whether the vessels were gigantic single-purpose ore carriers or large multiple-purpose OBOs or much smaller general-purpose SD-14s. One has only to look at the voyage charter fixture lists compiled annually by the charter market analysts to see that the average lot sizes have grown remarkably in the ore, coal and grain trades although spot fixtures in the 10,000- to 20,000-ton range are still quite common.[40]

A popular carrier for the major bulk trades by the mid 1980s was one with a cargo capacity of 25,000 to 35,000 tons, adequate cargo gear to be self-sustaining and sufficiently shallow draught for access to most bulk commodity ports.[41] In all the big dry bulk trades there were many carriers far larger than this providing periodic tramp service. Many of the large ore carriers, OBOs, etc strayed at times from industrial carrier service to take spot voyage charters.

The single-purpose dry bulk carrier

With the total seaborne trade of all mineral ores amounting to only 25 million tons in 1937 there was no prewar need for large bulk carriers; small tramp vessels provided the necessary transportation service.[42] There had been some early experimentation with small single-deckers in short-distance European ore trades and with Great Lakes ore carriers of up to 18,000 dwt. Bethlehem Steel had also built four 24,000 dwt ocean-going ore carriers in the late 1940s, to be used for Chilean ore movements to the United States east coast, and Swedish and other European shipyards were designing 24,000 deadweight bulk carriers by the 1950s. Japanese shipyards in the 1950s began 'jumboising' (lengthening) Liberty ships for the ore trade and, when released from early postwar shipbuilding restrictions, they rapidly

35. Bes, *op cit*, p473.

36. Branch, *op cit*, pp46–7.

37. Fearnleys *Review*, 1989.

38. Bes, *op cit*, p477; Branch *op cit*, Fig 3.3.

39. Kendall, *op cit*, p40.

40. Maritime Research Inc, *Chartering Annual 1989*.

41. Kendall, *op cit*, p74.

42. Couper, *op cit*, p133.

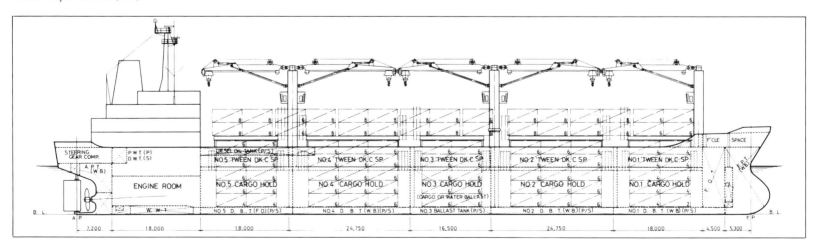

One method of obtaining a larger vessel without buying one is by 'jumboising'. This method has been in use for decades but postwar has become quite common. Many standard vessels built in the Second World War were jumboised – including 'Liberty' ships – to increase their carrying capacity or at the same time as conversion to a different role. Here, the 1959-built British-owned Niceto de Larrinaga, *built by Short Bros Ltd, Sunderland, is at the Harland & Wolff shipyard at Belfast in 1964 for the insertion of a new forward cargo section. Originally of 11,700 dwt and 491ft in length, she emerged at 13,742 dwt and 558.5ft.* (Harland & Wolff)

at reasonable cost, which is the *raison d'être* of bulk carrier service, was fuelled in the 1950s first by shipping space needs engendered by the Korean conflict, then by the enormous industrial expansion of the mid-1950s in Europe and Japan and by the Suez crisis of 1956 which immediately created an alarming, and, to industry, a very costly, shortage of shipping space. The coking coal and iron ore import needs of western Europe and Japan were especially pressing. Naess, in retrospect, calls 1953–57 his 'golden years', in terms of the kinds of innovative financing, building, chartering and operating activities in which he was engaged.[45]

captured the world lead as a builder of large bulk carriers.[43] It is no coincidence, perhaps, that the Japanese themselves rely more heavily than any other single nation on bulk commodity imports – oil, coal, iron ore and grain in especially large volume.[44]

Some of the great shipping tycoons, throughout the 1950s, were experimenting with larger-size ocean-going bulk carriers for both the liquid and dry bulk trades. Ingenious contractual arrangements were made with Japanese and European shipyards, United States and European banks, and with some of the very large oil and steel corporations including state-managed firms and their supply agencies in Britain and Italy for example. The great Japanese trading companies also became heavily involved in some of these ventures.

They were experts in the matter of raw material procurement.

The requirement for ocean transport of large quantities of bulk materials, regularly and

43. Manners, *op cit*, p182.

44. Fearnleys, *World Bulk Trades*, 1988.

45. Naess, *op cit*, p120.

In the 1970s the Danish shipbuilder Burmeister & Wain of Copenhagen designed and produced what turned out to be a popular series of Panamax size bulk carriers of around 61,000 dwt. Apart from domestic purchasers, several vessels of the type joined the fleets of shipowners outside Denmark, including some in the UK. Morelia *was built for Det Ostasiatiske Kompagni (East Asiatic Co) and completed in 1976. Gross tonnage was 35,904 and deadweight was 60,920. The vessel has seven hatches (each 14.4m × 15.0m) and seven holds with a total bulk capacity of 79,900cu m.* (East Asiatic Co)

Hanjin Dampier, *a 207,346 dwt bulk ore and coal carrier was built by Hyundai Heavy Industries and delivered to Hanjin Shipping Co, of South Korea, in 1989. Bulk carriers of over 200,000 tonnes, engaged primarily in ore and coal trades are a new generation, and whilst a few were afloat in the 1970s, they reflect a trend of the '80s, which carried on into the '90s. The largest pure bulk carrier afloat in 1992 is the 1986-built ore carrier* Berge Stahl *of 364,767 dwt.* (Hyundai)

From 1958 on through the early 1970s there was a dramatic rise in the world fleet of ore carriers and great increases in individual vessel size.[46] Lawrence, accepting the simple (but arbitrary) definition of the bulk carrier as 'all single-deck ships of over 10,000 dwt', claims that bulk carriers had by 1967 captured eighty-five per cent of iron ore shipments.[47] The largest of the newbuildings were consigned to high-volume routes feeding major steelworks with deep water facilities.[48]

The energy crisis and world recession in the mid 1970s, coupled with a peaking of shipyard deliveries of 'supercarriers', created a catastrophic glut of shipping space. Steel industry production, hence raw material and shipping needs, faltered. Shipowners became much more cautious about ordering new ships, especially the very large, therefore very inflexible, single-purpose bulk carriers. This caution persisted throughout the 1980s. In 1988, although there was one 360,000-tonner in operation and twenty-one more over 200,000 dwt with six more ordered, the most popular dry bulk carrier size in the world fleet was in the 25,000 to 40,000 dwt 'handy size' range, which contained 1842 bulk carriers totalling fifty-eight million dwt.[49]

A typical Japanese ore carrier, of over 100,000 dwt, is too large for the Panama Canal, but able, fully laden, to transit the Suez. According to contemporary jargon, it is larger than 'Panamax' but a bit smaller than 'Suezmax' and in the 'Capesize' range. It is a single-decker with large hatches over large, self trimming, holds. Wing tanks and bottom tanks are provided for ballast steaming and the deep bottom tanks raise the centre of gravity and reduce empty hold space to improve the laden vessel's response in heavy seas. The vessel is adequately compartmented and structurally strengthened for the carriage of a very dense commodity. Superstructure and engine room are located aft. There is no attached cargo handling equipment. Conveyor belts or other shore-based gear would be provided, and very rapid cargo-handling rates should be expected.[50,51]

As mentioned, the most popular dry bulk carrier size in recent years has been considerably smaller than the Japan-built ore carrier described above; however, there are a number of ore trades today that can use vessels of this or larger size. Australia-Japan and Brazil-Japan ore movements via the Cape of Good Hope are especially voluminous, for example. The economies of large-carrier, large-volume, ocean transport are especially apparent on the long journeys. Clearly, for a specific vessel, both the total voyage cost and the cost-per-ton of cargo carried are going to be more for a long journey than a short journey. Clearly, also, a large ship is going to cost more in absolute terms to build and more in terms of total voyage costs to operate than a small ship. The important point is that these absolute costs do not rise in direct proportion to distance or to vessel size (capacity). The abstract illustrations on page 66 explain the theoretical rationale for increasing vessel size. Figure 1 indicates that the building costs expressed in terms of costs per ton of deadweight capacity tend to decline with size of vessel under construction. A 100,000-tonner, for instance, has twice the capacity of a 50,000-tonner but the construction costs are far less than twice as much. This can be explained by the fact that a major part of the materials cost – steel plate, for instance – is related to the surface area or the ship's dimensions squared rather than to cubic capacity or dimensions cubed. Moreover, steel tends to cost less when ordered in large than in small quantities.

Figure 2 shows the hypothetical relationship between freight cost per ton and vessel deadweight size for different journey lengths. For the longer journey there is a particularly notable decline of voyage cost per ton carried with vessel size increases. The fact is that many of the vessel operating costs including capital costs, as mentioned, but crew costs and fuel costs too do not increase in direct proportion to the carrying capacity of the vessel and this is especially noticeable on long voyages for large ships when 'zero-distance costs', incurred in port, are a minor component of total voyage costs.

There are many factors, however, that limit the feasible size of ore carriers. Not least are the canal dimensions and the draught limitations, terminal capacities, berth lengths, etc of many of the world's ore ports. In determination of the optimum size of vessels to be built to supply Italian state-managed steelworks in the 1960s the cost of deepening Italian ports and improving port facilities had

46. Manners, *op cit*, Table 43, pp184–5.

47. Lawrence, *op cit*, pp89–90.

48. Manners, *op cit*, p183.

49. Fearnleys, *World Bulk Fleet*, July 1988.

50. Branch, *op cit*, p56.

51. A D Couper, *The Times Atlas of the Oceans* (Van Nostrand Reinhold, 1983), p139.

The Norwegian ore/bulk/oil carrier Sibotre *is typical of OBOs built in the 1960s and early '70s. At 77,727 dwt, with a cargo capacity of 88,834cu m (grain)/77,842cu m (oil)/48,307cu m (ore), she has nine holds/tanks and nine hatches. She was built in 1968 at the Gotaverken Arendal shipyard in Sweden, also known for series production of VLCCs. Swedish ship yards were among the first involved in the building of OBOs and the ore/oil carriers which appeared in large numbers in the late 1960s and '70s. (Gotaverken)*

to be considered. The water depth and berth limitations of foreign loading terminals, both for ore and coal, were relevant considerations too, as was the perceived need to diversify supply sources for political or security of supply reasons. Eventually, the Italians decided on bulk carriers of modest size, about 45,000 dwt, that could carry either iron ore or coal, and they supplemented their owned fleet with long term as well as spot charters of outside tonnage.[52]

BISCORE, the British ore-procurement organisation, part of the British Iron & Steel Corporation, relied very heavily on time-chartered vessels in the 1950s and '60s. While they controlled these vessels, acting as an industrial carrier, their freight costs tended to be high since they were obliged to use rather small vessels because of draught limitations at most of the British coastal steelworks in those days.[53] The Japanese steel industry, on the other hand, starting from virtually zero in the early 1950s, had built up the largest national ore fleet in the world by 1965 and many of their ore and bulk carriers were in the 50,000 to 70,000 dwt range. Japan took maximum advantage of their deep water berths. To feed their fast-growing industries Japan had the most voluminous raw material procurement needs of any nation and they became masters of 'contractual tramping' and of industrial carrier service.[54] Their long term Australian ore and coal purchasing and shipping arrangements were especially notable.

The multiple purpose bulk carrier

There had been experiments in the 1920s with small vessels that could carry, alternately, dry cargo and wet cargo. In the development of the Liberian ore trade from Monrovia to the United States east coast after the Second World War, Republic Steel entered a shipping venture jointly with a New York-based shipowner. Several oil/ore carriers of 24,000 deadweight were designed in the late 1940s, built in European yards and delivered in the early 1950s. While waiting for the port of

Monrovia to prepare facilities for iron ore exports Republic's first vessel was fixed on charter to Anglo-Iranian for the Persian Gulf – western Europe oil trade. Oil loaded in side tanks and bottom tanks could put these vessels down to their marks, or they could reach their marks with iron ore loaded in centre holds rather high up over the deep bottom tanks. Swedish shipyards were among the first in these oil/ore ship designs. By the early 1970s ore/oil carriers of 250,000 deadweight were being used.[55]

Many ship operators wanted more versatility and more cargo options than the early oil/ore ships afforded. Furthermore, there was an inevitable wasting of space. When ore was carried, much of the tank space was unused. When oil was carried the centre holds were empty. Erling Naess' account of his pursuit of the multi-purpose bulk carrier is enlightening.[56] Here was someone who was acutely aware of the directional imbalances in the dry cargo trades. Holding down the number of ballast days relative to loaded days was the secret of successful bulk carrier operations. Naess wanted vessels that could engage in coal, bauxite, phosphate rock and grain trades as well as ore and oil. In the 1950s he envisioned future contracts of affreightment covering coal and ore moving to Japan and backhauls of Indonesian oil to the next outbound movements of coal and ore. In 1960 a Japanese yard delivered to Greek operators a relatively small ship designed to carry any one of various dry bulk commodities or oil. Naess' team watched the operations of this antecedent of the OBO (oil/bulk/ore) type carefully, finding a few design characteristics that diminished the vessel's dry

cargo handling performance. Eventually in 1965 after collaboration which included technical assistance from Britain, Sweden and Germany, a Bremen shipyard delivered *Naess Norseman*, an OBO of 71,183 deadweight tons, drawing 44ft 10in on summer marks. This ship, registered in Liberia, was considered by many to be the first operationally successful OBO.

The concept of the OBO appealed to the great industrial shippers as well as the independent carriers in the 1960s and early 1970s. By the 1970s, many new buildings exceeded 200,000 dwt. Typically these larger vessels have superstructure and engines aft. Of the eleven holds to carry oil, seven can, alternatively, be used for ore or other dry bulk cargoes. Hatch openings are large, allowing expeditious handling of dry bulk cargoes. Hatch covers are oil-tight and gas-tight. Portable heating coils for the oil trade are provided as are special cleaning systems. Double bottoms are the rule. Typically the construction costs of an OBO run about 15 per cent higher than those of a tanker or an ore carrier of similar carrying capacity.[57]

In a sense the large OBO combines the improved freight earning potential of a multiple purpose ship with the operating economies that come with large size. Although the loaded

52. Manners, *op cit*, pp194–5.

53. *Ibid*, pp193–4.

54. *Ibid*, pp193.

55. Naess, *op cit*, p222.

56. *Ibid*, Chapter 21.

57. Branch, *op cit*, pp54–6; Naess, *op cit*, pp148–51.

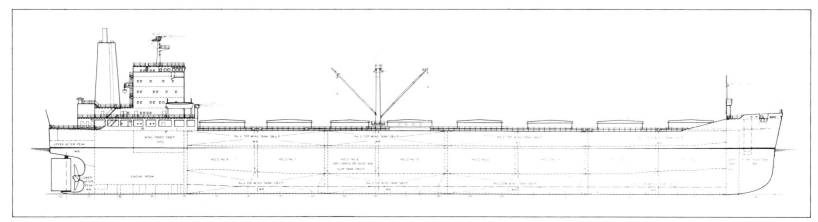

Table 1/1: Bulk tonnage on order, January 1992.
(Vessels over 10,000 dwt; numbers of ships and ,000 dwt)

Country of build	Tankers		Combined carriers		Bulk carriers		Total	
Japan	124	18,712	–	–	56	2893	180	21,605
Korea	59	9529	12	1370	28	3763	99	14,662
Denmark	7	1960	8	624	1	73	16	2657
Taiwan	3	349	–	–	13	1937	16	2286
China	22	1162	–	–	20	1072	42	2234
UK	4	592	–	–	6	960	10	1552
Yugoslavia (ex)	17	1124	–	–	5	162	22	1286
Brazil	13	921	–	–	4	272	17	1193
Romania	9	405	–	–	5	777	14	1182
Spain	10	1106	–	–	–	–	10	1106
Italy	12	778	–	–	2	282	14	1060
Poland	4	224	–	–	5	578	9	802
Turkey	2	314	–	–	4	202	6	516
Bulgaria	8	164	–	–	5	158	13	322
India	3	285	–	–	1	26	4	311
Finland	2	182	–	–	–	–	2	182
USSR (ex)	2	58	–	–	–	–	2	58
Argentina	1	30	–	–	–	–	1	30
Pakistan	–	–	–	–	1	17	1	17
Singapore	1	12	–	–	–	–	1	12
Total	303	37,907	20	1994	156	13,172	479	53,073

Source: *Fearnley's World Bulk Fleet*, January 1992.

A standard 55,000 dwt OBO (ore/bulk/oil) design developed by Swedish shipbuilder Uddevallavarvet. It has an oil tank capacity of 63,000cu m and its grain holds capacity is 65,795cu m. It is of Panamax size with an extreme breadth of 32.6m. (Uddevallavarvet)

draught of the large OBO excludes it from many ports and a few canals, straits and shallow seas, there are still many potential patterns combining different commodity trades that enable these vessels to reduce ballast days relative to loaded days for extended voyages. Paying for this flexibility by somewhat higher construction costs seemed reasonable to many shipowners in the 1960s and 1970s.

Unfortunately and somewhat paradoxically, the OBO can be plagued by what Sargent once called the 'want of balance' in ocean trades and the periodic fluctuations and variations in the different dry bulk trades – grain especially.[58] This means that the OBO operator is often trying to combine bulk carrier service for a steady movement with tramp service for spot movements which requires a complicated juggling of contracts of affreightment, long term charters and short term voyage charters. The Japanese, with their enormous bulk commodity requirements, may have been best equipped to mastermind and set in motion the trading patterns that the OBO requires, and OBOs have been heavily used in Japanese dry and liquid bulk movements.

New orders for OBOs are sparse, however. The concept is appealing but to operationalise the concept, contracting for the proper trade

58. Sargent, *op cit*, p24.

The largest dry cargo vessel built in the 1990s is the 320,000 dwt Bergeland, *a product of the Hyundai shipyard at Ulsan, South Korea.* Bergeland *and the larger* Berge Stahl *(364,767 swt) are the world's biggest ore carriers and are owned by Bergesen dy AS, Norway, a company with a fleet totalling over 9,220,000 dwt in service or under construction. (Bergesen dy AS)*

combinations, is not easy during an era of surplus bulk tonnage.

The shock of the oil crisis of the 1970s on the shipping community, the well-publicised bankruptcies, vessel lay-ups and scrapping have tempered the enthusiasm of ship owners for 'super-carriers'; the popularity of the large combined carriers has faded in recent years. One analyst observes, 'Many consider them either sub-optimal tankers or sub-optimal bulk carriers. The attractiveness of the flexibility to switch between oil and dry bulk is apparently not sufficient'.[59]

Table 1/1 shows the bulk tonnage (ships over 10,000 dwt) on order as of January 1992, specifying the shipbuilding country and differentiating between oil tankers, combined carriers (eg OBOs), and other bulk carriers (eg ore carriers). Most of these vessels are to be delivered in 1993–94, and almost two thirds of the tonnage will come from Korean and Japanese yards.[60]

The trades

A great surge of ocean-borne bulk commodity shipments occurred, as already mentioned, in the 1950s with a remarkable increase also in the following decade, especially in the crude oil trades. Iron ore and coal movements generally reflected the burgeoning needs of the steel industries of Japan, western Europe and America. The average journey lengths for oil, iron ore and coal were increasing during this period as the economies of long distance, large bulk carrier transport became ever more apparent, and as vessel size began to preclude conventional routeing via the Suez or Panama Canals or the Malacca Strait.

New trans-shipment terminals and new offshore loading facilities also changed the networks and itineraries of ships engaged in the bulk trades. A Cape of Good Hope routeing was necessary not only for large oil tankers on the Persian Gulf to western Europe route but also for the large bulk carriers in the Brazil-Japan ore trade and in the United States east

In 1973 Sunderland Shipbuilders Ltd delivered the 161,805 dwt ore/bulk/oil (OBO) Naess Crusader, typical of such carriers which became popular in the 1970s. Its maximum capacity was 172,906cu m of oil carried in eleven tanks or an alternative ore/grain capacity of 170,762cu m. The Harland & Wolff/ B & W 28,000 bhp engines gave a service speed of 15kts. (Sunderland Shipbuilders)

coast-Japan coal trade. Tankers and ore carriers over 200,000 dwt bound for Japan, steaming eastward across the Indian Ocean, used Lombok Strait and Makassar Strait rather than the Malacca Strait.

The grain trade in the 1950s and 1960s was quite uneven from year to year and sales depended, as they do now, on harvest conditions all over the world, on relief programmes, on various national agricultural policies, grain trade policies and, not least, on the sometimes mysterious strategies of a handful of major grain-dealing companies – Continental, Cargill, Bunge and the like.[61] Eventually, in the 1960s and with increasing needs in the 1970s, the Soviet Union and China became large purchasers of foreign grains. At first, this simply added to the uncertainty in the grain markets. Suddenly there would be huge grain purchases; suddenly there would be large demands for shipping space; suddenly the movement would cease. On some of the established routes, for instance, United States Gulf ports to western Europe or western Canada to Japan, heavy grain moved regularly enough to provide base parcels for cargo liners. The total volumes moving were impressive but regular bulk carrier service was not often needed. It was difficult to make long term contractual arrangements for shipping when the commodity supply was unpredictable. Thus tramp service was frequently used and vessels of very large size infrequently used.

The major bulk commodity trades

Table 1/2 presents a twenty-year series of world seaborne cargo movements, listing each of the major bulk commodity trades separately. Other bulk commodities and general cargo of all types appear in aggregate in the 'other cargo' column.[62] One sees here in very broad perspective the accommodated needs for liner, tramp and industrial carrier service. Clearly, shipping space requirements for oil, iron ore, coal and grain are not very closely synchronised – the movement of grain can go up as oil trade goes down, for instance. However, the trend is upward for all the listed commodity trades except crude oil, a general reflection of economic growth trends especially those of the world's industrial economies.

Iron ore and hard coal shipment requirements tend to move somewhat in tandem and are, as mentioned, related to the steel industry's needs. Nearly half the listed coal shipments, however, are energy coals rather than coking coals, and this adds other dimensions to the picture. Nevertheless, long term projections of shipping space needs are probably easier to calculate for ore and coal than for any of the other bulk commodities. This predictability together with the role of large corporations, especially the big steel making and mining firms, in these trades encourages bulk carrier service and, more specifically, industrial carrier service, and also it encourages long term contractual arrangements. While there are many different iron ore export sources, Brazil and Australia now ship huge annual volumes to Japan and western Europe, providing a large cargo base for bulk carrier service. Australia, the United States, South Africa and (western) Canada are the great coal exporters

59. Fearnleys, *World Bulk Fleet*, July 1988, p5.

60. *Ibid*, (January 1992), p19.

61. Morgan *op cit*, pp4–5.

62. Fearnleys, *Review* 1989 and 1990.

Table 1/2: World seaborne trade 1975–1990 in (millions of tonnes)

Year	Crude Oil	Oil Products	Iron Ore	Coal	Grain	Other Cargo	Total Trade
1960			(101)	(46)	(46)		
1965			(152)	(59)	(70)		
1972			(247)	(104)	(139)		
1975	1263	233	292	127	137	995	3047
1976	1410	260	294	127	146	1075	3312
1977	1451	273	276	132	147	1120	3399
1978	1432	270	278	127	169	1190	3466
1979	1497	279	327	159	182	1270	3714
1980	1320	276	314	188	198	1310	3606
1981	1170	267	303	210	206	1305	3461
1982	993	285	273	208	200	1240	3199
1983	930	282	257	197	199	1225	3090
1984	930	297	306	232	207	1320	3292
1985	871	288	321	272	181	1360	3293
1986	958	305	311	276	165	1370	3385
1987	870	313	319	283	186	1390	3461
1988	1042	325	348	304	196	1460	3675
1989	1120	335	352	321	192	1540	3877
1990	1190	(340)	347	342	192	(1610)	4021

Source: Fearnley's Review 1989 and World Bulk Trades, 1990. Figures in brackets are estimated.

including Russia) but large quantities move also to African, Latin American, Indian Ocean and other destinations. Although the United States-Far East and United States-Europe routes are especially important, the fluctuating volumes from year to year and the geographical spread and variety of grain ports worldwide encourage tramp service.

The oil trade, discussed in more detail in Chapter 4, has unique features also, dramatically shaped by changing economic and political conditions since the 1973 Arab oil embargo and the ensuing uncertainties of oil supply availabilities and price. The energy crisis of the

The Brazilian shipbuilder Companhia Comercio e Navegacao had considerable success with its Prinasa PRI-26/15 type bulk carrier design. It has five large holds, and five clear opening hatches, which can be served by four cranes of 25 tons or an optional five cranes of 16 tons. Cargo capacity is 32,000cu m and grt is about 16,025. The design commenced production in 1978, and by the end of 1982, twenty-two had been delivered. (CNN)

with western Europe and Japan again very heavy importers. The two most important single coal trades are United States east coast to Japan and Australia to Japan, also providing a base for bulk carrier service.

The grain market is quite unlike the others and shipping space requirements for any specific grain trade route cannot be accurately predicted long in advance. The weather, the prices, and the politics are too variable. The rather surprising stability of the annual world oceanborne grain trade volumes over the past ten years (see Table 1/2) masks large fluctuations from one year to the next on some of the individual routes. In the statistics used here 'grain' includes wheat, maize, soya beans, sorghum, barley, oats and rye but does not include rice (which moves mainly in short sea trades). Wheat and maize are by far the largest grain export items. The United States is the world's largest grain exporter (from all coasts). Canada, Argentina, Australia and France have long established grain export trades. The importers are many in number and global location. Japan and other Far Eastern imports are very significant as is western Europe (notably

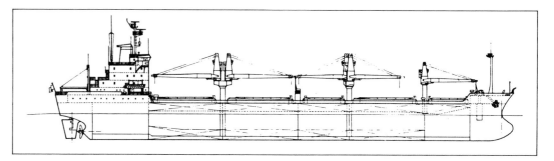

A successful standard type of bulk carrier produced during 1978–82 was the Prinasa PRI-26/15 type from Rio de Janeiro builders Companhia Comercio e Navegacao (CCN). Amongst the twenty-two vessels in the series was Cape Finisterre, one of five built for UK owners. In 1984 CCN introduced an updated version known as PRI-GC26, which was basically similar but had a more economical main engine fitted. (FotoFlite)

1970s profoundly disturbed the entire world economy and the impact on the shipping world was huge. The clearest evidence was the great glut of unemployed tankers, created by the market dampening effect of oil price rises together with unstoppable shipyard deliveries of large new tankers ordered before the crisis.

Seeking more reliable and easily accessible petroleum supplies the United States looked toward Mexico, the Caribbean and the North Slope of Alaska (Alaska shipments are 'domestic', that is intra-USA, therefore are not included in the foreign seaborne trade figures of Table 1/2). North Sea oil development provided a valuable new supply source for European consumers. The Soviet Union also began delivering oil to various European destinations by pipeline and short-haul tankers. After the Arab oil embargo (when the Suez Canal was still closed) the average distance of the loaded voyage for tankers of over 60,000 dwt decreased steadily from 7500 miles in 1973 to 4080 in 1985 with a slight increase thereafter.[63] In the Middle East there were new developments that changed some of the specific routeings of the tanker trade. The Suez Canal, reopened in 1975, was subsequently deepened and widened to permit transit of laden tankers of 150,000 dwt and much larger sizes in ballast. Also the Yanbu pipeline gave Saudi Arabia a new oil terminal on the Red Sea shortening the tanker voyage to European destinations and obviating Persian Gulf and Strait of Hormuz transit which was precarious during the Iran-Iraq war. The Sumed pipeline provided an alternative to transiting the Suez Canal for oil moving from the Red Sea to the Mediterranean, but, of course, this requires two tankers, one at each end of the pipeline. These and other alterations to the oil distribution system, including a complex network of European pipelines, have changed the geographical configurations of the tanker trades over the past two decades. Not only the large oil companies and their controlled fleets but the independent ship operators owning combined carriers and tankers promoted, encouraged and even financed some of these changes themselves. Al-

ternative routeings could only be to their advantage in the long run.

The huge volume of the seaborne oil trade, although it has declined from its peak in the 1970s, provides a *raison d'être* for bulk carrier service and one which was clearly perceived by shippers and carriers as early as the 1950s. The low transport costs derived from supertanker operations gave added stimulus to long distance trades – to Europe via the Cape, to Japan via the Lombok Strait, etc. The oil trade promised new and remunerative patterns of operation for the combined carrier operators.

The Middle East, exporting from Persian Gulf, Red Sea and Levant coast terminals, remains the dominant region in the oil export trades, regardless of embargoes, price hikes, world recessions and regional wars. Japan, western Europe and the United States are especially heavy importers. Caribbean, West African, North African and Indonesian exports to the major oil markets also figured in the trading patterns for combined carriers.

The OBO operators, while some tended to favour short term charters to retain operating flexibility, were more likely to survive the crisis of the mid 1970s if they had long term shipping contracts.[64] Those who were concentrating on spot demands in the oil trade – that is, the ones providing tramp service – suddenly found themselves missing an essential leg in their combined trade system.

Seaborne trade of bauxite and alumina in 1988 reached nearly 48 million tonnes, phosp-

hate rock almost 44 million. Many millions of tons each of manganese ore, various non-ferrous ores, sulphur, scrap, salt, oil-cake, tapioca, raw sugar, cement, petroleum coke, potash, gypsum and others are shipped in bulk. Iron and steel products and wood products are often shipped in unpackaged form and are potential cargoes for dry bulk carriers. One analyst estimates a total seaborne trade of forest products of over 150 million tonnes annually.[65] In global perspective these minor bulk trades offer attractive possibilities to the wide-ranging tramp or bulk carrier operator. The handy-size tramp vessel, for instance the SD-14, has the designed flexibility to participate in any of these bulk or neo-bulk shipments.

Some actual operating patterns

The versatile tramp operator moves his fleet in and out of various trades, tying together otherwise unrelated cargo movements.[66] Not only are the same vessels used in different trades, but the freight rates for commodities shipped on entirely different routes are interrelated when the extended voyages of individual vessels incorporate one route and one commodity after another. Also the mere potential of tramp

---

63. Fearnleys, *World Bulk Trades*, 1983 and 1988.

64. Lawrence, *op cit*, p92.

65. Simpson, Spence & Young, *op cit*, p26.

66. Fleming, *op cit*, p30.

The bulk carrier Sandra Marie, *owned by Intercontinental Shipping Pty Ltd, Sydney, is engaged on Australian coastal voyages. Built at Tomago, NSW, in 1986, the vessel has two hatches and two holds and is equipped with a 25-ton capacity crane. She has a multi-purpose role, capable of carrying general and bulk cargoes (586cu m), containers can also be carried – 81 TEUs in the holds and 60 TEU on deck. The managers of the vessel are Howard Smith Industries Pty Ltd.* (Howard Smith Industries)

Many specialised vessels, such as cement carriers, and others solely employed in carrying powdered cargoes, have onboard discharging gear. Fewer, however, are the versatile bulk carriers, employable in diverse trades, which carry self-discharging equipment. Amongst these are vessels owned by Norwegian Atle Jebsen, controller of a group of companies with vessels under Norwegian, German, UK, Philippines, Liberian and Netherlands registration. Telnes (10,110 dwt), registered in London, and owned by Jebsen Thun Beltships Investments Inc, operates in a pool marketing self-discharging bulkers with Swedish owner Thunrederierna. (FotoFlite)

and combined carrier fleets to switch trades affects the freight rate markets, as Metaxas and others have pointed out.[67] The combined carrier's adaptability for quick movement between dry and liquid bulk trades establishes a closer relationship between tanker and dry cargo freight rates.[68]

The tramp operator's objective, in simple terms, is to find efficient and profitable patterns of operation. It might be mentioned that technical efficiency of vessel operations and profitability in terms of the firm's net earnings are not always, and not necessarily, synonymous.

In the early postwar days a tramp operator using low-cost, multiple-purpose 10,000-tonners had a multitude of trading options despite many artificial obstructions – for one example, freight payments in blocked sterling. The division between tramp and liner operations was sometimes quite nebulous so that vessels frequently provided liner service on one leg of a voyage and tramp service on another. For a time in the 1950s a United States controlled, Norwegian registered, fleet of six Liberty vessels was engaged by oil interests to provide regular service from the United States Gulf to the Persian Gulf for the heavy movements of various types of oil drilling equipment. The ship operators could quote reasonable, less-than-conference, freight rates only if they could obtain onward or return cargo. The oil interests then offered drummed lubricating oil from Bahrain to several destinations in Madagascar and East Africa. The ship operator then negotiated voyage charters for full cargoes of ore from either Beira or Lourenço Marques in Portuguese East Africa (Mozambique) or Durban, South Africa to Baltimore. A pattern such as this was both efficient and profitable while it lasted, but the variations in reliability and timing of these different cargo movements always presented potential problems. The commodity shippers were not willing to commit themselves to long-term contracts.

There are a multitude of modern combinations of trades that enterprising tramp operators, using handy-sized, multi-purpose ships, have discovered, each hoping to find a special geographical niche undiscovered by others. Tracing the recent voyages of a few of the ships handled by General Steamship Corp, one of the busiest ship agents in the Pacific Northwest, one finds, for instance:

Motor vessel Sammi Frontier (Korean flag), combination container carrier/bulk carrier of 26,700 dwt, loaded full cargo of forest products (logs) in Pacific Northwest, departing Grays Harbor in May 1990 for Korea, off-loading forest products in June, loading Korean steel in July for August arrival United States Pacific Coast.

Belforest (Norwegian flag), combination container carrier/bulk carrier of 39,218 dwt, loaded full cargo of wood products topping off at Coos Bay, Oregon in May 1990, arriving for discharge at Ghent in June and loading steel at Newport (South Wales), Brake (Germany) and Antwerp, sailing early July for California ports of discharge.

North Wind (Bahamas flag), reefer ship of 6352 dwt, loaded apples in New Zealand in June for Seattle, ballasted to Alaska to load frozen fish for Japan, thence in ballast back to New Zealand.

Frio Merchant (Panamanian flag) reefer ship of 4750 dwt on maiden voyage, ballasted from Japan to New Zealand in July 1990, loaded full cargo of kiwi fruit for Seattle, arriving 20 August for cargo discharge, then ballasted to Mexico for cargo of frozen fish for Japan.[69]

On a grander scale one European analyst has calculated for 1988, by general regions of origin and destination, the total volume of dry bulk shipments by bulk and combined carriers of a vessel size over 50,000 dwt (see Table 1/3). The totals include dry bulk commodity shipments of major consequence – iron ore, coal, grain, bauxite and alumina and phosphate rock – but also almost 90 million tons in the 'minor' bulk trades (eg wood products, etc) served by vessels over 50,000 dwt.[70] The analyst notes that in 1988 there was a substantial switch of combined carriers (OBO and ore/oil) from oil to dry bulk trading. These statistics give a reasonable impression of the patterns and possibilities for large bulk carrier operations in the dry cargo trades. The multi-purpose bulk carrier which Naess and other shipping magnates could only look forward to in the 1950s, gives ship operators the potential of putting together heavy volume trades in combinations reminiscent of tramp trading of the past. Vessels built in the 1980s for the carriage of automobiles, alternatively dry bulk, and other vessels for containers, alternatively dry bulk, are also classified as bulk carriers and these ships obviously offer some new trading options.

A gross generalisation of Table 1/3 statistics reveals that Australia and the Americas are the

67. Metaxas, *op cit*, pp70, 118.

68. Naess, *op cit*, p150.

69. *Lloyd's Shipping Index; Lloyd's Voyage Record*; General Steamship Corp office records.

70. Fearnleys, *World Bulk Trades*, 1990.

Table 1/3: Dry Bulk Shipments by Bulk and Combined Carriers 1990. Commodities and Areas (in ,000 tonnes)

| | FROM the areas with: | | | | TO the areas with: | | | |
	Iron ore	Coal	Grain	Others	Iron ore	Coal	Grain	Others
UK/Continent	–	1040	6090	5440	101930	62710	9830	25260
Mediterranean	–	–	160	650	19420	24400	8360	9230
Other Europe	17170	7730	820	2880	15000	21970	20230	8700
Africa	29060	38390	70	13070	800	2060	4210	400
North America	22900	103460	79010	25630	14440	320	1110	19110
South America	130850	10060	10830	22200	4150	11910	490	7640
Asia	29740	10730	80	7690	168140	140480	54980	19140
Australia	94740	92440	2150	12280	580	–	–	360
Total 1990	324460	263850	99210	89840	324460	263850	99210	89840
Total 1989	336770	247530	97990	105830	336770	247530	97990	105830

Notes: The term 'Others' here comprises bauxite and alumina, phosphate and other bulk commodities. Australia also includes New Zealand and Pacific Islands; includes vessels over 50,000 dwt only.

Source: Fearnley's World Bulk Trades, 1990.

huge dry bulk exporters and Europe and Japan enormous importers. However cleverly the dry bulk carriers devise their itineraries, there are going to be some long ballast journeys for some of the large carriers simply because of the relative geographical locations of the major exporting regions and the major importing regions and the directional imbalances of cargo flow. There is not enough bulk cargo moving in 'opposite' directions' to accommodate the total demand of the ship operators.

Of course, the bulk carrier operators, like tramp operators, are always seeking a favourable geographical niche which, they hope, can be consolidated by long term contractual arrangements. When there is a surplus of shipping space, a condition that has very often prevailed since the mid 1970s, the niches are more difficult to find and long term contracts of affreightment difficult to arrange. In general, bulk commodity shippers are much more in control in the 1970s and '80s than they were in the 1950s when space was in short supply. Many carriers, and not just those in industrial

carrier service, have recently consigned their large economical vessels to one dependable trade with long ballast legs between port of discharge and next port of loading. Many of the single-purpose vessels were, in fact, built with that probability in mind.

While emphasis in this chapter has been placed on trading possibilities for the ship operator it should be remembered that the demand for shipping space is essentially derived from the demand for the commodities shipped. The enormous bulk material requirements of Japan, for instance, are suggested but only partially shown in Table 1/3. Japanese industries, or the trading companies representing them, have contracted for great quantities of these materials to be supplied by Australia, Brazil, the United States, South Africa, etc, and contracted with shipyards to build large bulk carriers or with vessel operators to provide bulk carrier service. The industries are 'calling the shots' and they may think that cross-trading is a luxury and a complication. Regular, dependable, reasonably-priced service is top priority.

Ownership and management

Independent shipowners and operators have always frequented the tramp trades. Firms and fleets vary enormously in size from the single vessel enterprise to large tramp divisions within a corporation that provides liner and large bulk carrier as well as tramp service. The tramp ownership structure has not changed remarkably over the past forty years. Recently there has been a flurry of 'limited partnerships', spawned especially in Norway and making use of the new Norwegian international registry. There is not a high degree of concentration in the tramp shipping market and governments have not, as a general rule, involved themselves in tramp shipping as much as they have in liner service. Even Eastern-bloc fleets, while they are state-owned, have operated very competitively as non-conference tramps, cross-trading in the west; however tramp service, by its very nature and definition, seems much more a phenomenon of capitalism than socialism.

In bulk carrier services the enterprises tend to be larger; at least, larger capital investments are necessary. Often, as was the case with Erling Naess' bulk carrier operations, what started as a small experimental venture developed into what was in the late 1960s the world's largest dry bulk carrier fleet.[71] There were other success stories but many failures as well, when shipping markets slumped in the 1970s and tramp operators could not survive on spot charters.

Part of the world's bulk carrier fleet belongs to large industrial corporations. Various United States steel companies, for example, have owned and operated ships under subsidiary companies. Experts in the industry have been sceptical of industrial carrier service, noting the inflexibility of itineraries, the internal corporate pressures on the shipping division from production or marketing personnel who know nothing about transport economics, and so forth. Some national governments, for in-

71. Naess, *op cit*, p192.

The 'Cardiff' class bulk carrier Cinchona was the twenty-first of this type to be built and one of a pair built for East Asiatic Co, Denmark. The 'Cardiff' class was the result of close co-operation between Upper Clyde Shipbuilders and the Cardiff shipowner Sir William Reardon Smith & Sons. The final design was a good general trader, suited for the usual bulk trades such as grain, ores and coal, but also very attractive to the forest products industry. (East Asiatic Co)

stance British and Italian, have been interested in bulk carrier operations, and in some instances they have been active participants as owners or long term charterers of ore carriers. In other instances, government agencies, such as Japan's Ministry of International Trade and Industry, have in many different ways facilitated the build-up of a national ore fleet, privately owned but publicly encouraged.[72]

The development of much of the world's bulk carrier fleet was undertaken by private companies, assisted by banks, shipyards, steel companies and others who would be the eventual users of the bulk carrier services. Frequently one of the legendary shipping entrepreneurs from Norway or Greece or Hong Kong was the 'diplomat' who put things together, who consolidated the necessary linkages. One leader offered this comment on building bulk carriers in Japan, 'The job was to tie up the links in the chain. The steel companies would buy the coking coal to produce the steel which the shipyards would use to build the ships which I would order to carry the coal'.[73]

Recent estimates show that, measured by deadweight tonnage, the independently-owned tanker fleet was three times the size of the oil-company owned fleet. Independently owned combined carriers also predominated.[74] In the dry bulk fleet independent ownership is also prevalent. It should be noted, however, that long term charters and other contracts can shift the control to the industrial corporation and the result is industrial carrier service on many of the major bulk commodity routes.

One aspect of ownership that has evolved into a fascinating and complicated puzzle is the matter of flag and registry. The rationale for open registries and the hoisting of the so-called 'flags of convenience' is rather straightforward. The open registry offers the shipowner geographical freedoms in the building, crewing and operating of the ship. Open registry may also signify low registry fees, low annual tonnage fees, freedom from taxation of fleet earnings in the host country and freedom from other regulatory requirements or restrictions. The tramp operator or bulk carrier operator, seeking flexibility and seeking low operating costs, is drawn to flags of convenience – more so, certainly, than liner companies which tend to retain the national flag and, sometimes, its cargo and subsidy privileges.

Table 1/4 discloses the recent evolution of bulk fleets according to country of registry. Two huge open registries, Liberia and Panama, head the list. Liberian registry, which has been especially favoured by oil companies, has

Table 1/4: Existing Bulk Fleet, Flag Distribution 1970–1992.
(Vessels over 10,000 dwt; in million dwt)

Country of registry	1970 Jan	1975 Jan	1980 Jan	1985 Jan	1988 Jan	1989 Jan	1990 Jan	1991 Jan	1991 July	1992 Jan
Liberia	47.9	108.5	150.1	112.0	88.5	83.1	80.2	84.5	83.2	83.9
Panama	5.5	12.8	21.8	44.0	49.7	51.6	53.2	48.4	51.3	55.5
Greece	8.8	26.5	48.0	48.9	36.8	34.2	33.4	35.7	38.0	40.0
Norway	26.2	38.9	34.3	23.2	9.9	18.2	29.9	35.5	35.4	34.6
(whereof NIS)					(6.8)	(16.8)	(28.6)	(34.2)	(34.2)	(33.4)
Cyprus	0.2	1.5	0.7	9.5	25.2	28.2	26.8	28.8	30.0	29.6
Japan	25.6	50.7	52.8	48.5	38.1	34.3	30.4	28.5	28.7	27.5
Bahamas	–	–	–	6.0	13.1	13.7	16.3	20.1	23.5	26.0
UK	25.1	44.9	39.0	27.9	27.2	28.0	27.9	23.1	21.4	19.6
USA	9.3	9.7	14.7	14.7	15.7	15.6	14.5	14.2	14.0	13.2
Malta	–	–	0.1	1.8	3.1	4.4	5.1	6.7	8.3	12.1
Philippines	0.3	0.3	1.4	5.0	11.9	12.2	12.6	12.0	11.8	11.9
China	0.2	1.3	4.8	6.9	9.7	10.0	10.3	11.1	11.2	11.2
USSR (ex)	3.9	5.4	9.1	10.4	11.5	12.0	12.7	11.6	11.0	10.8
Singapore	0.1	3.4	8.5	7.7	8.2	7.9	9.0	9.8	10.1	10.3
Korea, South	0.6	1.4	4.7	8.6	8.9	10.0	9.9	9.7	9.1	8.9
Brazil	0.9	2.8	5.3	7.7	8.1	8.2	8.5	8.6	8.5	8.6
Italy	7.0	12.7	15.9	12.1	8.5	8.0	8.4	8.8	8.7	8.2
India	1.8	3.9	6.8	8.1	7.8	7.9	8.3	8.5	8.4	8.2
Iran	0.1	0.1	1.1	2.9	6.5	7.4	7.9	7.9	7.6	7.6
Taiwan	0.6	1.2	1.6	4.7	4.5	4.4	5.0	6.3	6.3	6.5
Turkey	0.2	0.7	1.4	4.8	4.0	3.7	4.0	5.2	5.5	5.9
Denmark (DIS)	2.9	5.5	6.4	5.2	4.5	4.6	4.4	4.6	4.9	4.9
Spain	2.3	5.8	11.5	8.6	5.9	5.4	4.8	4.6	4.5	4.1
France	6.1	14.4	18.4	11.2	5.2	5.1	4.6	3.9	3.9	3.9
Marshall Islands	–	–	–	–	–	–	0.5	3.0	3.4	3.8
Romania	0.3	0.7	1.8	2.9	3.7	3.8	4.2	4.4	4.4	3.7
St Vincent	–	–	–	0.2	0.7	0.9	1.1	1.7	2.0	3.3
Poland	0.5	1.6	3.0	2.5	2.8	2.9	2.8	2.8	2.9	2.9
Australia	0.9	1.2	1.9	2.6	3.0	3.1	3.0	3.0	2.8	2.8
Vanuatu	–	–	–	0.1	1.0	0.9	1.1	2.6	2.6	2.4
Sweden	5.3	9.4	5.0	2.0	0.5	0.5	1.2	1.8	2.1	2.3
Luxemburg	–	–	–	–	–	–	–	–	2.0	2.1
Kuwait	–	0.8	2.5	2.2	0.6	0.4	1.9	1.7	1.6	1.5
Yugoslavia (ex)	0.8	1.2	1.9	2.3	3.1	3.3	4.0	4.1	3.9	1.5
Argentina	0.7	1.0	2.1	1.9	1.7	1.7	1.9	1.8	1.5	1.4
Bulgaria	0.4	0.7	1.2	1.4	1.5	1.5	1.4	1.4	1.4	1.4
Iraq	–	0.3	2.1	1.4	1.4	1.4	1.5	1.5	1.4	1.3
Germany	5.0	9.6	9.2	4.5	1.6	1.4	1.4	1.3	1.3	1.3
U A Emirates	–	–	0.1	1.1	0.7	0.8	0.8	0.9	1.0	1.3
Netherlands	3.8	5.5	5.6	4.1	1.6	1.1	1.1	1.2	1.2	1.2
Portugal	0.3	1.1	1.6	1.9	1.4	1.4	0.9	1.1	1.1	1.2
Burma (Myanmar)	–	–	–	–	0.2	0.5	0.7	1.1	1.1	1.1
Libya	–	0.3	1.5	1.4	1.1	1.1	1.1	1.1	1.1	1.1
Egypt	–	–	0.1	0.3	0.7	0.8	0.8	0.8	0.8	1.0
Others	5.3	8.4	14.7	20.2	16.0	15.3	14.9	13.6	11.2	10.6
Total	198.9	394.2	512.7	493.4	455.8	460.9	474.5	489.0	496.0	502.0

Notes: NIS = Norwegian International Ship Registry; DIS = Danish International Ship Registry.
Source: Fearnley's World Bulk Fleet, January 1992.

seen a decline from its peak at the end of the 1970s, just as the world tanker fleet, in general, has dwindled in size since 1979. Panamanian registry, on the other hand, has experienced steady increases, and the numbers of vessels in the Panamanian flag bulk fleet now exceed the numbers but not the total deadweight capacity in the Liberian fleet. Panama has an especially large number of dry bulk carriers. Of the other open registries, Cyprus has become progres-

sively more important, especially as a haven (with special ties to Greece) for dry bulk carriers. The Bahamas has also risen to significance.

Among the curiosities of the flag of conve-

72. Manners, *op cit,* p195; Naess, *op cit,* p139.

73. Naess, *op cit,* p139.

74. H Clarkson, *op cit,* p41.

The British crown colony of Hong Kong is home to a substantial ocean-going fleet, many under the local register, but the majority under flags of convenience such as Liberia and Panama. One of the largest fleets managed in the colony is that of World-Wide Shipping Group, with the majority of its vessels consisting of tankers and bulk carriers. One under the local register is World Dulce, *a 75,485 grt bulk carrier, built by Hitachi Zosen, Nagasu, Japan, and delivered in January 1981. All vessels in the fleet are registered in the name of 'one-off' companies –* World Dulce *is owned by World Fairbanks Shipping Ltd. (FotoFlite)*

nience phenomenon are the emergence of the registry of Vanuatu, a small Pacific archipelago, and the development of domestic flags of convenience like Isle of Man for the United Kingdom and Kerguelen (Indian Ocean) for France. The impermanence of specific registry arrangements is revealed by the overnight emergence of new registries and the 'flagging out' and flagging back in of vessels during the Panamanian political crisis in 1989.

The establishment of the new Norwegian International Ship Registry (NIS) offers owners low registration fees, little or no taxation and a free hand in crewing the vessels. NIS, as indicated in Table 1/4, has drawn back ships to the Norwegian flag from other flags, which was, of course, the intention. Interestingly, the general idea behind the new Norwegian registry, established in 1987, was proposed four years earlier by Erling Naess who had retired in the 1970s from active operations as a shipowner.

Clearly, the flag of convenience is an artificiality, a technical loophole that the shipowner has found. It can be created and erased by law. Paradoxically, something artificial has enabled the bulk carrier operators to express themselves naturally by shopping around internationally for the best places to finance, build, crew and manage their vessels. It is essential in their global business to make these international comparisons, especially if they are considerate of the interests and costs of the consumers of their own shipping services.

Table 1/4 also reveals that two of the great cross-traders and tramp operators of the past,

Greece and Norway (with old and new registries), still have prominence in the size of their bulk fleets. And two of the largest bulk materials importers of the past, Japan and the United

Built for UK registration, but later transferring to Hong Kong, the 173,028 dwt British Steel *was one of the largest vessels in the UK fleet, and the largest bulk carrier then built in Europe. Built to carry iron ore for British Steel Plc's UK plants, this vessel is owned by Lombard Finance Ltd, on bareboat charter to British Steel and managed by Furness Withy (Shipping) Ltd. A product of the Harland & Wolff shipyard at Belfast in 1984, which also built the later sister-ship* Ironbridge, *the vessel has a gross tonnage of 90,831 and is 286.95m in length. (FotoFlite)*

Kingdom, understandably have sizeable bulk fleets. The Russian, Chinese and South Korean bulk fleets have increased impressively.

Although there is a good deal of imprecision in the statistics on beneficial ownership and identification of 'controlling interest', analysts agree that the flag of convenience fleet directly owned or controlled by United States companies has been well over twice the size of the United States flag fleet in the 1970s and 1980s and the proportion of convenience flag is even greater for the bulk fleet component. It has been claimed that the Greek-owned open registry ships together with the Greek flag ships made the world's largest combined fleet in the mid 1980s. The Norwegians also claim a very large combined fleet through direct as well as indirect control in the late 1980s. The beneficial ownership and control by Hong Kong interests of open registry vessels has been notable; in the early 1980s only the United States had more tonnage under beneficial ownership. Japan, finally, supplements its large fleet under Japanese registry with an open registry fleet of significant size, and one suspects it has considerably more control by means of long term charters than the records of ownership would suggest.

Because of the open registry phenomenon and the difficulties translating the statistics of beneficial ownership to the realities of actual control, any list of merchant fleets by country of registry leaves many unanswered questions. From where are these fleets managed? Where are the head offices, the loci of control? For the traditional maritime nations one usually expects the head office to be found in the country's busiest maritime centre. For tramp shipping and bulk carrier ventures, London, New York and Tokyo are places where carriers and shippers converge to make vital shipping arrangements. These are the world's three greatest control and shipping management centres where trading information is most timely and abundant.

London is a special case. The Baltic Ex-

The long-established German shipping concern Egon Oldenorff, of Lübeck, manager of the Liberian-flag bulk carrier Yeoman Burn *(77,548 dwt), completed in 1991.* Yeoman Burn *has been chartered to the Foster-Yeoman group, which, at Glensanda, in western Scotland, is excavating granite from a 2000ft-high mountain. Crushed granite is transported to a plant on the Isle of Grain, for use in the Channel Tunnel, to Europe, and to Texas.* Yeoman Burn *has a cargo capacity of 72,103cu m, and with nine hatches and seven holds, she is fitted with self-unloading equipment. (Egon Oldendorff)*

change is really the only institution of its kind, where chartering brokers still meet daily, face to face. With computer scopes and modern communications this sort of meeting place is certainly less essential for negotiation purposes than it once was, but the perennial value of shipping gossip is undeniable and this comes easily in small 'social clusters'. In volume of

shipping management decisions London does more than hold her own. Greek and other European shipowners often have a very large, if not their largest, office in London. It is a logical point from which to manage a fleet.

New York, on the other hand, has tended to decline in recent years as a chartering and shipping management centre. One reason is the deconcentration of both the shipping industry

and manufacturing industry in the United States, with head offices dispersing to other parts of the country, especially to the west coast in concert with new 'Pacific Rim' trade orientations.

Tokyo until recently has not been a great centre of international financial and shipping control. However, the enormous postwar growth of Japanese industries and shipping

Typical conventional and multi-purpose cargo vessels in service since 1945

Ship (Class)	Flag	Built	By	GRT DWT	Length (oa) × breadth × depth × draught Feet–Inches Metres	Cargo handling gear	Engines	Speed	Remarks
'LIBERTY' type	Many	1941–45	US	7176 10,400	441–6 × 56–11 × 37–4 × 26–10 *134.7 × 17.33 × 11.38 × 8.18*	Derricks 1 × 50 or 30 tons, 1 × 30 or 15 tons, 5 × 5 tons	3-cylinder triple-expansion 2500ihp; 1 shaft	11kts	5 holds 5 hatches
FERNSTATE	Nor	1958	C Connell & Co, Glasgow	6759 11,847	511–0 × 64–3 × 41–6 × 28–6 *155.760 × 19.59 × 12.65 × 9.16*	Derricks 1 × 50 tons, 4 × 10 tons, 4 × 7.5 tons, 13 × 5 tons	1 Barclay Curle/ Doxford diesel, 8500bhp; 1 shaft	17kts	5 holds, 5 hatches, 4 pass, 710m³ ref
BENVALLA	UK	1962	C Connell & Co, Glasgow	11,391 13,249	549–7 × 71–3 × 44–5 × 33–7 *167.52 × 21.72 × 13.54 × 10.22*	Cranes 2 × 5 tons; derricks 1 × 50 tons, 1 × 20 tons, 10 × 10 tons, 10 × 5 tons	1 Rowan/Sulzer diesel, 15,000bhp; 1 shaft	20kts	5 holds, 7 hatches, 12 pass, 419m³ ref
NICOLA (SD-14 type[1])	Grc	1967	Austin & Pickersgill, Sunderland	9069 15,363	462–6 × 67–1 × 38–6 × 28–6 *141.0 × 20.48 × 11.74 × 8.86*	Derricks 10 × 5 tons	1 Hawthorn Leslie/ Sulzer diesel, 5500bhp; 1 shaft	15kts	5 holds, 5 hatches
KHIAN CAPTAIN ('Freedom' type[2])	Grc	1967	IHI, Tokyo	9918 14,153	465–1 × 65–1 × 40–6 × 28–10 *141.76 × 19.84 × 12.35 × 8.78*	Derricks 12 × 10 tons	1 IHI/Pielstick diesel, 5130bhp; 1 shaft	14.5kts	4 holds, 6 hatches
MELAMPUS	UK	1976	Mitsubishi, Nagasaki	16,031 21,618	540–4 × 85–6 × 34–10 × 28–8 *164.7 × 26.07 × 10.62 × 8.74*	Derricks 3 × 35 tons, 5 × 22 tons, 1 × 10 tons	1 Mitsubishi/Sulzer diesel, 16,800bhp; 1 shaft	18kts	5 holds, 9 hatches, 773 TEUs incl 76 ref
BAAB ULLAH	Ina	1983	Sasebo HI, Sasebo	9471 13,645	439–8 × 71–4 × 39–5 × 31–0 *134.02 × 21.75 × 12.02 ×9.46*	Cranes 2 × 35 tons; derricks 2 × 15 tons	1 Mitsubishi/B&W diesel, 11,600bhp; 1 shaft	17kts	3 holds, 6 hatches, 1001m³ liquid cargo in deep tanks
LELIEGRACHT	Ne	1987	Miho Zosensho, Shimizu	5994 9601	371–2 × 63–1 × 37–1 × 28–0 *113.14 × 19.23 × 11.31 × 8.54*	Cranes 2 × 50 tons	1 Hanshin diesel, 5350bhp; 1 shaft	14kts	1 hold, 2 hatches, 564 TEU

Notes: [1,2] Variations in specification to suit owners specific requirements.

means that very large tramp, bulk carrier and liner service decisions are, in fact, made in Tokyo. Huge Japanese industrial and service corporations, including some very powerful trading companies, are making daily decisions of great consequence to the shipping world. These decisions in Tokyo tend to revolve about Japanese trading interests whereas those in London are more 'international'.

Hong Kong has emerged as an important centre of control and management of shipping ventures. Both Hong Kong and Singapore owe their start as commercial control centres in large part to the farming out of British monies and ships to havens with somewhat looser regulatory control, or, put another way, to places offering more freedom to behave as profit-seeking enterprises. This, of course, has particular appeal to shipowners imbued with a tramp philosophy.

Other shipping control centres of note, to-day, must include Piraeus, Oslo, Hamburg, Paris, Rotterdam, Moscow, Genoa, Beijing, Seoul and Taipei.

A final word is needed regarding the thousands of ship agents scattered around the world that husband the tramp and bulk carrier vessels. Every port has them. Large shipping lines may have several offices of their own in several countries and literally hundreds of agents, one for each port, to handle their vessels elsewhere. Large ship agencies may have a dozen or more branch offices, and handle the basic needs of a ship in port – tugs, pilots, line handlers, fuel, cleaning, inspecting holds, provisions, crew replacements, medical attention, ship repair and maintenance work, cargo handling and documentation, customs, immigration and consular formalities, etc – which have not changed radically over the past fifty years.

There are some new considerations such as large scale waste and ballast disposal, and also some streamlining of old procedures, especially in cargo documentation. The revolution in communications equipment and procedures has vastly improved the speed and volume of information flows between ship and agent and owner and commodity shipper. However, there remains a special flavour to the tramp shipping and bulk carrier operations – there is a certain unpredictability, a knowledge that every ship will bring some new problem to be solved, some new story to be told.

D K Fleming

Acknowledgements

The assistance and encouragement of General Steamship Corporation (Seattle) and Simpson, Spence & Young (London) are appreciated.

Typical bulk and ore carriers 1966–1990

Ship (Class)	Flag	Built	By	GRT DWT (Cargo capacity m³)	Length (oa) × breadth × depth × draught Feet–Inches Metres	Cargo handling gear	Engines	Speed	Remarks
CAPE ST VINCENT	UK	1966	John Brown & Co, Clydebank	12,835 20,022	528–1 × 72–5 × 41–6 × 31–7 *160.96 × 22.12 × 12.65 × 9.62*	Cranes 2 × 7.5 tons; derricks 1 × 8 tons	1 Brown/Sulzer diesel, 9600bhp; 1 shaft	15.5kts	5 hatches
GRISCHUNA	Lib	1968	Nippon Kokan, Tsurumi	28,403 60,639	742–10 × 104–3 × 57–5 × 42–4 *226.42 × 31.78 × 17.51 × 12.9*	Gearless	1 Uraga/Sulzer diesel, 17,600bhp; 1 shaft	16.25kts	12 hatches
VANCOUVER CITY ('Cardiff' class)	UK	1970	Upper Clyde SBs, Govan	16,644 26,289 (38,361)	569–6 × 83–9 × 46–0 × 32–8 *173.59 × 25.51 × 14.03 × 9.96*	Cranes 5 × 15 tons	1 Kincaid/B&W diesel, 11,600bhp; 1 shaft	15.25kts	Crew 37 5 holds, 5 hatches
CHERRY FLOWER	Grc	1978	IHI, Kure	13,663 22,670 (30,800)	539–3 × 75–2 × 44–6 × 32–4 *164.35 × 22.92 × 13.57 × 9.85*	Cranes 5 × 10 tons	1 IHI/Pielstick diesel, 8000bhp; 1 shaft	15kts	Crew 27 5 holds, 5 hatches
RAVENSCRAIG	UK	1979	Harland & Wolff, Belfast	64,651 119,500 (131,875)	857–11 × 133–9 × 72–2 × 53–2 *261.5 × 40.75 × 22.0 × 16.2*	Gearless	1 Harland & Wolff/ B&W diesel, 24,800bhp; 1 shaft	15kts	Crew 40 9 holds, 9 hatches
WORLD DULCE	HK	1982	Hitachi Zosen, Nagasu	75,485 133,361 (153,709)	888–9 × 141–3 × 81–4 × 53–7 *270.9 × 43.06 × 23.8 × 16.35*	Gearless	1 Hitachi/B&W diesel, 18,400bhp; 1 shaft	14.5kts	9 holds, 9 hatches
CAPE FINISTERRE (Prinasa 26/15 type)	UK	1982	CCN, Niteroi, Brazil	16,023 26,003 (34,038)	568–1 × 87–6 × 44–4 × 32–0 *173.16 × 26.67 × 13.52 × 9.75*	Cranes 4 × 25 tons	1 Pesada/MAN diesel, 13,300bhp; 1 shaft	15kts	5 holds, 5 hatches
BRITISH STEEL	UK	1984	Harland & Wolff, Belfast	90,831 173,028 (194,254)	941–5 × 154–5 × 78–9 ×58–5 *286.95 × 47.07 × 24.01 × 17.8*	Gearless	1 Harland & Wolff/ B&W diesel, 19,713bhp; 1 shaft	14kts	Crew 32 9 holds, 9 hatches
BERGE STAHL	Nor	1986	Hyundai HI, Ulsan	175,720 364,767 (199,324)	1125–4 × 208–4 × 99–1 × 75–7 *343.01 × 63.51 × 30.21 × 23.03*	Gearless	1 Hyundai/B&W diesel, 24,858bhp; 1 shaft	13.5kts	10 holds, 10 hatches ore
AURIGA	Ita	1990	C N Italiani, Monfalcone	131,479 260,783 (157,000)	1059–9 × 178–0 × 90–2 × 67–3 *323.0 × 54.25 × 27.5 × 20.5*	Gearless	1 Italiani/Sulzer diesel, 16,900bhp; 1 shaft	13kts	7 holds, 7 hatches

2

Conventional General Cargo Liners and Refrigerated Ships

A CARGO liner is a ship which operates a regular scheduled service on a fixed route between designated ports, and carries many consignments of different commodities. It appeared primarily after the mid nineteenth century when steam propulsion, and the opening of the Suez Canal in 1869, made international scheduled services more possible.

Conventional general cargo liners

Many cargo vessels were, by the late nineteenth century, designed for specific trades. They had heavy-lift gear where tropical hardwood logs were loaded or the handling of heavy equipment was common; deep tanks for service in vegetable oil and latex producing regions; strong rooms for bullion and valuables; and refrigerated space in the meat and dairy product trades. Some combined many of these and other special features, and all had several decks and an array of derricks

During the 1950s the People's Republic of China, through its shipping entity China Ocean Shipping Co (COSCO), made inroads into the international shipping scene, at first slowly, but reaching a peak in the 1970s when through COSCO and a number of subsidiary companies in Hong Kong and Macao it purchased a very large number of new and secondhand vessels of all types. In 1976 alone it added ninety ocean-going vessels to its controlled fleet, comprising mainly good quality secondhand purchases. One of the purchases about then was Glenogle *(built 1962, 11,918 grt), previously owned by Glen Line Ltd, London, a typical large cargo liner of the period. Many purchases were from European and Japanese liner companies, which with the increase in container traffic provided the ship sale market with a steady supply of good quality, but redundant, general cargo vessels. Even these by the early 1990s were disappearing from the Chinese fleet due to that country's involvement in containerisation. (Glen Line)*

for the stowage and handling of hundreds of items of cargo.

In the early 1960s new general cargo vessels were still primarily multi-purpose common carriers with special equipment and able to accept a great range of commodities each in small quantities. These included manufactured goods, foodstuffs, fruits, refrigerated items, tea, coffee, cotton, textiles, vegetable oils or latex in tanks, and other relatively high value products. The long-distance ships were generally about 15,000 dwt, had a speed range of 15–20kts, the bridge, engine room and accommodation were amidships – often with cabins for up to twelve passengers (if more than twelve a full-time doctor had to be on board). There were five to six hatches; each hold had one to three tween-decks and four derricks for cargo handling. Short distance liners were of 4000 dwt to 7000 dwt, and possessed some similar characteristics.

By the late 1960s, there were more variations in general cargo liner design. The single tween-deck 'open' ship with very wide hatches became increasingly common. By the mid 1970s longer multi-purpose vessels of about 22,000 dwt were being built, and the bridge, main engine and accommodation were now aft in all modern liners. Some ships had twin hatches one to starboard and one to port to facilitate faster cargo handling and they were fitted with shipboard cranes. These were also

capable of lifting 25-tonne containers carried on deck. The operational speeds were around 20kts.

Table 2/1: Typical cargo liner of the 1960s

mv *Benvalla*
Owners: Ben Line Steamers Ltd, Leith, Edinburgh
Built by Charles Connell & Co Ltd, Glasgow; completed September 1962

Gross tonnage:	10,926
Net tonnage:	6249
Deadweight tonnes:	13,249
Length (oa):	167.52m
Length (bp):	154.87m
Breadth (max):	21.72m
Depth:	13.54m
Draught:	10.22m
Capacities: (cubic metres)	Grain 20,664
	Bale 17,433
	Refrigerated 419
Machinery:	15,000bhp (11,033kW) Rowan/Sulzer diesel
Speed in service:	20kts
No of screws:	1
Five holds	
Seven hatches	
Twenty winches	
Cranes:	2 × 5 tons
Derricks:	1 × 50 tons, 1 × 20 tons, 10 × 10 tons, 10 × 5 tons

Accommodation for twelve passengers

One of the most sophisticated groups of cargo liners of the 1970s was built for British owner, the Ocean Transport & Trading Group, of Liverpool. Here, Melampus, *one of seven near-sisters, four of which were built in Japan, is carrying a large cargo of containers, and some motor cars on deck. Her multi-purpose capabilities made her eminently suitable for all the trades in which the Ocean Group was involved, including Europe–West Africa, Europe–Australasia, Europe–Far East, and trans-Pacific. The large container capacity of 773 (407 below deck, 366 above) was useful for charters into regular container service requirements. The general cargo capacity was 30,335cu m. Equipped with seven derricks ranging from 10 to 35 tons capacity, the vessel had capability to load and discharge in ports where shore facilities were limited or non-existant.* (FotoFlite)

The multi-purpose cargo carriers with containers on deck were the ships destined to be displaced by fully containerised vessels on the North Atlantic and cross-Pacific trades. Their major defect was, in spite of many design improvements, the individual handling of each item of break bulk hold cargo and the consequent protracted time in ports.

The conventional cargo liner is still used in the medium distance Mediterranean/north-west Europe route and also in the trades of some of the developing countries and the People's Republic of China but even in these they are in ever-diminishing numbers due to the increase of container and roro facilities. The particulars of a typical small sized modern cargo liner owned by a developing country, completed in 1987, is shown by Table 2/2.

A special type of cargo liner is the refrigerated ship. The 'reefer' has multi-tween-decks, and can also carry non-refrigerated cargoes if need be and containers

Table 2/2: Small size general cargo liner of the late 1980s

mv *El-Djazair*
Owners: General National Maritime Transport Co, Libya
Built by Kyokuyo Zosen KK, Chofu, Japan; completed in 1987

Gross tons:	8195
Net tons:	3411
Summer dwt:	9614 tonnes
Length (oa):	125.0m
Breadth:	20.0m
Depth:	11.8m
Summer draught:	7.2m
Diesel engine:	6000 bhp
Service speed:	14.8kts

Four ship cranes (capacities 1 × 26, 2 × 20.5, 1 × 15.25 tonnes)
Three holds; total capacity 14,746 cubic metres

Containers:	320, including 20 refrigerated
Crew:	27

on deck. However, it has very special functions and is therefore discussed separately in this chapter.

In the past the majority of cargo liners operated within conferences – owners in the same trades co-ordinating their sailings and agreed levels of freight rates. The first conference was the UK–Calcutta (1975), and today, although with much reduced influence, conferences still function in the majority of liner trades in both the conventional and containerised sectors.

A D Couper

Refrigerated transport

Maritime transport plays a particularly important role in the efficiency of the world-wide commercial circulation of perishable products. These can be grouped as (1) early, and other fresh or frozen or refrigerated fruits and vegetables (in addition to apples and pears, there are also essentially Mediterranean products and tropical and equatorial fruits) and (2) perishable foodstuffs which include, in particular, fresh, frozen or refrigerated meat and fish, eggs, milk and the whole range of dairy products.

As a result of the technical revolution in transportation over the past thirty years, with the introduction of multi-temperature refrigeration, of pallets and of containers in ships, there has been a progressive increase in the volume of refrigerated trade world-wide,

although the major routes and the considerable importance of some large pools of transporters remain unchanged.

Continuity and growth in flow of refrigerated trade

The tonnages of refrigerated commodities are relatively small. If the French ports are taken as an example, refrigerated maritime trade represented at the end of the 1980s an annual flow of about 4 million tonnes. It is small compared with grain flow shipments which accounted for 17 million tonnes and only as much as the traffic of animal feed. It is half the traffic of fertilisers and almost one-fortieth of petroleum (crude and products) shipments. However, for many port communities it is a profitable traffic; the refrigerated trade in the port of Nantes, for example, provides about 20 per cent of dockers' employment.

The world's refrigerated vessel fleet is correspondingly small; it represented in 1989 only 1.84 per cent of the number of ships and 1.61 per cent of tonnage and this is not expected to rise due to the marginal increases in refrigerated cargoes in containers, particularly on the Australasian and South American trades.

In 1989, according to the UNCTAD *Commodity Yearbook*, 6.8 million tonnes of bananas were imported by developed market-economy countries out of a total of 7.5 million tonnes (90.5 per cent). Developing countries' exports represented 7.2 million tonnes. In 1990, the annual increase was 4 per cent up from 1989 with 8.4 million tonnes.

In 1989, bovine meat represented more than

Typical of refrigerated cargo vessels of the 1970s was Gladiola, *completed in February 1972 by Aalborg Vaerft AS, Denmark. With a B&W diesel engine rated at 23,200 bhp, and a service speed of 23.5kts, she was suitable for world-wide reefer trading, and for much of her career was attached to the Salen reefer pool based in Stockholm.* Gladiola *was owned by Adelaide Shipping Lines Ltd, London, an associate of Maritime Fruit Carriers Corp, of Israel.* (Skyfotos)

3.8 million tonnes carried world-wide but 3.22 million tonnes came from developed countries (84.2 per cent) and it is the exchanges between developed countries which dominate (2.5 million tonnes); the developing countries importing only 0.9 million tonnes.

The total trade in fresh meat – refrigerated and deep-frozen – represents about 8 million tonnes world-wide. Among the zones of exportation, northwest Europe is ahead of North America, Australia and New Zealand, while the portion of the other regions of the globe can be considered as negligible. Importing countries – eastern Europe aside – are mainly in northwest Europe (34 per cent), southern Europe (20 per cent), North America (12 per cent), Asia (17 per cent) and in the Middle East (6.5 per cent). However, although

Discharging refrigerated cargo by 'traditional' means at Wilson Quay, Nantes, is the Moroccan reefer vessel Ifni. (Port of Nantes-St Zaire)

tonnage is rather small, the value of the product is high – about $20 billion.

The maritime transportation of fresh and deep-frozen fish accounts for 4 million tonnes with a value of more than $10 billion. There are three major areas for exportation and importation – Europe, North America and Asia. As in the case of meat, the demand for the transport of fish in Asia is generated mainly by Japan, and to a lesser extent by Hong Kong, Singapore and South Korea. The exchange of refrigerated products is linked to the concentration of centres of production and consumption and so, in the southern hemisphere, where population density is low, there is little activity.

These examples show the influence of wealthier consumer countries in generating import and export flows of refrigerated products.

Diversification of maritime refrigerated trades

The traditional consumers of the northern hemisphere have found new products in recent years. As far as fruits are concerned, beside the classical traditional goods such as oranges and other citrus fruits, pineapples, apples and pears, 'new' fruits have appeared in the form of mangos, pawpaws, lychees, kiwi fruit and others.

New markets have appeared in Asia. For example, 80 per cent of the exported apples

from Washington State via the port of Seattle go to Asian countries of the Pacific rim: Taiwan was the first buyer of these fruits in 1989 (up to $22 million), Hong Kong the second (up to $11 million), followed by Thailand, Singapore and Malaysia. The total exports of fruits through Seattle reached 200,000 tonnes or $200 million in 1990 (81,600 tonnes and $64 million in 1980). It is not by chance that Lauritzen Asia Ltd, a wholly-owned subsidiary of the well-known Danish company, was established in Singapore in 1985. It shows the effort of the group to spread its network over the Asiatic market where the demand for refrigerated products is increasing. It is also expected that the People's Republic of China will become more and more a fruit exporting country. Just as Bangkok has become a centre for the exports of frozen fish, this market is also growing in the Philippines and Malaysia.

The example of the maritime transportation of bananas shows that this evolution has been a gradual one, through a series of modifications and minor developments rather than any dramatic change.

Traditionally, export companies had concentrated on the Caribbean which was the zone best placed to serve Europe and North America. However, with the increase in the consumption of bananas in Asia, new trade routes have developed from Ecuador across the Pacific. In Asia itself, banana cultivation has developed; as is true of the Philippines, which supplies some of Japan's banana imports, and countries such as India and Thailand have become surplus producers. Inter-Asian trade routes have thus been created.

Thirty years ago, Central America was dominant in its role of generator of maritime banana transport. Now there is a tendency towards an even greater dispersion of zones of production and exportation. It was not until the 1970s, however, that a non-American supplier – the Philippines – took third place behind Ecuador and Costa Rica and ahead of Honduras.

Parallel to this growth in markets and to the technical improvements in vessels there has,

of ships were flagging out, particularly under the Cyprus flag.

The major fruit producing companies, most notably North American firms which dominate the world banana market, control the fleets of refrigerated ships, often placed within major pools and working under flags of convenience. One can mention United Brands (trademark *Chiquita*) which operates about sixty ships, a dozen of which operate through the management of their British E & F Ship Management Ltd (better known as Elders & Fyffes), and Castle Cooke (trademark *Dole*) which beneficially owns several vessels under Liberian and Panamanian registration.

over a period of several years, been a geographical shift in the ownership of tonnage.

The development of new maritime inputs

In 1966, 77 per cent of refrigerated maritime potential was to be found in Europe, of which 35.8 per cent belonged to the member countries of the European Free Trade Zone (EFTA), 33.1 per cent to the six members of the EEC, and 8.1 per cent to the countries of eastern Europe. America represented only 13.7 per cent (8.6 per cent belonging to the USA), and Asia represented 4.7 per cent of potential.

In 1989, Europe remained in control of a large percentage of the world fleet, but it no longer enjoyed a monopoly, representing now no more than 15 per cent. During the period

1966–89, there were considerable advances on the part of vessels under flags of convenience (27 per cent), the fleets of the former socialist countries (33 per cent) and of Asia. It is significant that the world's largest refrigerated fleet in 1989 was the Soviet Union (325 ships), the second, Panamanian (202 ships) and the third, Japanese (201 ships) out of a total of 1402 reefer ships.

The big refrigerated fleet of the Soviet Union was shared between companies like Black Sea Shipping, the Latvian Shipping Company and the Far Eastern Shipping Company. But the very rapid changes in the countries of eastern Europe since 1989 has upset this situation. The 'former' socialist European and Russian fleets are now being ruled by the market economy; in 1990, dozens

Improvements and evolution

The great diversification of maritime refrigerated routes is closely linked to the technical transformations which have revolutionised the ships themselves.

The traditional single temperature vessel

The resolution of the problem of the transportation of perishable goods began towards the end of the nineteenth century, in particular

Following the Second World War the majority of maritime nations put in hand programmes to re-establish refrigerated cargo carriers, scores of which were lost during 1939–45. By the mid-1950s numerous new vessels had entered service in the fleets of established refrigerated cargo ships owners, particularly in Scandinavia. However, many vessels which survived the war carried on in service until the late 1950s and even into the '60s. One such vessel was Jamaica Producer, *built in 1934 for Jamaica Banana Producers Steamship Co Ltd, capable of carrying over 4000 tons of fruit at a service speed of 15.5kts. (Skyfotos)*

following the work of British engineers and also of the Frenchman Charles Tellier, who was responsible for the first international transportation of refrigerated meat from Buenos Aires aboard *Frigorifique*. The transportation of fruit which, in order to avoid premature maturing, must be kept at between 12.5 °C and 13 °C lead to the development of the banana carrier. With the encouragement of the British government the Elder Dempster company, then franchise holder of the Britain-Jamaica route, launched in 1901 *Port Morant* (2800 dwt). This experiment was imitated a few years later by the United States company, United Fruit.

The number of single temperature refrigerated ships, specialised either in the transportation of fruit or meat, each of which requires a different temperature, then increased. Even though these ships were relatively small, mass transportation had been chosen as the only option which would allow the delivery to distant markets (6000nm) between Puerto Bolivar and Hamburg) of products capable of competing with local produce.

Even until the 1960s modifications had been limited to improvements in operating speeds and hold capacities, and virtually little else.

For example, the Lauritzen vessels at the beginning of the 1930s had an average hold capacity of 2800m³ and a speed of 13kts, while at the end of the decade new reefers had an average capacity of 5180m³ and a speed of 15.5kts.

The multi-temperature refrigeration and pallet revolutions

The single temperature refrigerated vessel of the 1950s was still, generally, a small highly specialised ship. From 1955 to 1965 technical improvements did not fundamentally change such things as the quality of ventilation of fruit

transporters, the development of automatic temperature control or increases in operating speed. Vessels which did not incorporate these improvements were often sold to Eastern-bloc countries or to the Third World.

The multi-temperature refrigerated ship appeared in the 1960s and it has since become the standard means of transport. This new vessel was capable of transporting every sort of merchandise, a fact which greatly increased its flexibility and thus its profitability. Fruit transportation requires different temperatures of refrigeration, but always takes place above freezing point. Meat and fish need a temperature of a few degrees below zero, and deep-frozen goods must be transported at temperatures of around –25 °C. There were many such vessels in service by the end of the 1960s, mainly in service with Scandinavian concerns, particularly Sven Salen of Sweden.

The same period saw the development of a standard sized pallet (1.20m × 1.0m) which has optimised handling, and the internal layouts of multi-temperature refrigerated ships have been designed taking these dimensions into account. Out of a total of 280 cargo vessels of more than 3500m³ built during 1984–90, only about twenty were not pallet compatible. Further-

'Unitised' meat cargo being discharged from a reefer vessel at the Commerce Quay, St Nazaire, France. (Port of Nantes-St Nazaire)

more, most of these ships were destined for the ex-Communist bloc. This change has taken place with considerable speed, since in 1975, only ten per cent of the refrigerated fleet was pallet compatible.

It could be said that maritime cold transport, which, in the past, was technically relatively dependant on the products exported, has been able to free itself from this limitation by carrying a whole range of products. This has been reinforced by the phenomenon of containerisation.

The revolution of the refrigerated container

It was at the beginning of the 1970s that containerisation made its appearance. The first experiments in this field, as far as the transportation of tropical fruits is concern, were carried out by United Brands through its British subsidiary Fyffes, with which, in 1972, two small container ships *Barranca* and *Bayano* (4087 dwt) entered service on the Honduras-US route (Puerto Cortès – Galveston). Containerisation also enabled companies operating regular routes to enter the refrigerated market. Their ships, particularly if in service on a certain trade route may offer a very large hold capacity.

For example, on the West Indies-Europe route operated from France by the Compagnie Générale Maritime, the single temperature refrigerated banana carrier *Barfleur* (3111 grt) built in 1938, had a hold capacity of 4620m³ and a speed of 13kts. *Fort Joséphine* (4150 grt), one of the first multi-temperature vessels which had a minimum temperature of –10 °C and was completed in 1964 had a capacity of 6440m³, while the second generation multi-temperature ship *Pointe Madame* (6561 grt), launched in 1973, had a minimum temperature of –25 °C and a speed of 20kts for a capacity of 8600m³. However, the series of refrigerated container ships built after 1978, such as the *Fort Royal* (32,671 grt) with its speed of 22.6kts and with 915 refrigerated containers providing

a capacity of 20,508m³, show the degree of competitiveness regular containerised lines can provide.

The owners of regular shipping lines are developing the refrigerated chain. Operators of regular lines work on a fixed route with containerships able to carry refrigerated products. Either the containers are autonomous (80 per cent of the fleet, about 277,500 full reefer containers in 1990) and have their own refrigerated system, or they are Conair-containers (20 per cent of the fleet, about 69,500 units); this latter system is fairly new, appearing about twelve years ago and is based on the principle of air circulation inside the container (fresh air is drawn in and warm air forced out).

For the owners, the risks of the refrigerated products market can be counterbalanced, to some extent, by the transport of other non-refrigerated goods. The owners of regular lines offer a refrigerated chain door-to-door and improve it to cope with both competition and growing demand, as in the case of the Sea-Land, one of the greatest regular companies in the world.

The electric boxes fleet of Sea-Land Service was composed of 13,000 units at the end of 1989, following a new investment programme of over $150m dealing with new refrigerated containers, new staff, and a computerised information system able to manage a set of services to cope with a boom in demand, especially in some markets. For example, the meat exports from the United States to Asia

were expected to increase by seven to eight per cent during 1990–92. Sea-Land is pursuing a policy of quality within the perishable products market. It explains the setting up from 1 January 1990, on the world-wide network, of the marketing programme named 'Reefer plus'. It includes a package of specific guarantees such as 'seaclean' (comprehensive washing providing high standard container interiors), 'seafresh' (constant control of humidity levels for cargo) and 'seawatch' (high technology to assist the cargo).

The refrigerated transportation of bulk liquids

It was in 1982 that the first refrigerated tankers appeared and by 1990 there were six in service, all specialised in the transportation of orange

Refrigerated containers of Sea-Land Service Inc on the land-bridge railroad flats of the New York & Southwestern Railroad. (Sea-Land Service)

juice. The traditional form of packaging consisted in casks stocked in a cold room, but the size of Brazilian exports to the United States and Europe encouraged the development of this type of vessel. Brazil and the United States are the world's two major producers, but it is possible that the market will expand to other regions. The Americans are big consumers of orange juice and export very little of it, and so virtually all the maritime transportation of orange juice is of Brazilian origin. The ships' capacities vary from 5131m³ to 12,184m³ (in the *Uchoa* and *Bebedouro* respectively), and the orange juice is transported in tanks at the temperature of −10 °C.

Both *Bebedouro* and *Uchoa*, which are representative of this new type of vessel are under Liberian registration and managed by a Hong Kong company. *Bebedouro* (10,195 grt) was purpose-built by Hyundai Heavy Industries, Ulsan, South Korea, and completed in August 1986. There is a fuller description of this vessel in Chapter 7.

However, *Uchoa*, a pioneer in the trade, was a conversion from a refrigerated general cargo carrier, and now has a cargo space consisting of twelve stainless steel tanks with an aggregate capacity of 5131 cubic metres. Powered by a 4500bhp Mannheim diesel engine, she was built at Galatz, Romania, in 1974 for a Norwegian owner, and was acquired by her present owner, Overseas Navigation Ltd, in 1981.

This type of vessel illustrates, as do those mentioned above (multi-temperature and container ships), the way in which maritime cold transport is able to impose its own norms along the chain of distribution. The port of arrival in Europe for orange juice tankers is Ghent which, in December 1982, opened a specialised terminal. Affiliated to the Brazilian group Citrosuco and operated by the Citrus Coolstore company, the Ghent installation is composed of a reception centre for bulk fruit juice (20,000 tonnes) and a terminal for the reception of fruit juice conventionally transported in casks (35,000 tonnes). Two other firms, the American Cargill group and the Brazilian Cutrale group share the world market. The countries of eastern Europe and of Asia provide promising new potential markets for the sale of fruit juice.

However, whatever the diversity of refrigerated transport on liners, or on tankers,

Typical of the large refrigerated carriers of the 1980s is the Hong Kong-registered Spring Delight, *built in South Korea in 1984. This 18kt vessel, fitted with a Hyundai/B&W 10,440 bhp diesel engine, is designed for world-wide trading and has 12,830cu m of refrigerated cargo carrying space. Her four 16-ton electric cranes serve four hatches and seven holds.* Spring Delight *can carry 290 TEUs – 128 in holds and 162 on deck.* (FotoFlite)

they are overtaken, with regard to capacity, by the potential of the specialised fleet often with very specific owners as can be seen in gas transport, forest products or car carriers.

The large pools and their organisation

The shipowners who operate by international tramping have a specialised refrigerated fleet whose operations depend upon the offer of cargoes and contracts. Because of the risks existing on this market, the owners must operate at a global level so that the negative effects in one place may be counterbalanced by positive effects in another place.

Six major groups dominate the market: Cool Carriers, Seatrade, Lauritzen Reefers, Alpha Reefer Transport, Star Reefers and Universal Reefers, and other Netherlands, British, German, Greek, Japanese and South African operators are also very important. All six together comprise a fleet of about 250 ships. There are also notable companies of less importance. They own refrigerated ships and charter them on the world market.

Today, no single owner could expect to make a profit on a scale as those made by a pool which manages dozens of ships. A large fleet has several vital advantages including a strong marketing position, rapid response to the change of marketing needs, optimal scheduling, minimal waiting and idle time, high load factors and the ability to handle large contracts smoothly.

An example of the commercial management system is the Leonida system of the first reefer pool of the world, administered from Sweden by Cool Carriers AB.

The owners within the pool, such as Leonhardt & Blumberg (Germany), Christian F Ahrenkiel (Germany), Laeisz (Germany), Ahlers (Belgium), Mediteranska Plovidba (Yugoslavia), are responsible for registration, financing, technical management and crewing. The administration of Cool Carriers, with the

Leonida system, decides on and is responsible for marketing and contracting, scheduling and operation, bunkering and cargo handling. In exchange for this service, Cool Carriers' profit charge of 6.95 per cent is deducted from the total net earnings, whereafter returns are distributed on the basis of a formula which is supplied to each ship. The formula includes cargo carrying capacity, number of days in operation, where idle and waiting are included, and actual fuel consumption as well as trade factors, the ship's efficiency and suitability for world-wide reefer operations based on twenty-five factors revised periodically in response to long-term changes in the market. The system is based on computer management able to analyse about 750 voyages each year.

Cool Carriers has twenty per cent of the whole reefer market. Such a management system also exists with some minor differences, within other pools. Under the Cool Carriers commercial banner the ships' flags are various – there are ships whose owners are Japanese and who are operating with the Panamanian flag or that of Vanuatu or of the Philippines, for example.

The specialised fleets of major pools: J Lauritzen A/S, Denmark

The shipping companies, most particularly those based in Scandinavia around which several pools have been created, have traditional activities within the transportation of refrigerated products which go back to the very beginning of this century.

For instance, the Danish company J Lauritzen A/S, of Copenhagen, created in 1884 is one of the first which invested heavily in reefer transport. The beginnings of Lauritzen's interest in reefers can be traced back to 1905 when oranges were carried as a cargo by company ships trading between Britain and Spain's Mediterranean coast. This traffic continued for many years on a seasonal basis

before electrical ventilation was installed on several vessels, leading to increased cargoes and more regular services. Little by little, the market grew. In 1931, the company began to carry bananas between West Africa and Europe and foreseeing the promising trade offered by tropical fruit, Lauritzen increased his fleet of specialised ships adding to their name the word *Reefer*. Shortly before the Second World War, those ships (*African Reefer, Canadian Reefer, Brasilian Reefer, Chilean Reefer, American Reefer* and *Australian Reefer*) began a world-wide trade which saw them carry pears, apples and citrus fruits from South America to Europe, bananas from Central America to the USA and Europe, and other trades.

It was on December 1971 that the Lauritzen Reefer Pool was formed (together with Finnish shipowner Gustaf Erikson) and as a continuing process the fleet was renewed and ships became larger and more efficient. The company has also had an association with P & O.

The company took delivery of three vessels during 1990, each of them costing about $41m. The biggest of the series, *Ditlev Lauritzen* (14,406 grt) is also the biggest reefer ship in the world with a capacity of 21,684cu m and 16,950 dwt. In comparison, the ships which entered the fleet in 1957–59 *Arabian Reefer, Belgian Reefer* and *Chilean Reefer* were 6800cu m vessels. So reefer maritime transport has also been affected by the race towards gigantism, just like other branches of maritime transport.

The new vessel, *Ditlev Lauritzen*, efficient with regard to bunker consumption, can be manned with a crew of seven persons. This is the result of a joint programme of research with the company and the Danish Ministry of Industry. *Ditlev Lauritzen* obtained the ICC (Integrated Computer Control) standard of Lloyd's Register because of the high integrated level of information and means of control aboard ship. The five holds where the temperature can be set from −29 up to +13 °C, include 23 compartments thanks to between-decks dividing nine subdivisions of temperature. The whole surface amounts to around one hectare (about 2.5 acres or exactly

The sophisticated reefer vessel Ditlev Lauritzen *was completed in 1990 by Danyard AS, Frederikshavn, for J Lauritzen AS, Copenhagen. With the most up-to-date automation, this vessel, equipped with a Korea HI/B&W diesel engine of 15,288 bhp, can operate with a crew of seven to nine. The first of four sister-ships,* Ditlev Lauritzen *is engaged in world-wide reefer trades as part of the international fleet of fifty vessels which make up the fleet of Lauritzen Reefers.* (J Lauritzen AS)

9070sq m) which permits the loading of 7000 standard pallets.

Ditlev Lauritzen which has five deck-cranes can also accommodate 236 containers in the hold and 186 on the upper deck. These provide the chance to make a profit during the trip towards the port of loading and also of carrying products inside the refrigerated containers (332).

As with the other such vessels, the refrigeration is provided by cold air flowing under a wattle-floor where there are pallets or cardboard-boxes with fruits, or animal carcasses. Naturally, the holds are insulated. The cooling of insufflated air is provided by a plant working with *Fréon R22*, a gas which is considered to be ozone-friendly.

A range of specialised ships

Every company tries to offer the most reliable equipment. The example of Lauritzen is not the only one. During 1989–91 the fleet managed by Cool Carriers was augmented by four large reefer ships, *Hansa Bremen, Hansa Lübeck, Hansa Stockholm* and *Hansa Visby* owned by the German company Leonhardt & Blumberg. They are of 15,576cu m capacity, 12,943 dwt and the refrigerated compartments

Carrying refrigerated produce from the West Indies to Barry, South Wales, is Geestbay, *one of a small fleet operated by Geest Industries Ltd, Spalding. Geest shipping operations started with short-sea carriers linking mainly the UK and Netherlands, the home of the Geest parent concern. The company's ocean-going development brought with it a number of high-class vessels which additionally became popular with accommodation for passengers.* Geestbay, *with accommodation for twelve passengers, a cargo capacity of 12,954cu m, and service speed of 19.5kts, was built by Smith's Dock Co Ltd, South Bank, Middlesbrough, in 1981.* (FotoFlite)

have eight subdivisions of cold between –30 °C and –12 °C, can carry 290 containers and have four deck cranes.

The race for increased hold capacities undertaken by the principal companies has not resulted in the obsolescence of smaller vessels, and construction is not limited to units of 10,000 dwt. In May 1991, ninety-one refrigerated ships were under construction in shipyards throughout the world. Nineteen had a a deadweight of less than 5000, twenty-seven a deadweight of between 5000 and 7500, twenty-three between 7500 and 10,000 dwt; only twenty-two ships were larger than this, of which six were of a series of 13,100-tonners being built for Chiquita Brands. The large shipowners have small vessels too. Gustaf Erikson has for example four refrigerated vessels of 5150 dwt on order as well another series of eight ships of 11,000 dwt.

In today's Lauritzen fleet, there is a whole range of ships, from the pride of the fleet, *Ditlev Lauritzen* down to the *New Zealand Reefer* (1982) which, like her sister-ship, *Nippon Reefer* has a capacity of 8657 dwt (11,043m³).

Having in mind the nature of products transported and the distances involved it is not necessary to have a fleet composed only of large, rapid vessels. The pools have great freedom of movement to adapt to the demands of the market. Herein lies a whole business strategy. The advantage of quicker ships, negligible over short distances becomes, on the other hand, very noticeable on longer voyages – this fact having to be taken into consideration along with the cost of fuel.

For instance, on the Ecuador–New Orleans route (2250nm), the journey time at 17kts is five days thirteen hours, and four days two hours at 23kts. The difference is therefore not very large, which is far from being the case for the Ecuador-Japan route: nineteen days and fourteen hours at 17kts; sixteen days and fourteen hours at 20kts; fourteen days and twelve hours at 23kts.

Reefer ships which are operated by pools benefit from a structure which optimises the high investments of the reefer chain, which account for the predominant position of wealthier countries in this market.

Domination of maritime groups and production companies

There are few producing countries, particularly among the developing countries, which are free from the domination of the major group.

It is well known that the production of the banana republics of Central America is controlled by great multinational companies such as Castle & Cooke, United Brands, and Del Monte. Even in countries where this domination is much more limited, the influence of wealthier consumer countries exists, most particularly in respect of maritime exports.

The Chilean owner, Compania Sud Americana de Vapores (CSAV) has become involved in the maritime export of Chilean fruits with four modern refrigerated ships. Although not a very substantial fleet, and with limited capacity of up to 12,975 dwt, the arrival of competitors on the trans-Pacific routes, has diminished the Chilean share of the trade. In 1989, Chile exported 105 million cases of fruit, of which CSAV carried 45 per cent. In 1990 Nippon Yusen Kaisha, of Japan, entered the market and took 15 per cent. The share of CSAV fell to 35 per cent.

For the most part, national owners are very dependant on the major multinational producing firms. For example, Ecuador, the first banana exporting country in the world, is one of the very few countries of the Third World to have a noteworthy fleet (tenth in the league in 1989 with eighteen vessels of 126,545 gross tons).

It is the private Ecuadorian owner Naviera del Pacifico – managed from Antwerp – which exports bananas of the parent company, Noboa group, with ten or so refrigerated ships. Another Compania Maritima Agmaresa, is a subsidiary of the Castle & Cooke group.

Further examples of multinational involvement exist in Cameroon, where Del Monte and United Brands are present. Here the national maritime company, Cameroon Shipping Lines, subcontracts the maritime transport to the pool Seatrade Groningen (Netherlands) and in the Ivory Coast, Société Ivoirienne de Transports Maritimes charters ships to Cool Carriers.

Conclusion

The maritime transport of refrigerated products is an activity which is shared between international tramp traders and regular shipping lines. Given the revolution in this sector over the last thirty years, it is possible to predict a development in traffic in the future, parallel to an extension of activity world-wide. Ports have understood this and are continuing to invest in specialised installations in the knowledge that the needs of consumers will continue to increase.

Anywhere in the world, or more exactly in developed countries, anybody can taste strawberries in winter; seasons no longer exist thanks to refrigerated transport chains organised essentially by maritime pools.

Moreover, the organisation of this maritime trade is particularly concentrated. The maritime flow of refrigerated goods is based on the theory of an oligopolistic market, distinguishing it from the traditional model which assumes an open system of maritime transport.

Jacques Marcadon

Maritime Fruit Carriers Co Ltd, of Haifa, Israel, was founded in the 1960s and before the end of that decade owned a substantial fleet of reefer vessels. Sabracore, built by Akers MV, Oslo, was typical of these, and had a cargo capacity of 11,774cu m. Principal particulars were 8035 grt, 9866 dwt, length 147.83m, breadth 20.05m, and speed 20kts. The owning company, which had extensive interests outside Israel, including the UK and USA, was liquidated in the 1980s. (Aker Group)

Typical refrigerated cargo vessels in service since 1945

Ship (Class)	Flag	Built	By	GRT DWT (Cargo capacity m³)	Length (oa) × breadth × depth × draught Feet–Inches Metres	Cargo handling gear	Engines	Speed	Remarks
JAMAICA PRODUCER	UK	1934	Lithgows, Port Glasgow	5464 4900 (6773)	423–0 × 54–9 × 33–6 × 23–10 128.93 × 16.69 × 10.21 × 7.25	Derricks, 1 × 25 tons + others	Quad exp. Rowan steam; 1 shaft	15.5kts	—
ARGENTINEAN REEFER	Dmk	1945	Aalborg Vft, Aalborg	2808	374–0 × 51–7 × 29–1 × 19–4 114.0 × 15.71 × 8.87 × 5.89	Derricks 1 × 15 tons 10 × 5 tons	2 Helsingfors/ B&W diesels 3700bhp; 2 shafts	16kts	4 pass 23 crew
BELGIAN REEFER	Dmk	1958	Aalborg Vft, Aalborg	4871 5850	437–7 × 59–3 × 37–5 × 25–11 133.36 × 18.06 × 11.41 × 7.89	Derricks 8 × 5 tons	2 B&W diesels 8160bhp; 2 shafts	18.5kts	24–27 crew; bulbous bow fitted 1963; speed to 19.5kts
S A ZEBEDIELA	SA	1968	Verolme, Heusden	6311 10,529 (14,147)	521–5 × 65–7 × 40–1 × 25–3 158.93 × 20.0 × 12.22 × 7.7	Derricks 12 × 10 tons	1 Verolme diesel 9600bhp; 1 shaft	17kts	6 holds 6 hatches
SABRACORE	Isr	1968	Akers MV, Oslo	8035 9866 (11,774)	485–0 × 65–7 × 41–0 × 30–0 147.83 × 20.0 × 12.5 × 9.16	Derricks 2 × 15 tons 8 × 5–10 tons	1 Nylands/ B&W diesel 11,500bhp; 1 shaft	20kts	7 pass 4 holds 4 hatches
SNOW FLAKE	Swe	1972	La Ciotat, La Ciotat	11,422 12,782 (17,319)	568–8 × 81–0 × 48–11 × 33–9 173.31 × 24.69 × 14.91 × 10.3	Cranes 8 × 5 tons	1 Sulzar diesel 23,200bhp; 1 shaft	22.75kts	5 holds 5 hatches 16 TEUs
GEESTBAY	UK	1981	Smith's Dock, Middlesborough	7729 9970 (12,954)	521–9 × 70–1 × 41–11 × 29–0 159.04 × 21.37 × 12.76 × 8.83	Cranes 2 × 12.5 tons 2 × 8 tons; derricks 4 × 5 tons	1 Kincaid/ B&W diesel 13,100bhp; 1 shaft	19.5kts	12 pass 4 holds 4 hatches 72 TEUs
SPRING BLOSSOM	Swe	1984	Koyo DY, Mihara	12,105 10,098 (13,077)	498–9 × 79–0 × 44–0 ×28–4 152.03 × 24.08 × 13.42 × 8.63	Cranes 4 ×16 tons	1 Mitsui/ B&W diesel 11,600bhp; 1 shaft	19kts	36 crew 7 holds 7 hatches 287 TEUs
LINCOLN UNIVERSAL	SL	1987	Hayashikane DT, Shimonoseki	9622 11,055 (12,743)	474–1 × 74–3 × 42–7 × 30–4 144.51 × 22.64 × 13.0 × 9.26	Cranes 2 × 30 tons 2 × 10 tons	1 Mitsui/ B&W diesel 10,672bhp; 1 shaft	19kts	4 holds 4 hatches 66 TEUs
DEL MONTE PLANTER	Lib	1989	Ast. Espanoles, Seville	8945 9867 (10,477)	462–7 × 73–3 × 41–10 × 30–2 141.0 × 22.33 × 12.75 × 9.2	Cranes 4 ×	1 Espanoles/ B&W diesel 13,250bhp; 1 shaft	20kts	4 holds 4 hatches 124 TEUs
HANSA BREMEN	WG	1989	Bremer Vulcan, Bremen	10,842 19,461 (15,576)	513–6 × 75–7 × 43–4 × 31–4 156.53 × 23.04 × 13.2 × 9.53	Cranes 2 × 18 tonnes	1 Bremer V/ B&W diesel, 15,254bhp; 1 shaft	21kts	10 pass 24 crew 4 holds 4 hatches 290 TEUs
DITLEV LAURITZEN	Dmk	1990	Danyard, Frederikshavn	14,406 16,950 (20,894)	539–1 × 78–11 × 51–6 × 32–10 164.33 × 24.05 × 15.7 × 10.0	Cranes 3 × 36 tonnes 2 × 8 tonnes	1 Korea HI/ B&W diesel 15,288bhp; 1 shaft	20.2kts	7–9 crew 5 holds 5 hatches 480 TEUs

3

Container Shipping

IT could well be argued that, for most of maritime history, development of the ship has proceeded faster than that of cargo handling technologies. When in recent times handling technologies started to develop rather more rapidly, it was in the liquid bulk and major dry bulk sectors that the process began. So far as general cargo was concerned the labour intensive conventional cargo handling technology proved much more resistant to change. Certainly it sustained little improvement from the late nineteenth century to the middle of the twentieth. And even as late as the 1980s systems which contained elements of conventional handling were characterised by poor productivity and slow ship turnaround in port.

As a result of a high labour content, low productivity and the eventual increase in the power of stevedoring unions, the conventional system eventually came to be associated with relentless increases in cargo handling costs.

Table 3/1: Loading Costs in London 1870 to 1970

Year	£ per dwt	Actual Value index	Value in 1870 terms
1870	0.03	100	100
1910	0.05	1662	208
1930	0.09	300	280
1940	0.17	566	468
1950	0.52	1733	737
1960	0.73	2433	647
1970	3.33	11,100	1989
1975	8.03	26,777	1598

Source: Costs of Operating British General Cargo Ships 1870–1970

This point is illustrated in a study by P M Alderton of the liner trade between London and Sydney (see Table 3/1). This covered the period from 1870 to 1970 during which time Alderton found that cargo handling speeds altered little, with two to four weeks required for the single port turn round of typical tramp trades, and four to six weeks for the multi-port operations of liner trades. Power cranes were always available and their use increased steadily, but their impact was on working conditions rather than cargo handling speed, as the critical job was working in the ship's hold which, until the larger hatch openings of the 1950s and the unitisation of the 1960s remained a manual operation.

The beam and containers on deck stacked four-high are clearly seen in this view of TFL Adams, *operated by Trans Freight Lines Inc, New York, for a Europe–US east coast service. The vessel, owned by Germany, can carry a total of 1152 TEUs, 662 of which are on deck.* (FotoFlite)

When expressed in 1870 prices here was a sixteen-fold increase in prices over the period. But the most dramatic growth was in the 1960s when costs tripled. There was a further very rapid increase in costs in current prices between 1970 and 1975.

The problem of escalation in cargo handling costs first became acute in the United States. In 1960 McMillan and Westfall studied the operations of conventional shipping companies. They showed that direct labour (including ships' crew as well as dockers), accounted for some 50 to 60 per cent of the costs of sea transport and that between 60 and 70 per cent of total costs (including the costs of ships' time) accumulated in the port. They also calculated that the costs of United States shipping companies had risen by almost 8 per cent compound throughout the postwar period without any increase in productivity, and estimated that containerisation could reduce cargo handling costs between 65 and 80 per cent and ship time in port by more than 80 per cent.

It is often thought that the problem of high stevedoring costs and the low overall economic efficiency of conventional shipping was solved by containerisation. Containers certainly have the highest profile of the new systems, but they were by no means the only one. What happened was that a number of new cargo handling technologies were employed across the general cargo and tramp sectors. These included, *inter alia*, liquid and dry bulk handling systems for some of the more specialised elements within the sector like oils and fats and cement; specialised car and truck carriers for vehicles of all types and large items of equipment; a number of unit load systems (which did not make use of containers) for steel, forests products and some general cargo foodstuffs; containers themselves, and (on short sea trades) road trailers. In some cases these technologies required specialised ships and in others they could use general-purpose vessels. As a result of the broad spectrum of development in cargo handling systems there was a re-structuring of the tramp and liner sectors which fragmented into a number of sub sectors. The allocation of cargo to the different systems depends both on commodity and the size of the cargo flow, and the general cargo sector tends to take the small flows of cargo across the board.

In the reshaped liner sector the cellular container system took an early lead on routes between the developed countries. There was nevertheless an active debate on the merits of various alternative systems like roll-on/roll-off (roro), semi container and (for a short time) barge carrying ships such as 'LASH' and 'Seabee'. At the same time the cellular container system was widely believed to be unsuitable for developing countries on account of its perceived capital intensity. In this area roro and semi-container vessels were considered to provide an effective alternative. There were indeed particular problems in developing countries, and it has recently come to be widely accepted that the cellular container system can serve their needs extremely well. In general, modern shipping technologies of one form or another are now clearly a necessary precondition for economic development, whilst the cellular system is of particular value in providing low cost and high quality services for manufactured exports.

The early experiments

The earliest precursor to radical change was in the roro sector. A number of rail/car ferries operated between the wars on services in the Baltic, in Japan, on the Great Lakes and in the Caribbean. During the Second World War, the United States military developed a series of landing ships employing roro methods, the largest of which were landing ship tanks (LSTs). This development culminated in 1953 in the construction of *Comet*, the first purpose built roro ship. Towed LSTs were also used in trailer operations in United States trades to Puerto Rico in the early 1950s, whilst at about the same time Colonel Frank Bustard began using them across the Irish Sea and the English Channel.

Although some observers have pointed to examples of the use of containers in experiments on the railways in the early decades of the twentieth century, these did not contain within them the seeds of revolutionary change. The real origins of the modern container system were post Second World War. One company started taking converted truck trailer bodies from which the wheels had been removed as deck cargo from Fort Lauderdale to Ponce in Puerto Rico in 1951. However, they then moved over to the trailer style operation, employing three LSTs and 700 used road trailers on the route.

The most important developments started in

January 1955 when Malcolm McLean, a United States trucker, diversified into shipping with the foundation of McLean Industries and the purchase of Waterman Steamship Corporation and its subsidiary Pan Atlantic. McLean set about applying the lessons of integrated road transport systems to general cargo shipping. In 1956 he began experiments with 33ft × 8ft × 8ft containers carried as deck cargo on Pan Atlantic tankers running between Houston and New York. Pan Atlantic soon moved into full container operations on its coastal services, with converted general cargo ships (C2s) with a capacity of 236 containers. McLean used a road trailer (chassis) operation in the terminal and ships with their own cranes (for a system which at that time had to be self contained as well as integrated. Quite early on he considered the idea of using roro ships carrying containers on trailers, but he rejected this because of high trailer costs and the poor utilisation of space in the ship. He proceeded with converted Second World War tonnage and in 1961 entered the trade to Puerto Rico. In the same year Pan Atlantic was renamed as Sea-Land Service Inc.

By 1964 Sea-Land was contemplating expansion into the deep sea liner trades and in October that year entered into an agreement with Litton Leasing for the purchase and conversion of six rather larger general cargo vessels (C4s). This was part of a US$46 million

The deck of a container vessel showing the slots that fix the containers in position. Each hatch cover section in the foreground has spaces for 8 TEUs. (Hapag-Lloyd)

deal which made provision for six new containerships of 1261×35ft container capacity. These particular ships were not built, but it is extraordinary that Sea-Land was considering vessels some five times the size of conventional liners several years before containers were introduced to the deep sea trades. In a major change of policy in the mid 1960s Sea-Land completed its preparations for international deep sea routes by switching to the use of shore based gantries ordering eighteen between 1965 and 1967. In 1967 the company began operations on the north Atlantic, signalling the start of the container revolution on the deep sea trades of the world.

Mention must also be made of the Matson Navigation Co, the other important container pioneer of the 1960s. Matson started rather cautiously in 1956 with a research programme which owed a lot to management theories current in the United States at the time. The company deliberately excluded those with experience in conventional shipping and concentrated on systems analysis and operations research techniques. The research programme was then enlarged to encompass engineering design and Matson led the way towards cellular vessels and modern container terminals served by shore based gantries, associating with the west coast crane manufacturer Paceco in this latter development. However, Matson never developed the entrepreneurial drive and expansionist policies of Sea-Land and remained a relatively modest operator in the Pacific trades.

The cellular container system

Container standards

One of the essential features of the cellular container system lies in the capacity of the box itself, in particular its high weight and space carrying capacities, its high ratio of payload to tare weight, its general ease of handling, stackability, durability and low cost. British railway companies had experimented with containers in the 1920s and 1930s, but the typical construction of the time, which was wood reinforced with metal, created a unit with a heavy tare weight of some three to four tons. The payload was also about four tons so that

A typical operator's container range.

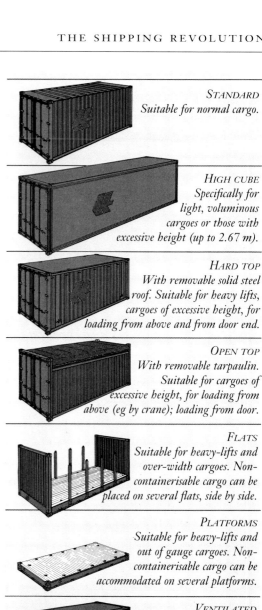

STANDARD
Suitable for normal cargo.

HIGH CUBE
Specifically for light, voluminous cargoes or those with excessive height (up to 2.67 m).

HARD TOP
With removable solid steel roof. Suitable for heavy lifts, cargoes of excessive height, for loading from above and from door end.

OPEN TOP
With removable tarpaulin. Suitable for cargoes of excessive height, for loading from above (eg by crane); loading from door.

FLATS
Suitable for heavy-lifts and over-width cargoes. Non-containerisable cargo can be placed on several flats, side by side.

PLATFORMS
Suitable for heavy-lifts and out of gauge cargoes. Non-containerisable cargo can be accommodated on several platforms.

VENTILATED
For cargoes requiring ventilation.

INSULATED
For cargo requiring transport at a constant temperature above or below freezing point.

REEFER
For cargoes requiring transport at a constant temperature above or below freezing point. With built-in reefer unit.

BULK
For loose/bulk cargoes.

TANK
For liquid chemicals. Containers are also available for the transport of liquids and liquid foods.

the tare to payload ratio was only about 1:1. This was no good at all and railway operations of the time were in any case fragmented and unsuited to intermodal transport operations.

When change came it was from association with the developing trucking industry in the United States. The lightweight container with a ratio of 10:1 or more between lifting capacity and tare weight was developed in road transport use and transferred to sea transport in the 1950s. The limits to container sizes were set in the United States and were closely related to truck regulations of the various states. The maximum width allowed on the roads at that time was eight feet. The maximum permissible height was 13ft 6in and with the standard chassis at 5ft 6in this left only eight feet for the container. With improved design the chassis height was reduced to 5ft 6in allowing the container height to be raised to 8ft 6in. Subsequently with the use of smaller road wheels and gooseneck trailers the height could be raised to 9ft 6in.

So far as length was concerned there was a 35ft trailer limit in the east coast and a 48ft limit in the west. In response to this Sea-Land chose a 35ft container length and Matson a 24ft length (this giving them the chance of hauling two empty or lightly loaded boxes on a single trailer). The US Federal Co-ordinator of Transport called for standardisation of equipment as early as 1953, but work did not start until 1959. In that year the eight foot width was accepted. At the same time many states raised the permissible lengths for road trailers to 40ft. As a result standards for 10ft, 20ft, 30ft and 40ft containers were published and an International Standards Committee was set up in 1961 to review this subject. After much discussion the American sizes were accepted as 'Series 1' containers in 1963–64. An 8ft 6in height was added a short time later. At the same time minimum design and test standards were established (ICHCA 1979).

International standards for containers have come under some pressure in recent years, with a desire in the United States and in Europe for an increase to 2.5m or 2.6m in width for greater compatibility with the standard pallets used in inland transport and distribution systems. There has also been pressure for greater lengths with a range of sizes from 45ft to 53ft being canvassed. Indeed a number of pools of special containers do exist in various trades. However, the agreement on international standards has been one of the major features of the container system, with a very high proportion of the world's fleet being built to Series 1 measurements. And in spite of the fact that with hindsight a few inches could have been added to the width, there can be no doubt that the success of the container system owes an enormous debt to the formulation and general acceptance of the Series 1 standards in the early years.

The 20ft × 8ft × 8ft 6in general purpose steel container will have a tare weight of some 2.3 tonnes, and on the road is usually allowed a total loaded weight of some 24 tonnes, giving a maximum payload of about 21.7 tonnes. It has a volumetric capacity of some 33 cubic metres. The standard 40ft container weighs in at about four tonnes. Depending upon limits set in the inland modes payload can go up to about 26 tonnes, whilst space availability rises to almost 68cu m. There is also a high cube 40ft container of 9ft 6in height with a space capacity of 76.2cu m. Finally, there are the non-standard containers in use in the United States, the largest being the 53ft × 8ft 6in × 9ft 6in, which has a tare weight of 3.3 tonnes, a space capacity of 108cu m and a payload on the railway of almost 60 tonnes.

Depending upon the size of the container and the characteristics of the cargo, a standard container will hold some five to twenty times the volume or weight that would be carried under the hook of a conventional crane. When dropped into the guides of a cellular vessel, stowage is automatic and no labour is required in the hold. Even on the weather deck, securing the box is a relatively simple question of twist locks and lashings, and there are now the beginnings of a trend towards the use of on deck cell guides. Finally, the gantry cranes designed for quayside use could in principle lift up to thirty containers per hour. This was seldom achieved in the early days, when some

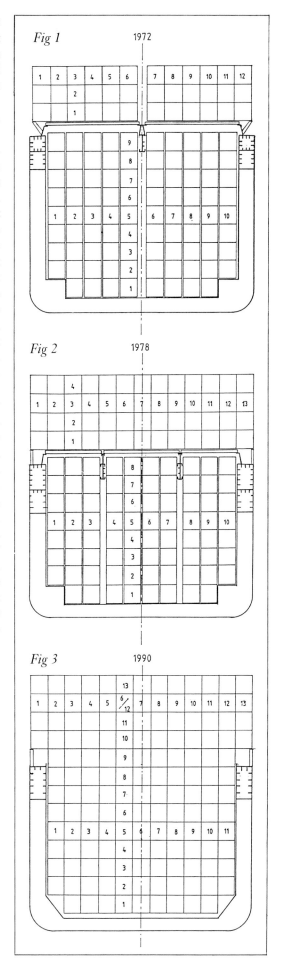

Cross-sections of typical midships container stowage arrangements of the average Panamax container vessels of 1972 (Fig 1), 1978 (Fig 2) and 1990 (Fig 3).

In Fig 1 the containers are stowed nine high and ten across, and on deck three layers of twelve containers are positioned on adjacent hatch covers. The majority of the cargo is transported in the holds.

During the 1970s changes took place which allowed the number of layers to be increased from twelve to thirteen. The depth of vessels had decreased, therefore giving savings in tonnage and port dues, etc. The container-carrying capacity was increased because the upper layer in the hold was shifted to the above deck position which has more container rows than the hold (Fig 2).

The 1990 vessel benefits from reduction in space between cell guides and the absence of longitudinal members on which hatch covers normally rest. It is thus possible to stow eleven rows across the hold (Fig 3).
(Nedlloyd)

The container handling cranes at Europe Combined Terminal (ECT), in Rotterdam. The size of the cranes can be gauged against Nedlloyd Asia *alongside the berth, which is 48,508 grt and 32.24m in breadth. Note the ship's deck cell guides which speed up loading.* (Nedlloyd)

ports found it hard enough to sustain rates of twelve movements per crane per hour. However, with the improvement in terminal systems and the development of new generations of cranes and yard equipment, crane handling rates are moving up to very impressive levels. Some terminals have reported rates of fifty moves per hour with modern cranes although this could not be accepted as standard. However, at major terminals cranes would now be expected to sustain an average of twenty moves per hour for a 24-hour day, which with two cranes on the ship would give 500 moves equivalent to 750 20ft equivalent units (TEU) with a 50/50 split between 20ft and 40ft containers.

The average weight per loaded TEU over a broad set of trades is about 10 tonnes, and the overall average per box move (taking account of returning empties) somewhat less than this, say at about 7 tonnes. However, with a standard two crane operation this still gives an overall cargo handling rate of some 8400 to 10,000 tonnes per day, at major terminals, compared to the 400 tonnes which was typical for liner (as opposed to semi bulk) cargoes in the conventional era, and the 1000 to 2500 tonnes per day which could be achieved by some of the better organised pallet systems.

Cellular container vessels

The development of the cellular container system removed the set of economic, technical and operational constraints to the growth of ship size which had held conventional tramps and liners to a maximum of about 14,000 dwt

for decades. The crucial constraint was economic, in that with slow cargo handling, the cost of ship time in port offsets economies of size at sea. However, there would also have been severe operational difficulties in handling large conventional stows, and a multi-deck conventional ship, in which all the tween decks have to open out quite widely to achieve effective vertical access (although technically feasible) would have been a heavy, costly and somewhat cumbersome creature. Multi-deck construction is rather easier utilising the roro technology, as ramps or lifts do not present quite the difficulties of wide tween deck hatches, and in the absence of the cellular container system this might have been the way in which the general cargo sector would have developed.

Containers provide a natural multi-deck capability, and utilising the cell guide system can be piled on top of each other with ease. The international standards eventually allowed for nine-high stacking below deck and with a five high stow on deck, the largest cellular containerships can stow cargo 120ft high, with only the weather deck itself to impede vertical access.

After the introduction of containers in 1955 there was a very rapid exploration of the technical, operational and economic limits of the new system. By 1962 Sea-Land was using jumboised tanker hulls to provide a container capacity of 476 × 40ft containers and by 1964 had completed the design studies referred to above for a fleet of vessels of 2200 TEU capacity.

The tanker conversions were undertaken at

United States shipyards and the re-born vessels emerged with a profile not at all resembling their former selves. The midships bridges had been taken away and the aft superstructure replaced. All that remained in fact was the original machinery and the hull, although this had been 'jumboised'.

The first batch of vessels, dating from 1942 were given the names *Elizabethport*, *Los Angeles*, *San Francisco* and *San Juan*, giving a clue at the same time to their principal ports of call.

In the late 1960s containers were introduced to the Atlantic and Pacific trades, in 1969 to the Europe-Australia trade and in the early 1970s to the Europe-Far East trade. A first generation of vessels widely used in the Atlantic trade were of about 1000 TEUs at 20kts, and a second generation of 1500 TEUs at 23kts soon followed.

The Europe/Australia trade saw the first large scale British involvement in container shipping with purpose-built vessels for Overseas Containers Ltd (OCL) and Associated Container Transportation (Australia) Ltd (ACT). These were groups which had as their partners long-established British liner companies such as Port Line, Ellerman Lines, Blue Star Line, Furness Withy, P & O, British & Commonwealth, Ocean Transport & Trading and Shaw Savill. The first ships appeared in 1969–70, with now familiar names such as *Botany Bay* and *Moreton Bay* (26,876 grt) and *ACT 1*, *ACT 2* (24,892 grt).

On the Atlantic a long list of well-known companies joined the container revolution, with Hapag-Lloyd (West Germany), United States Lines, Seatrain Lines (United States) and Dart Containerline (international consortium) to the fore.

At about the same time Sea-Land astounded the shipping world with plans for a fleet of eight 33kt vessels of 2192 TEUs requiring 120,000shp and burning 500 tonnes of fuel a day. These ships were at the frontiers of technology particularly in respect of propulsion systems, where the 60,000shp per screw went way beyond the pre-existing maximum 45,000shp. They were to be deployed sailing to major container ports, served by feeder ships and inland road transport networks and backed by sophisticated control and data transmission

systems. Employed in both transatlantic and trans-Pacific routes, these vessels started with *Sea-Land McLean* (41,127 grt) in 1972, followed by seven sister-ships by the end of the following year.

However, they have all been withdrawn from service and by the end of 1982 were added to the ranks of the United States Reserve Fleet. The last to be withdrawn were *Sea-Land McLean* and *Sea-Land Galloway*, also built in 1972 and the second vessel in the series. In response to this development a consortium of British, Japanese and West German lines, which was at the time designing ships for the important Europe-Far East route, produced the third generation Panamax vessel.

This consortium, known as Trio, was worried both by the prospect of Sea-Land's SL7 type vessels (as they were known) operating on round the world services, and also by the Trans-Siberian Railway, which in principle had the capacity to offer fast transit times in competition with the sea mode. There

was some considerable debate about the advisability of matching the Sea-Land vessels for speed, but caution eventually prevailed and a speed of 27kts was chosen which required only 40,000 shp per screw and a fuel consumption of about 300 tonnes per day. These *Liverpool Bay* class vessels were of full Panamax size with 289m length and 32.3m beam. Draught through the canal was only about 11m, but at full load the vessels would draw 13.0m. There was a two or three high stow on the weather deck, and the ships were variously rated at between 2600 and 3000 TEUs. The 2600 TEU figure was based on an assumption of 20 tonnes per container, the cargo deadweight of the vessels being just under 50,000 tonnes, whilst the 3000 figure represented the maximum number of container spaces and was based on assumption of rather low cargo density.

The sheer pace of these developments was

extraordinary, and it led to some expectations of the construction of a fourth generation of even larger vessels of at least 5000 TEUs. This was technically feasible even in the early 1970s, but it did not happen, and in fact there was not even much further construction at the top end of the existing range. The big ships designed in the era of low bunker costs turned out to be much too fast, with 33kts for the SL7s being penal after 1975, and even the 27kts of OCL's *Liverpool Bay* class Trio ships being unsustainable. In the mid 1970s, following the OPEC oil price increases the emphasis was on speed reduction. In the new environment medium sized slower speed vessels could compete quite effectively with the fast Panamax ships and newbuildings were concentrated on medium sized and medium speed vessels, with most ships being of under 2000 TEUs and under 23kts.

According to the *Containerisation International Yearbook* of 1979 there were 297 cellular ships in the world fleet. Of these only thirty-

The 2240-TEU Ever Guard *was one of a series of twenty vessels built for Evergreen Lines in Japan and Taiwan in 1983–84. She is pictured here in 1983; just one year later she was lengthened and capacity increased to 2728 TEUs. Other vessels of the series were either lengthened following completion or during construction. By 1988 Evergreen Lines was the world's largest container vessel owner with over fifty in service.* (FotoFlite)

Eleven of the ships were destined to be of around 40,600 grt, but the specification of each was increased and those which had been completed in 1986–87 were taken in for lengthening, whilst others were increased in size before completion. The alterations saw an increase in the TEU capacity from 2940 to 3428 and an increase in overall length from 242m to 269.7m.

This was followed by the United States Lines order of the twelve Econships for its eastbound round the world service. In all 102 large container ships were built in the five years to 1988. This trend was also supported by jumboisation of many medium sized vessels.

Technically all of these vessels were still Panamax and some of them were actually built to less than the full length of the Panama Canal locks. Indeed the Panama Canal constraint (which does not effect the *Liverpool Bay* class vessels, on their trade from Europe to the Far East), is a firm constraint for ships on round the world itineraries and on many other multi-route operations.

All of the new designs have much higher TEU ratings in relation to principal dimensions and deadweight capacity than the old third generation vessels. Part of the extra capacity is found below deck, being brought about by slower speeds, giving a reduced requirement for engine space and bunker capacity, as well as a rather fuller hull form. However, much of it is above deck and is the result of rating the ships with a five-high weather deck stow. This compares to the two

three vessels were above 2000 TEUs in size including fifteen Panamax vessels on the Europe-Far East route and the eight SL7s deployed on the Atlantic and the Pacific. Apart from this the workhorses of the world fleet were 165 first and second generation vessels of between 1000 and 2000 TEUs supported by 99 vessels of between 500 and 1000 TEUs. There were fifty-seven ships of over 23kts including as before the SL7s and the third generation Panamax ships. In the late 1970s many of the early third generation ships were either re-engined or had their propulsion systems modified to enable them to compete and even as late as the early 1980s third generation ships were largely confined to the Europe-Far East route.

In the 1980s large vessels returned to favour and from being a relatively small class they have become dominant on major routes. Speed was held down, most of the benefits being taken in pure cost reduction. The new era began on the Pacific when in the early 1980s

American President Lines built three quite fast ships of 2450 TEUs for its service from the Far East to the West Coast. These new ships, named *President Lincoln*, *President Monroe* and *President Washington* (all of 40,627 grt) appeared in 1982–83. But the decisive move was taken by Evergreen with its new G class ships of which no less than thirty-one were ordered for delivery between 1983 and 1987. Twenty-five of these vessels were for a new round the world service and six for the Pacific.

The new Evergreen ships, run by Evergreen Marine Corp of Taiwan, not only increased the owning company's capacity several times over, but was notable in that the result was the promotion of Evergreen to the world's largest container shipping concern. Its new ships range in gross tonnage from 37,023 to 46,410.

Hapag-Lloyd's Nurnberg Express *is one of four sister-ships employed on the company's North Atlantic service. With an original TEU capacity of 1758, these four vessels effectively replaced 1114-TEU 'first generation' carriers which Hapag-Lloyd had placed on the North Atlantic in 1968–69. In the mid-1980s* Nurnberg Express *and its sister-ships were lengthened and this increased the TEU capacity to 2594.* (Hapag-Lloyd)

or three tiers of the earlier version of the third generation each additional tier adding some 250 to 300 TEUs.

The third feature of the new vessels is their reduced fuel consumption. One major reason for this was the reduction in speeds to between 20kts and 24kts, fuel consumption varying broadly in proportion to the cube of the speed. In addition to this the switch from twin screws to single screws is estimated to save about six per cent in fuel consumption. Finally, whereas the steam turbines of the early 1970s consumed as much as 190 grams per shaft horsepower hour, the fuel consumption of modern slow speed diesels has come down progressively from some 155 grams per brake horsepower hour in the early 1970s to about 124 grams today. As a result of this fuel consumption has been reduced to under 150 tonnes a day for most of the new third generation vessels, with many vessels consuming under 100 tonnes per day.

Turning to the other main component of operating costs, there have been continuous reductions in manning levels on vessels of all types. Many general cargo liners of the 1960s had crews in excess of thirty men, and some of the early third generation cellular container ships were crewed with as many as forty-five. This has been successively reduced as a result of automation, changes in working practice and the reduction in the amount of on board maintenance. In principle modern ships could probably be operated with as few as twelve to fourteen hands. However, there are a number of disadvantages to this, partly sociological and partly that there are few hands to cope with emergencies and the more labour intensive operations such as docking. Many European carriers now choose to operate with twenty-three man crews. Evergreen Marine Corporation operates with a seventeen-man crew on many of its vessels.

During the mid 1980s many vessels were ordered and built at very low prices. For example, the early 43,000 dwt G class vessels built in Japan for Evergreen in 1983–84, cost only about US$28m per ship. The 53,000 dwt

version built in 1986 cost some US$37m, but much of this increase was the result of a substantial strengthening of the yen. In the last few years, with a return to some sort of balance in the world shipbuilding market there has been a very sharp escalation of prices, so that a large moderately fast third generation vessel now costs about US$100m. If one looks at the very large amount of steel, machinery and equipment in a large container vessel it seems more than likely that these higher prices are here to stay.

No discussion of the third generation ships of the 1980s would be complete without some reference to United States Lines' twelve Econships. These vessels were the largest third generation ships of the 1980s at a rated capacity of 4480 TEUs with a dwt of 58,943 tonnes. The extra capacity was achieved by taking a slow maximum steaming speed of just over eighteen knots, thus allowing a small engine capacity of only 28,000bhp and a very full hull form. One interesting thing about these vessels is that they were built by Malcolm McLean, who left Sea-Land in the 1970s and returned to the industry by taking over United States Lines some years later. So the man who built the SL7s at 33kts, in the heady days of the container revolution also produced the slowest vessels of the mid 1980s. The Econships were all built in South Korea and delivered in 1984–85 by just one shipbuilder, Daewoo Shipbuilding & Heavy Machinery Ltd, Koje. The familiar names with the prefix *American* were adopted, followed by an American state, eg *American Alabama*, *American California*, etc.

In the late 1960s the rallying cry was high speed, service quality and intensive use of capital on concentrated itineraries. In the 1980s it was low slot costs, economy and the new concept of the round the world service. The SL7s caused Sea-Land great financial problems before they were eventually purchased by the United States military strategic reserve. The Econships were deployed on an eastbound round the world service, where their large slot capacity was not of maximum possible use, because of the high proportion of heavy cargoes eastbound between Europe and the Far East. United States Lines cut prices very aggressively in entering the Europe-Far East trade as an independent carrier. However, they did not succeed and went into liquidation. The common features of the two opposing strategies were a strong entrepreneurial drive, allied to extreme, or at least radical, technical and operational philosophies. The bankers were convinced, but both extremes lost out in the market place.

After the liquidation of United States Lines, the Econships eventually found their way into the hands of Sea-Land at a price of some US$15m each. Sea-Land did a sale and lease back deal with the vessels and put them into a consortium with Trans Freight Lines and Nedlloyd operating three Atlantic services. They were renamed the Atlantic class and de-rated to some 3200 TEUs. Speed has been raised to about 19kts, at which they provide adequate service quality for the relatively short deep sea routes across the Atlantic.

The containership Sea-Land McLean *(1972) was the lead ship in a series of eight vessels, the introduction of which astounded the shipping world. With a speed of 33kts, provided by four General Electric steam turbines, their 120,000shp was far above the then normal rating. The series was intended for both transatlantic and trans-Pacific routes and could carry 2192 TEUs. These fuel-hungry vessels, popularly known as the SL7 type, were withdrawn from service within 10 years and transferred to the US Reserve Fleet. (FotoFlite)*

Post Panamax ships

In the late 1980s, towards the end of a hectic period of ordering of large containerships, the Panama Canal barrier was at last broken. This was by American President Lines, who built five American President class C10s of post Panamax beam for their Pacific southwest service. In order to understand the potential of these new vessels one must take account of the fact that Panamax ships are artificially constrained in terms of beam, with a nine to one length to beam ratio instead of the seven to one which is generally preferred by naval architects. For this reason stability is somewhat limited, a problem which has to be countered by carrying ballast and careful stowage of containers by weight. The problem is not quite so acute now that speeds have been reduced and hull fullness increased, but it is still important. At 39m beam the C10s have a more normal length:beam ratio. They have a quoted capacity of 4340 TEUs and can be jumboised with a 30m mid section to 5300 TEUs. Stability is much improved, the need to carry ballast greatly reduced the weight constraints on the positioning of boxes lifted. At the same time the ships have the finest lines (lowest block coefficient) of any containerships since Sea-Land's SL7s which makes for a very efficient propulsion system. The C10s stayed within the range of a single slow speed diesel engine. They achieved 26kts in trials and have a service speed of 24kts, which can be achieved with a full load of containers at 12 tonnes average per TEU, for a fuel consumption of 150 tonnes per day. With the benefits of an unconstrained stowage plan and the installation of new high speed cranes in port, there is no increase in round trip time. These ships could operate with a crew of twelve, although they have entered service with nine officers and twelve ratings.

Since the dimension which has been increased is beam, rather than length or draught, post Panamax vessels do not create any particular problems with respect to access to ports unless there are locks in the system of less than 39m width. In the port sector post Panamax gantry cranes have become a virility symbol and they are becoming very widely available on the high density trade routes of the world.

There has not been any particular rush to build post Panamax vessels and many large carriers are sticking to the Panamax classes. Routes transiting the Panama canal are still important for many carriers, including the two largest container operators of the present time Evergreen and Maersk. Thus for post Panamax vessels to take over completely, either the present multi-route strategies would have to be abandoned or a new canal would be required with a width of about 40m. There have, however, been some further orders, this time for the Europe-Far East route, and looking to the future it seems quite likely that post Panamax vessels of around 5500 TEUs could become the workhorses of the high density trades during the first part of the twenty-first century.

Economies of ship size

There were a number of factors which combined to bring about the rapid growth in the fleet of large containerships. First, it was fuelled by the enormous growth of demand in the Pacific trades. Second, as might be expected, a very high proportion of capacity was ordered by the newly industrialised countries in the Far East as they took advantage of the huge increases in their trade to build up their positions in the world market. In total orders from these carriers rather outweighed those of United States, European and Japanese lines. Third, supply conditions were propitious. The new vessels could take advantage of reductions in design speed and increases in propulsive efficiency giving smaller engines, greater cargo capacity and substantial savings in fuel consumption per TEU mile. They were also designed for very much lower manning. Finally, most of them were built in Far Eastern yards at a time when they were offering exceptionally low prices. As a result of this the large modern vessels operate at costs only about half those of a European vessel of 1500 TEUs built in 1980.

However, the choice of large vessels was not simply a result of design improvements and the special conditions prevailing in world shipbuilding. After all, carriers could have built very efficient medium sized ships to compete with the existing fleet. Both capital and operating costs at sea are reduced as ship size increases, the constraints to growth being the size of the cargo flow available to individual carriers, as it affects load factors, and any diseconomies which may occur from increased time or cost in port. In fact the cargo flow available to individual carriers has been increased partly by the growth of traffic on the mainstream trades, and partly by the United States Shipping Act of 1984 with its greater freedoms for joint services and rationalisation on the Pacific and Atlantic routes. At the same time the proportion of 40ft containers in the world container fleet has risen steadily over time to about half of total TEU capacity, whilst port performance has also improved steadily. As a result of this, cargo handling performance has kept up with the growth in ship size, so that diseconomies in port have been avoided.

When completed in 1981 by Howaldtswerke-Deutsche Werft, Kiel, the containership Frankfurt Express was the world's largest container carrier. The 58,384 grt vessel has capacity for 3045 TEUs, and the 54,400 bhp MAN diesels give a service speed of 23kts. She was Hapag-Lloyd's fifth third-generation container carrier and was placed with four of the same owner's similar sized but older vessels on the Trio service, run by a group of European and Japanese operators on the Europe–Far East service. (FotoFlite)

German owners operate one of the world's most modern fleets of ocean-going container carriers, with large numbers in the 12,000–20,000 dwt range. Built at Szczecin, Poland, in 1983, the 20,011 dwt Laredo *can carry 1074 TEUs. Under Liberian registration and beneficially-owned by a Hamburg company, the vessel was seventh in a series of twelve from the same shipyard and destined for several owners. (FotoFlite)*

Flexible ships

Although the cellular system is the dominant one on world routes, other container-carrying vessels still make up a large part of the world fleet. They are not simply competitors to the cellular system but meet a whole variety of special needs. There is also a great deal of variety in this sector and of ingenuity in terms of concept and naval architectural design.

Semi containerships

The modern semi container vessel, which has a container, break bulk and in many cases roro capability, can be traced in a direct line of design evolution right back to the tramps and liners of the conventional era. However, during this process this class has lost its star status and performs in a number of supporting roles.

In the liner sector semi containerships were for a while thought of as a flexible alternative to the cellular system on routes to developing countries. And in South America, India and Africa there was considerable reliance upon them, support coming from the carriers from developed nations operating on the routes as well as from the countries themselves. This was in spite of some early studies which suggested

that (in lift-on/lift-off systems at least) mixed container and break bulk handling would always remain inefficient, ship turnaround time being largely controlled by the non container element.[1]

Much later on these initial findings were re-confirmed in a study for the World Bank.[2] This examined operational performance on several hundred voyages between Europe and West Africa, comparing semi containerships and conventional liners of up to about 14,000 dwt with self-sustaining cellular ships and roro ships of up to 1400 TEUs. The round trip distance was about 10,000nm to northwest Europe, with sailing time just over three weeks. It was found that the cellular vessels and roro ships were completing their voyages in about five weeks, whilst the smaller conventional and semi containerships were taking seven or eight. As a result of this, together with higher fuel and crew costs per unit of capacity, the conventional and semi containerships were much less efficient. The disadvantages were substantial when looked at in terms of TEU capacities, but they remained even when combined vessels were evaluated on the basis of the extra cargo carrying capacity available from a combined container and break bulk stow. There are now only a few liner trades which rely on semi containerships, and most of them

are in the process of transition to more modern systems.

Outside the liner sector conventional style vessels can handle a wide range of bulk and semi bulk cargoes. But here too their role has been limited by technological innovation. In this case it has been the development of a whole range of bulk carriers from 25,000 dwt upwards, which now carry most of the major and minor bulks on the world deep sea routes. As mentioned above the structural evolution of the industry gave rise to new sectors, particularly the neo bulks sectors for self unitising commodities like steel products, and forest products. Conventional vessels still carry these cargoes in harness with a range of rather larger specialised ships.

In spite of the tremendous reduction in their market role, semi containerships remain an important and numerous class of vessel. As mentioned above there is still a considerable volume of major, minor and semi bulk cargoes moving in small ships. Much of this is on short and medium sea routes where economies of size are constrained by route length. Some of it consists of small parcels of cargo moving on rather longer routes, and there are also cases where ship size is limited by draught constraints. These combine with feeder and relay roles on container routes, and employment in some of the north-south liner markets, to provide a broad spectrum of trading opportunity.

In a sample of 561 chartered container carrying vessels taken in 1984 by *Containerisation International*, 210 were in the semi container class. Of these 114 in the smaller size ranges were employed on short and near sea routes most of them operating in and around Europe. Of the remaining ninety-six operating in the deep sea trades, one half were employed on routes to Africa, whilst the rest were spread around the world with only fifteen on mainstream routes. This sample is probably not a precise reflection of overall

1. D C MacMillan and Westfall, 'Competitive general cargo ships', *Transactions of SNAME* 68 (1960).

2. Gilman Associates, *Liner Shipping in West Africa* (The World Bank, 1983).

In 1983 Farrell Lines of the USA sold four semi-container vessels to United States Lines, including Austral Puritan *which was renamed* American Puritan. *The vessel was jumboised and converted to a full containership, with a corresponding increase in capacity from 1708 TEUs to 2326 TEUs. Later in the decade, with the collapse of United States Lines, the vessel passed to Sea-Land Service Inc, one of the pioneers of sea-going containerisation.* (FotoFlite)

deployment because many deep sea liner operators own rather than charter, but it still gives an indication of the breadth of use and of the types of routes where these vessels are employed.

The world fleet of semi container vessels is concentrated in the smaller size ranges. A study shows that 67 per cent of the semi container capacity in TEU terms in 1988 was in vessels of under 500 TEUs with the average size in this range being 248 TEUs. A further 30 per cent was in vessels of between 500 and 1000 TEUs with the average for this larger group being 644 TEUs. In fact at the end of 1988 there were only some fifteen semi container-ships of over 1000 TEUs in existence.

Technological elements in design evolution

General developments

The earliest technical developments were pre-container and applied to tramps as well as liners. Their main features were the provision of wider weather deck and tween deck hatches, the removal of deck obstructions to provide flush surfaces for fork lift handling, and in some cases the provision of side ports for pallet operations. At the same time there was a small increase in maximum ship size up to about 15,000 dwt. In the tramp sector this was for a time the end of design evolution. From the mid 1960s on attention was concentrated upon the large market for Liberty ship replacements of which a number of designs were developed for series production. These are typified by Austin & Pickersgill's SD-14 a 15kt ship of some 760,000cu ft bale capacity and 15,000 dwt. The SD-14 and the similar Japanese and Spanish 'Freedoms' were immensely successful and some hundreds of these vessels were built.

In the liner sector design evolution continued with a strengthening of all decks to take the weight of containers, together with a selection of deck heights and hatch sizes for compatibility with container dimensions. There was also an evolution in cargo handling gear, with larger capacity derricks and cranes being provided to cope with container weights.

In the early 1970s certain of the charter operators, in response to trends in the market, began to optimise their designs for container carriage, and by the late 1970s this had led to the development of a series of very efficient compact ships.[3] Containers can be stowed efficiently only in the square of the hatch, so hatch sizes are increased to cover up to about 80 per cent of the available deck area. Space loss along the length of the ship is reduced by limiting the number of crane installations to two. Pontoon hatch covers which are stored on the berth rather than the ship may also be selected. A couple of metres is added to the beam to improve stability and allow extra rows of containers, and the number of tiers on the weather deck is raised from two to a maximum of four. The increase in beam also reduces the need to carry ballast (to compensate for the weather deck stow) and allows for the development of a fuel efficient hull form.

The development of semi container designs can be traced by examination of the relationship of bale space to the container bale. When containers are stowed below deck in a semi container ship there is a loss of some 50 per cent of bale space. This is mainly a function of space between containers, and the space taken up by the boxes themselves and the tween decks. (There is a considerable loss even in a cellular ship, although this is of a slightly lower order because the cell guides can follow the lines of the deck rather more closely, there is less impedance from hatches, no crane installation and no tween deck.) This loss of space below deck is recovered by the use of a substantial weather deck stow, so that a cellular ship has more internal bale space within the containers than that possessed by a conventional ship of similar dimensions. In the case of semi container ships the ratio of container bale to conventional bale depends upon how advanced is the design. In the case of the older ships the container bale may be only 30 per cent or so of the conventional, whilst in the case of more modern ships it may approach 100 per cent and in compact containerships may reach 130 per cent. There may be some loss of deadweight capacity, which is the difference in the weight of the tween decks of the conventional vessels and the weight of containers.

Conclusions

Semi container ships are still a large class of vessel trading across a wide range of routes and commodity sectors. Because of the need for trading flexibility there is a high proportion of chartered vessels in the fleet. Following a long process of design evolution two main groups may now be identified, the 'compact' vessels

3.Dieter Ahrens, *The Role of Tramp Tonnage in Containerisation*, (CS Publications Ltd, 1983).

Typical of small roro ships, Equimar Maritime SA's Gala del Mar (8639 dwt) was built by Enrique Lorenzo, Vigo (Spain). The vessel can carry container (533 TEUs) and roro cargoes simultaneously on a service between Europe and East Africa. Service speed is 14.5kts. (FotoFlite)

optimised for containers, and the liner vessels designed to carry break bulk or specialised cargoes in combination with containers.

The combination vessels are now a declining class. The reasons for this have been discussed at length above, and relate to lack of cargo handling and economic efficiency when engaged in mixed operations, a poor use of capacity when in the container mode and the limited size of vessel.

The compact vessels optimised for containers are likely to survive as a moderately important class. They are simply small and medium size self-sustaining containerships, which sacrifice cell guides for the advantages of being able to trade across bulk and semi bulk trades. However, it is the ability to switch trades and commodity sectors, rather than the ability to combine commodities within an individual voyage, which is important. The ability to switch trades can be achieved without compromising the efficiency and long term trading flexibility of the vessel, so long as there is not too much specialisation in the cargo spaces.

Even accepting the efficiency of the compact designs the average size of vessel is quite small. Vessels of up to 650 TEUs may be well suited to the short and medium sea container, semi

bulk and bulk trades and for acting as feeders or relays. But, they have little long term market opportunities for end to end services on deep sea liner routes. On the deep sea routes where they still trade, they are under attack, either from trans-shipment, or from processes of rationalisation which allow larger vessels to be employed.

Roro (roll-on/roll-off) ships

Early developments

Commercial roro ships have a capability of taking on and offloading 'wheeled' cargo, in the form of trailers with pallets, containers or packaged cargo, and the definition is extended to purpose built vehicle carriers. They are a

direct product of the unit load revolution being born in early development on short sea trades in Europe and on the medium sea trades from the United States mainland to Puerto Rico. However, the concept was developed for deep sea trades, partly to handle wheeled and non unitisable cargoes (including project cargo), partly for small flows of semi bulks, and partly as a direct competitor to the container system for a range of general cargo commodities.

The TEU capacity of roro containerships is fairly heavily concentrated in the smaller classes and according to the *Containerisation International Yearbook* 1988 one third of the capacity is in vessels of under 500 TEUs. This accounted for some 430 ships, their average size being about 260 TEUs. Most of these operate in short and medium sea markets. A further ninety-seven ships, were in the 500 to 1000 TEUs size range the average being 630 TEUs. In contrast to semi container sector, roro capacity does, however, extend into the medium size ranges, with seventy ships of 1000 to 1500 TEUs. However, there are relatively few large roro containerships, the *Yearbook* showing seventeen of above 1500 TEUs in 1988.

Small and medium sized roros

Within the class of roro vessels of up to about 800 TEUs, there is a considerable variety in

Something new on the container scene appeared in 1988 – the combination container/passenger ship Americana, built by Hyundai in South Korea, for service between the east coast of the USA to Rio de Janeiro and Buenos Aires. The container capacity is 1120 TEUs, in holds and and on deck, and the vessel carries 110 passengers in what is described as 'cruise ship standard'. Americana is 19,203 grt, 177m in length and its Hyundai/B&W diesel engine gives a speed of 18.25kts. (Hyundai)

design. Some of them are no more than semi container ships with a supplementary roro capability in the form of a small ramp, others lie mid way between the two classes using their ramps for most of the handling below deck but having cranes for a lolo weather deck stow of containers and other cargoes. Finally there are the pure roros, which have little or no lolo capability, although they will use shore based cranes where available for the weather deck stow.

One of the inter-deck ramps on board the roro/container vessel Atlantic Companion, *owned by Rederi A/B Transatlantic, Gothenburg, one of the partners in the long-established Atlantic Container Line consortium. Also shown is one of the vehicle deck areas giving an impression of the massive open garage space which is typical of a modern ocean-going roro.* Atlantic Companion *was built in 1984 and is of 57,255 grt and 44,988 dwt. (MacGregor Navire)*

The larger roro classes

The first generation The first generation of large roro vessels were cellular containerships with a supplementary roro capacity and were introduced on to the North Atlantic in the late 1960s. The early ships have now been scrapped and replaced by a new much larger class – the G3s – built in 1984. Their roro capacity is used for car and truck trades, non-containerisable items like earth moving equipment, locomotives and yachts, etc and semi bulks like timber, and forest products on trailers.

These ships were fairly successful in the early years when Atlantic Container Line had a substantial share of the transatlantic container market and the roro cargoes often commanded good rates. However, they were vulnerable to competition from the specialised vessels in the car trades and semi bulk sectors of their

market. In the early years the vehicle carriers were limited to cars, but they have evolved to encompass trucks and heavy roro cargoes, whilst the development of their operating and marketing strategies has given them the flexibility to compete for the smaller flows. In the semi bulk sector the large roros compete with the specialised forest products carriers as well as the open hatch bulk carriers and semi containerships.

Atlantic Container Line was formed as a consortium of six European and Scandinavian companies and commenced operations in 1967. When the final vessel for the services from the United Kingdom, northwest Europe and Scandinavia, to United States and Canadian east coast ports, was delivered in 1970, ten ships with TEU capacities varying between 441 (*Atlantic Saga*; A/B Svenska Amerika Linien, Sweden) and 966 (*Atlantic Causeway* and *Atlantic Conveyor*; Cunard Steam Ship Co Ltd), were in operation.

As a matter of comparison, the new G-type *Atlantic Conveyor*, owned by Cunard and perpetuating the name of the 1970-built vessel lost during the Falklands campaign, was built in 1984 and is of 58,438 tons gross (1970 vessel 14,946 grt), and has a TEU capacity of 2711.

The container roro is in effect a cellular container ship customised to provide a moderate capability outside of the cellular sector. In the early years the sums appeared to work out. However, when ACL built the G3s it was at a premium in capital costs compared to the large container ships being built at the time by companies like Evergreen. Together with the broad based competitive attack on rates in the roro sector this has combined to make them very much less attractive, and has probably rendered the design obsolete.

The second generation The so-called second generation of deep sea roro ships were an evolution of the design in terms of access, but they also involved a fundamental change of concept, dispensing with cellular holds in favour of multi-deck construction focused originally on non-containerised cargoes, with only a two high stow of containers on the weather deck and with internal decks not very well suited to container stowage. They followed Scandinavian concepts of cargo handling, dispensing with containers for self unitising cargoes like wool and forest products etc and having an excellent capability for vehicles, tractors and oversize items. Cargo

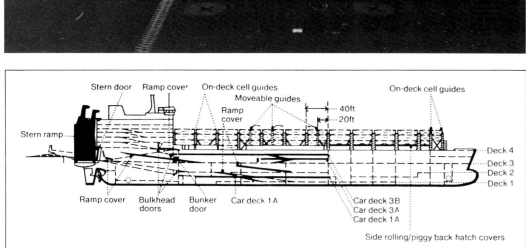

Profile of ACL's G3 class ConRo vessel Atlantic Companion.

handling rates of up to 10,000 tonnes per day
were claimed for Scandinavian ports. This was
rather exceptional but vessels of this type have
demonstrated an ability to handle 5000 tonnes
a day in a wide range of operating conditions.

The system soon had to evolve to develop a
container friendly capability, by taking a three
high weather deck stow and raising internal
deck heights for a more comfortable two high
stow. Some of these vessels even had a crane to
help with cargo on the forward part of the
weather deck.

The second generation has also failed to
become a popular class and the reasons for this
have already been touched upon above. Much
of their flexible capability is for the relatively
low rated cargoes and faces competition from
semi bulk ships and car carriers. This type of
competition is, however, more important for
them because of their greater commitment to
commodities of this type.

In operational terms there are also problems.
The system is relatively labour intensive in the
port sector and can run up against the
escalation of stevedoring costs. Further to this
a rate of cargo handling of 5000 tonnes a day is
equivalent to only about 500 TEUs, and
although this is tremendous in relation to lift-
on/lift-off handling for general cargo, it can
not really beat the cellular system for
containers, or the specialised carriers for
vehicles, project cargo, or semi bulks. The
system is ultimately more limited in terms of
development potential in the port sector than
the cellular system, and lacks scope for
automation. There are also stowage difficulties
on complex itineraries, and although small
roro ships can use less specialised terminals
than the cellular system, this advantage tends
to disappear as ship size increases. In fact large
general cargo exchanges require extensive land
and shed areas and very sophisticated systems
of terminal handling and management. Finally,
as is the case with the latest first generation
ships it now appears that there is a substantial

The angled stern door and ramp of Saudi Abha *is here*
in drive-on/drive-off position. (Kockums)

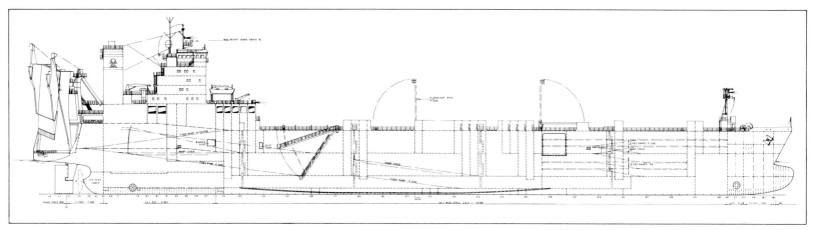

Profile drawing of Saudi Abha *type.*

premium in capital costs compared to cellular vessels.

There has been a long pause since the last large deep sea roro ships were built and during this time the large cellular vessels have moved into a position of total dominance on high density trade routes. Following some re-organisation in the trade the large roro ships are now operated by two carriers, Wilhelmsen of Norway and National Shipping Company of Saudi Arabia, and tend to be confined to rather specialised sectors of the market.

Roro container The pure roro ships operating as full container carriers were a limited class. One of the main operators was Merzario running out of Italy to the Arabian Gulf, the main reason for the choice of vessel lying in port limitations in both Italy and the Gulf in the mid 1970s. The other operator was Eastern Searoad Service (ESS) with a service between Australia and the Far East. Made up of a consortium comprising Kawasaki Kisen KK (Japan), and Flinders Shipping Co Pty Ltd and Australian National Line (both Australia), this carrier was strongly of the view that its particular type of roro ship was both cheap in construction and effective in operation, claiming that a combination of roro operations below decks and lolo on the weather deck (assisted by the use of cell guides) would give much faster handling than that of the cellular system.

As it turned out the system did not have operational advantages except in special circumstances. Handling was fast enough, but it could not maintain any significant long term advantage over the cellular system. The limitation in access below decks would also create stowage difficulties on complex itineraries. Because of this and the fact that the system was taken on by only a few operators and required a rather specialised approach in the terminal the ships lacked trading flexibility.

Conclusions

There has been a very long debate about the market role of roro ships and their efficiency *vis-à-vis* cellular and semi container systems. This started way back in the 1960s, when some of the proponents of roro argued that the inherent handling characteristics of the system were superior to those of lolo container systems and that large roro ships would be a serious competitor to cellular vessels.

So far as the large ships are concerned these hopes were to be dashed. The reasons for this have been competition from more specialised carriers in the semi bulk sector, the fact that handling performance could not match the cellular container system, and finally the emergence of a significant premium in the capital costs of the ships themselves. As a result of this these classes are now almost certainly obsolescent.

The smaller vessels are a somewhat different proposition. They are simpler in naval architectural terms, most of them having just one tween deck and rather simple roro access, and for this reason they do not bear too much of a cost premium. The modern vessels are very container friendly and can achieve good handling rates at limited port facilities beating older style semi container and conventional vessels and matching self sustaining cellular vessels. They also have a fairly wide range of trading opportunities. They are a moderately successful class, although there is some question about their long term ability to compete in the deep sea trades.

Bulk carrier containerships

Introduction

The bulk carrier-container fleet has grown quite rapidly in recent years and in 1988 there were 317 vessels in the world fleet with some 304,000 TEUs capacity. In TEU terms in 1988 the fleet was roughly equivalent to that of the roro ships and just under half the size of the semi container fleet.

Standard bulk carriers

Standard bulk carriers are ill suited to the container trades. They usually operate well down the speed range at some 13 to 15kts and have narrow hatches, which are neither sized for containers nor strengthened for a weather deck stow. The hold space in the square of the hatches has only a very limited container capacity, whilst stowage under the deck overhangs requires the use of a large fork lift truck. Finally they do not usually carry their own deck cranes. Together these features make for extremely awkward operations with limited capacity, slow handling and a relatively high propensity to container damage. These ships have had only a negligible presence in the container trades, the main operator being CAST Line (Canada) which used them in the 1970s, prior to the construction of its more specialised 'conbulkers'. There has, however, always been a number of self-sustaining bulk carriers in the handy size range up to 40,000 dwt. For ships of this type it is relatively easy to provide for a supplementary weather deck capacity for containers. Neither of these classes is of any great importance in container trades.

FPCs and other 'open hatch' vessels

Forest products carriers (FPCs) are fundamentally different from standard bulk carriers. Their cargo is in large units and this creates the requirement for the wide hatches and large square smooth sided holds which are the characteristics of the 'open hatch' design. Most FPCs are also self sustaining, many of them being equipped with two gantries, whilst they also tend to be a knot or so faster than similar sized bulk carriers. For these reasons they are much more expensive than standard bulk carriers, the open hatch design adding some 17 per cent to capital costs whilst gantries

may cost up to US$3 million apiece. These ships are naturally container friendly although the lack of cell guides is something of a disadvantage. They do participate in container trades, although their operational pattern is usually constrained by the need to marry a liner style service for forest products with containers. Among the tramps the modern vessels appear to be a little large and a little too slow to be chartered into container trades.

A typical example of this type of vessel is the Bahamas-registered *Hawk Arrow*, owned by Gearbulk Shipowning Ltd and managed by Jardine Ship Management Ltd, of Hong Kong. Built in South Korea in 1985, she is of 27,938 grt and 42,792 dwt, with a TEU capacity of 1392. With ten hatches and seven holds, the vessel does in fact have a total hold capacity for 1044 containers, while 248 could be stowed on deck.

Built primarily for the forest products trade out of the Canadian west coast, *Hawk Arrow*, has a speed in service of fourteen knots.

The general purpose open hatch bulk carriers are not very different from FPCs. They tend to have cranes rather than travelling gantries and in some cases a rather higher weather deck capacity.

Conbulkers

The main 'conbulker' classes were developed in the late 1970s by two operators, CAST on the North Atlantic and ABC operating a round the world service linking Europe, Australia and the United States east coast. CAST built quite large vessels of some 70,800 dwt with four pure bulk holds and three container holds. Weather deck capacity is 614 TEUs the boxes being

stowed around all holds and on the hatch covers of the container holds. Hold capacity is some 814 TEUs, but there is not too much of a concession to container handling as the ships retain deck overhangs and fork lift handling in the holds.

The CAST conbulkers, which are six in number, were built in South Korea and Yugoslavia. One of the series, *Cast Husky*, completed by Hyundai Heavy Industries, Ulsan, in 1982, is 40,924 grt and 70,912 dwt, and with her five sister-ships links Montreal and Zeebrugge.

ABC had a more radical approach, with changes in hold configuration towards an open hatch design in the early classes moving on to a cellular configuration in the later vessels and the addition of a reefer capacity. These are liner vessels with the addition of bulk holds, which are used for the service of along term mineral sands contract from Australia to the United States Gulf, and pick up whatever further bulks they can get which fits in with their itineraries.

In a detailed analysis of conbulker potential Reynolds defined the conditions required for them to compete in container trades. They required moderate sized parcels of high density bulk cargoes, which would not be suitable for large bulk carriers. If possible these had to be tied up with a long term contract. At the same time the route had to be one in which the largest cellular vessels could not operate. Further to this the geography of the bulk and container sectors had to be consistent, so that any diversions off the main route were kept to a minimum.[4] These conditions are extremely restrictive and the reality is that the purpose built conbulkers are very specialised ships. They have to be moderately fast to offer adequate service quality in container trades and they also require special strengthening to enable them to carry a mix of bulk cargoes and containers. This makes them far too expensive to trade flexibly in pure bulk markets, limiting

them to rather special combinations and with a requirement for long term contracts to guarantee the bulk component of their trade.

Conclusions

Among the bulk carrier container ships the most important class by far would appear to be the geared open hatch vessels in the 20,000 dwt to 30,000 dwt size range. As mentioned in an earlier section these are virtually an extension of the large semi container ships. They can trade flexibly across minor bulk, semi bulk and container trades, although the lack of a tween deck limits their ability to handle certain types of unit load cargoes. The FPCs are also an important class although the liners are rather limited in their operational flexibility in the container trades and the modern vessels tend to be rather too large and too slow for charter in container trades.

The small class of purpose built conbulkers has probably had much more publicity over the years than all the other classes, as CAST was for some time an important outsider in the North Atlantic and ABC Containerline made the first important attack on the strong closed conference in the Europe-Australia trade. However, this concept now appears at best of very limited application in the liner trades, and is probably obsolescent.

An assessment of the cargo handling revolutions

The unit load revolutions of the 1950s and 1960s produced a range of alternative systems.

They resulted in a radical structural change in the industry in which the large flows of semi bulk and specialised cargoes moved out of the tramp and liner sectors into their own individual systems. These sectors now handle a volume of cargo comparable with that of the container system itself. This change left a general cargo sector which was taken over largely by containers. It was somewhat reduced by loss of the semi bulk and specialised cargoes which it had previously carried, but for those in the industry the overall experience was one of dynamic growth fuelled first by the take-over from the conventional system and later on by the rapid growth of trade in manufactures and other containerisable products.

A cargo flow has to be of a certain minimum size in order to justify investment in specialised port facilities and handling systems. In some cases specialised vessels are also required. Where cargo volumes are not adequate to sustain such investments they remain in the general cargo sector. This has created opportunities for some carriers to operate with mixes of containers, unit loads, specialised cargoes and the residual of non unitisable cargoes. In particular it provided the window of opportunity for roro systems, which were particularly suitable for handling a variety of unit loads, and which some carriers, particularly the Scandinavians, believed would eventually prove more effective than the cellular container systems for handling containers.

4.G Reynolds, 'How Competitive are Conbulkers?', *MARIN* (1984).

Changes in trade patterns and operational requirements often cause owners to temporarily put their vessels out on short- or long-term charter. Nedlloyd Clarence, *owned by Nedlloyd Lijnen BV, Rotterdam, and built by Hyundai, South Korea, in 1983, was destined for its owner's liner trades, particularly between Europe and the Far East, but has changed its name a few times to conform with operational requirements such as charterers' preference. In 1992, for example, the vessel was renamed* Ibn Bajjah *for charter to United Arab Shipping Co, an Arab multinational entity based in Kuwait.* Nedlloyd Clarence *is 33,405 grt and carries 2003 TEUs. (FotoFlite)*

Within the general cargo sector proper the cellular container system quite quickly took the lead, dominating what are now called the mainstream routes, (linking Europe, the Far East and North America) as well as a number of important secondary routes to Australasia and South Africa. The large roro ships, also concentrated on these routes, albeit with a subsidiary role, as did the specialised conbulkers at a later date.

On many developing country routes the cellular system did not take hold straight away. A number of alternative policies were followed, the main approach taking the form of a slow evolution of the standard general cargo tramp and liner into semi containerships. There were a number of reasons for this; first the high costs of change over; second the problems of making modern systems work effectively and the high costs involved (in container damage and long dwell times inland etc) when they did not; and finally a lack of commitment to the new system resulting from a view that it was capital intensive and unsuited to the needs of developing countries.

Twenty years of competition have seen the resolution of many of the questions concerning the competitive efficiency of the alternative systems on both developed and developing country routes. Semi bulk systems predominate in the movement of some very large commodity groups like steel, forest products, bagged cement and fertiliser. Specialised systems have been equally successful in the movement of vehicles, oils and fats and many refrigerated cargoes. Many of these com-

modities are produced or packaged in large units at the point of manufacture and are not particularly vulnerable to pilferage and damage. The concentration in production leading to large parcel sizes is a further point in favour of purpose designed systems, whilst some commodities like vehicles and oils and fats achieve their best possible handling and stowage when they can be dealt with in specially designed vessels. As cargo volumes grow the semi bulk and specialised systems tend to develop technically and logistically and become more effective and competitive.

New specialised systems are under development as with high speed pallet loaders now being used in some fruit trades, or the development of a bulk carrier to handle the concentrated fruit juice which used to be a valued liner cargo out of Brazil. There are also some areas where the containers make inroads into a specialised system. For example the increasing size of containerships on mainstream routes, together with a degree of over tonnaging and a lack of balance between legs, has led to the entry of containerships into some of the forest products markets. There is also competition in the refrigerated sector in which container systems have made some inroads. This cut and thrust of competition between containers, semi bulk and specialised systems is likely to continue, although there is no longer scope for massive structural reorganisation of the type which has taken place in the last two decades.

The success of modern systems has implications for trade. In economic terms

transport is part of the production process, and those areas which do not have access to modern technologies find themselves at an increasing disadvantage as transport systems develop on the higher volume routes. Fortunately, some of the neo bulk and specialised systems can now operate at moderate scale, whilst the container system can use feeder services to bring quite small flows within the range of large vessels at moderate cost.

In the general cargo sector proper, choices have now been simplified by competition between the cellular system and its challengers. It has become clear that the flexible systems using large vessels which compete directly with the cellular system on mainstream routes, are either in retreat or have failed to make gains in a market which has grown quite dynamically in recent years.

Barge carriers have been the outright failure among the alternative systems and are now virtually obsolete although a few vessels of rather radical design are still trading. In this case the competition was only partly with the cellular system as barges handled large quantities of semi bulks.

The large roro ships have traded with a fair degree of success for many years, but full container ships with roro handling below the weather deck have almost died out, whilst the container roros and the full roros are confined to limited sectors, and have not been able to share in the growth of recent years.

In the semi container sector, those vessels which carry combinations of cargoes in specialised holds have been relatively unsuccessful, some of them rapidly becoming obsolete with the progress of containerisation in the trades they served. Turning to the combinations based on bulk cargoes, the CAST and ABC type conbulkers are not genuinely flexible ships, and appear destined to remain limited classes serving niche markets.

Some classes of flexible ships have proved to

The barge carrier revolution was a concept which did not advance at all well, and by the early 1990s accounted for very few vessels, including the Seabee class owned by Lyke Bros Steamship Co, of New Orleans, and put in to service between that port and northwest Europe. Built by General Dynamics Corp, Quincy, Massachusetts, in 1972, Doctor Lykes (21,667 grt) carried thirty-eight barges on board and was also able to carry containers. Access was by a stern door and barge lift, clearly seen in this 1973 photograph.

be quite successful. These include the compact semi containerships which can trade across bulk, semi bulk and container sectors and have a role in both deep and short sea trades. Their larger sisters the general purpose open hatch bulk carriers have also proved themselves, and may begin to take over the role of semi containerships in the deep sea trades. Finally, the small classes of roro vessel have proved successful, although with the growth of ship size on north-south routes and the increase in the fleet of self sustaining containerships their trading opportunities may be reducing.

Strategies for ship design

As a final comment upon the process of technological change one may distinguish between the strategies behind the various approaches to the design of ships and cargo handling systems. One successful theme has been segregation of the industry into pure sectors handling the large flow, which can then maximise economies of scale and take the full advantages of bulk and unit load handling. A related theme concerns the ability of the handling system to minimise labour costs and to develop in terms of automation and speed of cargo movement. In the deep sea liner sector the cellular system had undoubtedly been the most successful in these terms and has come to dominate the mainstream trades as well as many secondary routes.

The flexible classes which have been most successful are those which can trade across sectors, without too much additional expense in the vessel, and without compromising by too much their competitiveness in the most important of these sectors. These opportunities have been found among the smaller and medium sized vessels rather than the larger classes. They have also in general involved flexibility in the use of cargo spaces, rather than a combination of specialised cargo spaces. Finally, this type of vessel has been developed by charter rather than liner operators in a sector which encourages the search for the lowest common denominator.

Turning to the less successful elements one focus of attention must be on any high cost premium in the vessel. This is not always too easy to determine. For example, in the early days, such prices of the barge carriers as were available did not seem to be excessive, the real level of costs being hidden partly by subsidy to US shipbuilders and partly by an understandable coyness on the part of operators to discuss them at any length. For the large roros cost differentials did not seem to be great in the early years and a number of naval architectural studies seemed to confirm this point. Recently some rather larger differentials have emerged and ACLs G3s for example were about twice the cost of the Evergreen G class. Just how much of this reflects basic differences in the vessels and how much may be due to subsidy or differences between yards and shipbuilding regions is a matter for debate. But high building costs, together with competition for roro cargoes from other more specialised vessels like the car/truck carriers, severely limits their future role.

A second point concerns the way in which a flexible capability is achieved. Broadly, genuine flexibility is achieved when the individual cargo spaces can carry different types of cargo. When the ship simply has a combination of specialised cargo spaces it tends to lose trading flexibility, however effective it may be in the precise combination role for which it was originally designed.

On the revenue side the general problem with the strategy of carrying small flows of

During 1991–92 Nedlloyd Lines of Rotterdam commissioned five new container vessels for the northwest Europe–Far East service. The lead vessel of the series, Nedlloyd Asia, was built by Ishikawajima-Harima Heavy Industries (IHI), at Kure, Japan, and has a capacity of 3568 TEUs, and together with her sister-ships is the result of extensive research by Nedlloyd into the development of the ultimate container carrier (UCC), which gives a greater TEU capacity on a lower gross tonnage. (Nedlloyd)

semi bulk and specialised cargoes along with containers, is that this cargo may become subject to low cost competition. This reduces rates and creates the permanent threat of loss of the whole traffic. Where this type of competition applies, growth in the cargo volume tends to weaken the flexible system instead of strengthening it.

Conclusion

The cargo handling revolutions have been an extraordinary success. They have reduced both capital and labour requirements of the industry so that costs in real terms are a fraction of what they would have been under a conventional regime. At the same time the speed and security service has improved and this guaranteed regularity has supported the 'just in time' concept of manufacturing and the expansion of world trade.

So far as the container itself is concerned there is considerable pressure for increases in length and width, the justification for this being related to improved utilisation of equipment in inland modes and compatibility with inland pallet systems. However, although in physical terms the changes in width are only a few inches and those in length are only up to 13ft, the implications of any widespread change would be tremendous, involving massive re-investment and huge physical and logistical difficulties in ships ports, terminals and inland transport systems. Particular problems would be created in developing countries. These costs would limit the overall advantages and it seems likely that the industry will attempt to restrict the use of specials to limited trades.

In terms of the pure technology of shipping and cargo handling on the deep sea trades we may expect to see continuing evolutionary developments rather than another revolution. There have been some ideas for revolutionary developments in both ships and ports which would yield a further transformation in the container system. Articulated vessels unloading hundreds of containers at a time and completely automated multi-storey stacking for containers are two such possibilities.

These suggestions are not very widespread and do not have much force. The cellular system already has a huge scale of operations on high density-routes, with an established potential for yet further increases in vessel size to some 5500 TEUs. In the terminals some cranes are already achieving forty or fifty moves per crane per hour and as these rates become more sustainable, it can be seen that some 700 to 800 moves per crane per day could eventually come within reach, to give daily container exchanges for a two crane operation of up to 2400 TEUs (on the basis of a 50:50 split between 20ft and 40ft units). In the terminals there are increasing degrees of automation which could eventually reduce manning requirements. Most of these developments appear to be achievable without excessive pressure on port infrastructures at the major centres. These developments undercut the radical alternatives and we can look forward to further improvements along an evolutionary path and an enhanced service to trade, industry and economic development.

Sidney Gilman

Typical containerships 1958–1992

Ship (Class)	Flag	Built	By	GRT (TEU)	Length (oa) × breadth × depth × draught Feet–Inches Metres	Cargo handling gear	Engines	Speed	Remarks
1950s HAWAIIAN MERCHANT (C3 standard type)	US	1945	Ingall's SB, Pascagoula	7882	491–7 × 69–9 × 42–6 × 29–5 *149.82 × 21.26 × 12.95 × 8.97*	Derricks 2 × 30 tons + others	2 General Electric steam turbines, 9350shp; 1 shaft	16.5kts	24ft containers on deck; break-bulk cargo in holds; 12,177 dwt

Ship (Class)	Flag	Built	By	GRT (TEU)	Length (oa) × breadth × depth × draught Feet–Inches Metres	Cargo handling gear	Engines	Speed	Remarks
1960s									
ELIZABETHPORT	US	1942	Sun SB & DD, Chester, Pa	16,395 (476)	627–2 × 78–2 × 47–0 × 27–1 *191.17 × 23.83 × 14.32 × 8.26*	Cranes 2 × 27 tons	2 General Electric steam turbines, 10,000shp; 1 shaft	15kts	Converted from tanker 1962; lengthened; 15,770 dwt
First generation									
ATLANTIC STAR	Ne	1967	*France-Gironde, Dunkirk*	*15,054 (800)*	*731–9 × 98–5 × 62–4 × 30–1[1]* *223.02 × 30.0 × 19.0 × 9.17*	Roro	*1 MAN diesel, 20,700bhp; 1 shaft*	*20kts*	
Second generation									
ACT 1	UK	1969	Bremer Vulkan, Vegesack	24,821 (1414)	712–9 × 95–4 × 52–3 × 35–6 *217.25 × 29.06 × 15.93 × 10.83*	Gearless	2 Bremer Vulkan/ STAL-LAVAL steam turbines, 20,000shp; 1 shaft	22kts	4 pass 326 ref TEU
DART AMERICA	UK	1970	Swan Hunter SBs, Newcastle	31,036 (1535)	759–8 × 100–6 × 51–2 × 33–1 *231.55 × 30.64 × 15.6 × 10.08*	Gearless	1 Clark/Sulzer diesel, 29,000bhp; 1 shaft	23kts	
Third generation Panamax (1970s)									
LIVERPOOL BAY	UK	1971	Howaldtswerke-Deutsche Werft, Kiel	58,889 (2661)	950–0 × 106–1 × 80–8 × 42–9 *289.57 × 32.34 × 24.59 × 13.03*	Gearless	4 STAL-LAVAL steam turbines, 81,132shp;[2] 2 shafts	27.5kts	
RHINE MARU	Jap	1972	Mitsubishi, Kobe	51,040 (1836)	856–4 × 105–10 × 64–0 × 39–5 *261.02 × 32.26 × 19.51 × 12.02*	Gearless	2 Mitsui/B&W diesels, 55,200bhp; 2 shafts	23.25kts	
SEA-LAND McLEAN (SL7)	US	1972	Rotterdam DD, Rotterdam	41,127 (1095)[3]	946–3 × 105–10 × 51–11 × 34–10 *288.4 × 32.26 × 15.83 × 10.61*	Gearless	4 General Electric steam turbines, 120,000shp; 2 shafts	33kts	
Panamax after 1980									
AMERICAN ALABAMA (Econship)	US	1984	Daewoo SB, Koje	57,075 (4258)	949–10 × 105–10 × 70–6 × 38–4 *289.52 × 32.26 × 21.49 × 11.68*	Gearless	1 Hyundai/ Sulzer diesel, 23,620bhp; 1 shaft	18kts	146 ref TEU
EVER GUEST	Twn	1986	Onomichi Zsn, Onomichi	40,703[4] (2940)	792–10 × 106–0 × 62–10 × 38–2 *241.66 × 32.31 × 19.16 × 11.63*	Gearless	1 Hitachi/ Sulzer diesel, 23,180bhp; 1 shaft	21kts	
MARCHEN MAERSK	Dmk	1988	Odense Staals, Lindo	52,191 (3922)	965–8 × 105–10 × 70–8 × 44–4 *294.32 × 32.26 × 21.52 × 13.52*	Gearless	1 Mitsui/B&W diesel, 57,675bhp; 1 shaft	24kts	500 ref TEU
NEDLLOYD ASIA	Ne	1991	IHI, Kure	48,508 (3568)	741–5 × 105–10 × 76–3 × 41–0 *226.0 × 32.26 × 23.25 × 12.5*	Gearless	1 IHI/Sulzer diesel, 41,600bhp; 1 shaft	21.5kts	Crew 15
Post Panamax									
PRESIDENT TRUMAN (C10)	US	1988	Howaldtswerke-Deutsche Werft, Kiel	61,785 (4340)	902–11 × 129–4 × 77–6 × 41–9 *275.22 × 39.41 × 23.63 × 12.73*	Gearless	1 Korea HI/ Sulzer diesel, 56.960bhp	24.25kts	
Conbulker									
CAST CARIBOU	Bbd[5]	1982	Brodogradiliste 3 Maj, Rijeka	40,003 (1466)	771–0 × 105–9 × 44–3 × 61–1 *235.62 × 32.24 × 13.48 × 18.62*	Gearless	1 3 Maj/Sulzer diesel, 13,600bhp; 1 shaft	14.75kts	Bulk capacity 84,895m³

Notes:
[1] Dimensions as lengthened 1976; originally 501 TEU.
[2] Re-engined 1981, to diesel 50,880bhp.
[3] 35–40ft.
[4] As built – lengthened 1987: became 269.68 (oa) and TEU capacity 3428 incl 156 refrigerated.
[5] Later Yugoslav flag.

Oil Tankers, Chemical Carriers and Gas Carriers

T O UNDERSTAND the structure of the tanker market it is necessary to look at the patterns of production and consumption of oil. As we are examining the developments which culminated in the very large crude carrier (VLCC) and ultra large crude carrier (ULCC) in the early 1970s it is appropriate to look at the oil trades and the demand for tankers during this period.

Demand for tankers

From the early days of the industry in the nineteenth century until 1973, the world oil trade was dominated by seven oil majors sometimes known as the 'Seven Sisters' – Exxon (Esso), Gulf, Texaco, Mobil, Chevron, BP and Shell. Apart from the last two, they are United States owned and controlled. Between them the oil majors managed the exploration, production, transport, refining and marketing of oil in every country in which they were able to gain access. During those years they were amongst the largest multinational companies, and it was not unusual for some to have a greater income than that of the countries in which they operated. This power enabled them to manage the international oil industry in the way which best suited their interests.

When first produced crude oil is a mixture of many different components. Before it can be used it must be refined into products that the consumer needs, such as the petroleum gases butane and propane, liquid fuels including petrol, kerosene, diesel oil and fuel oil, lubri-

cating oils, and chemicals which are the base of many products in common use.

The first oil refineries were situated close to the oilfields and the products transported by sea to the markets. Examples of such refineries were the BP refinery at Abadan, Iran, and the Shell refinery at Curacao close to the oilfields of Venezuela. After the Second World War the oil companies changed their policy and located their refineries close to the major markets. There were two main reasons for this.

First, the immediate postwar period had been one of political instability in the Middle East, where most of western Europe's and Japan's supplies of crude oil originated. The nationalisation of the BP refinery at Abadan in 1951 led to a boycott of Iranian oil by the other oil majors in support of BP. When a settlement was finally achieved with Iran in 1954 the oil majors decided to locate their refineries closer to the markets to protect themselves from similar dangers.

Second, as refining technology was constantly being improved, there were no longer any unusable residues after crude oil was refined and no waste to be transported. The greater sophistication of the oil products themselves required blending from a number of different grades of crude oil, and it therefore made economic and operational sense to locate the refineries at deepwater terminals close to the consumers in Europe and Japan.

Since the Middle East War of 1973 the oil producing countries have gained control of their own oil production and are starting to reverse this trend in order to benefit from the added value of refining the oil.

Thus the scene was set for the developments in the tanker markets. These markets are divided into two large segments and a number of smaller niche markets such as liquefied petroleum gas and chemicals. The two main types of oil tanker are, firstly the crude carrier, designed to carry oil from oilfields to the refin-

When built in 1961, Naess Sovereign was one of the largest tankers of the time. Operating under the British flag as part of the then substantial Naess fleet, headed by Norwegian shipping magnate Erling Naess, this vessel had a deadweight of 95,386 tons – large by early 1960s standards. Pictured here at a discharge berth in the Thames, the network of on-deck piping can be clearly seen. (W R G Hopkins)

eries and the second type is the products tanker designed to take these from the refinery where they are produced to the consumer. Sometimes this involves discharging direct to a user such as a power station, but usually it is to a storage depot where it will be distributed by road or rail.

The products tanker

When the crude oil tanker developed into a large carrier optimised for the long distance trades from the oilfields to the refineries, the products tanker meanwhile developed as a separate type. In the days prior to and just after the Second World War, most tankers were

A postwar innovation has been the parcel tanker, capable of carrying simultaneously in independent tanks a variety of petroleum products or chemicals. In 1974 Panocean Shipping, a joint venture of P&O and Ocean Transport & Trading, commissioned Post Endeavour *(25,150 dwt), an advanced parcel tanker incorporating several technical advances, including the introduction of more stainless steel tanks (thirty-seven), ballast capability in double bottoms, and additional cargo pumps. Type A chemicals could be carried in independent stainless steel tanks on deck. (P&O)*

products carriers, transporting the refined oil from the Middle East and Caribbean to the markets. In practice there was then very little difference in design between crude oil and products tankers.

With the construction of oil refineries in market areas, the trade patterns for products tankers concentrated on the shorter voyages delivering the oil products to the customers, thus in areas such as northwest Europe, the average round voyage was comparatively short. These voyages did not offer any economic advantages for the larger ships and products tankers remained comparatively small as the ship size was dictated by the customer's requirements both with regard to volume of cargo and also by the type of port used for discharge at a customer's premises. There was, however, a small and steady increase in size from about 12,000 dwt in the 1950s to 24,000 dwt in the 1970s.

These ships spend a longer aggregate time in port than the larger crude tankers so cargo handling systems have been designed to keep port time to a minimum. As a result of their higher cost per tonne, owners aimed to maximise the time when carrying cargo. A crude oil tanker will carry cargo for only half the time she is at sea since for the other half she is returning in ballast to the loading port. The products tanker, however, generally has a varied trading pattern, and it is possible for an owner to manage its various charters to minimise the ballast voyages.

As the oil producers have built up their refinery capacity there has grown a demand for larger products tankers for the long-haul products trade. There were always what were known as 'balancing trades' where a surplus of products in one area would be shipped to another, but there are now regular long-haul products trades and the size of tankers used for these is approaching that of crude carriers.

The users of oil products, in particular the chemical industry but also the transport and other industries are demanding an increasingly higher specification for the oil which they purchase, and operators need to ensure that cargoes are delivered without any loss of quality. The main causes of quality loss are contamination between different products being carried in the same ship or by residues from a previous cargo. The difficulty is that a products tanker must be able to carry a wide range of products, perhaps three or four different grades on the same voyage, and these must be loaded and discharged without any contamination.

The developments that appeared in the products tanker were in the design of their

pipeline systems to give the required flexibility to enable the different grades to be loaded and discharged quickly and safely. Tank coatings were developed to protect the interior from corrosion and possible leaks between tanks and also to provide a hard and smooth surface that is easy to clean between voyages.

There are two principal types of products tanker – the 'clean' or 'white' product ship which carries oil with a colour specification such as petrol, kerosene and perhaps, the most difficult to carry, lubricating oils; the second type are the 'black' or 'dirty' tankers for the carriage of fuel oils. The important feature of these cargoes is that they must be heated in order that they can be pumped. To this end most product tankers are fitted with heating coils (pipes along the tank bottoms), and on some vessels, also the sides of the tanks, for steam to be passed through to heat the cargo.

Products tankers trade in either white or black oils because although it is easy to change from white to black (as long as the vessel has heating coils), it is not so easy to change the other way round as the tanks must be thoroughly cleaned to remove any residue which could contaminate a clean oil cargo. With modern tank coatings this does not present too much of a problem but charterers tend to prefer not to take what they see as a risk, and would prefer to stay with tankers which have traded in clean oils for some time.

Compared with larger crude oil carriers, products tankers require a more complicated cargo handling system, and on a cost per tonne basis these vessels are far more expensive than the crude oil tanker. Generally, freight rates reflect this difference.

The crude oil tanker

Having decided to relocate their refineries, it was the geography of the oil trades that led the oil companies to the development of large crude oil tankers. An examination of the map shows that in the 1960s most of the oil exported by sea came from the Middle East with smaller quantities from West and North Africa. The two main markets for this oil were western Europe and Japan. The recoveries of the European economy in the 1950s and the Japanese economy in the 1960s were based on less expensive Middle East oil replacing coal. Coal had been the main source of energy for the consumer countries. The use of increasingly larger tankers that were being developed during this period brought about lower unit costs.

The Suez Canal has had an important influ-

Cape of Good Hope was realised. It is interesting to note that the first 100,000-ton tanker,
large enough for the Cape/Cape route was delivered in 1959. This was the steam turbine-
powered *Universe Apollo* (114,356 dwt), built in
Japan for Universe Tankships Inc, beneficially
owned by a New York company. Her mar-
ginally larger sister-ship, *Universe Daphne*, was
delivered in 1960.

The canal was again closed in 1967 and this
time it had a profound influence on the development of the very large tankers.

Economies of scale

The concept of economies of scale in shipping
is as old as the ship itself; it is only the lack of
suitable technology that has held these developments back. Brunel's *Great Eastern* (1860)
at 18,915 grt was the largest ship in her day but
was too far ahead of her time to be a commercial success. By the end of the 1960s men had
visited the moon and there appeared to be no
limits to what technology could achieve. It was
the commercial constraints that paced the development of the large tankers.

The economies of scale in ships are based on
a few very simple principles:

The square/cube rule

Consider two cubes, one with sides 2m long
and the other with sides 4m long; the sides of
the second box are exactly twice those of the
first box. The volume of the first box is 2m ×
2m × 2m = 8cu m, and the volume of the
second box is 4m × 4m × 4m = 64cu m.

Now consider the surface area of each box:
the area of the first box is 2m × 2m × 6 (number
of faces) = 24sq m, and the area of the second
box is 4m × 4m × 6m = 96sq m.

Relating these examples to ships, the doubling of the size of the ship represents the problems that will be placed on ports and terminals
in terms of size and berth and depth of water.

The increase in surface area represents the
increase in costs of building the ship, mostly
composed of the extra steel required in the
ship's construction. The increase in volume
represents the increase in carrying capacity and
thus the earning power of the ship.

Thus for a doubling of size, the building cost
rises by a factor of four (2^2) while the earning
power increase by a factor of eight (2^3) – hence

ence on tanker development. The shortest distance from the Middle East to Europe is via the
Suez Canal, the distance from Kuwait to Rotterdam via the Suez Canal being 6572 miles
while the longer distance via the Cape of Good
Hope is 11,418 miles. Shipowners therefore
wanted tankers that were able to transit the
canal carrying a full cargo of oil. During the
postwar period, the Suez Canal has frequently
been deepened but it has lagged behind the
development of large tankers. Tankers which
have been able to transit southbound in ballast
have been unable to carry a full cargo north-

bound. Tanker owners frequently built ships
that were too large to carry a full cargo
through the canal anticipating that it would
soon be deepened and their ships would then
prove to be the right size. The canal has also
been associated with political problems; it was
the nationalisation of the canal by the Egyptian
Government which contributed to the Middle
East conflict of 1956 and the subsequent
closure of the canal. This led to a boom in
tanker freights and a rush to build new ships
but the canal was reopened before the idea of
building large enough ships to steam round the

When built in 1963 the 49,000 dwt British Dragoon *could still be described as a 'supertanker' in company publicity, but ships four times this size were on order within a few years.* (CMP)

the term 'square/cube rule'. This example is somewhat simplistic but it demonstrates that when the size of a ship is increased the earning power increases faster than any other parameter.

In practice there are other factors which show even greater benefits for the larger ships. *Crew costs*: the crew numbers do not depend on the size of the ship, but on the level of automation that the owner is prepared to pay for and the degree of onboard maintenance which the owner requires to be carried out. There has been a steady reduction in average crew numbers, from about forty-five to twenty-four, over the twenty years from the 1960s to the '80s. This was a result of owners taking advantage of improved automation and more reliable equipment. In practice the size of crew required to run a tanker is independent of the ship's size, hence the ratio of cargo carried per crew member increases with the ship's size.

Overheads: this is a similar position to crew numbers, with the overheads involved in running a large ship being the same as for a small ship, so the numbers of office staff, for example, depend on the numbers of ships rather than their size. In practice because of their trading pattern and types of cargo lifted the large tanker requires a smaller office staff than the smaller product tanker. Engine power is another area where the larger ship gains: other things being equal, the greater the power required, the greater the fuel consumption. The power required for any given displacement increases in proportion to two-thirds of the displacement. A ship of 60,000 dwt might need about 16,000hp for a loaded speed of 15kts while a ship of 260,000 dwt would need:

$$\frac{(60,000)^{2/3}}{(260,000)^{2/3}} = \frac{16,000}{42,500}$$

Construction costs related to deadweight size

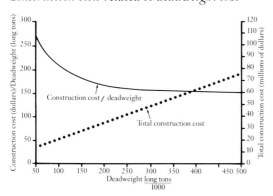

Although 42,500hp is a higher power, particularly when compared with existing ships of the later 1960s, it is only about 2.7 times what is required for the 60,000-tonne ship. The fuel consumption would be proportional to the power required and would only increase from about 53 tonnes per day for the smaller ship to about 140 tonnes per day for the larger ships.

Tanker size growth

These advantages had been understood for many years. In fact, Eagle Transport had built what for its time were very large tankers – 16,000 dwt – for transporting Mexican oil to the United Kingdom just before the First World War. The trend continued during the between-wars period, and during the Second World War the 'T2' of 16,400 dwt became the standard tanker.

A total of 620 of these turbo-electric powered ships were built between 1942 and 1946 in the United States in a shipbuilding

Shipment cost related to ship size and distance of bulk commodity source

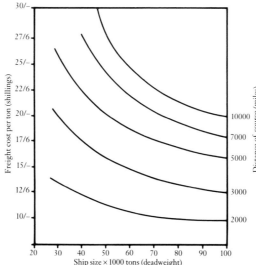

effort that was only exceeded by that of the better-known 'Liberty' ship. In the early postwar years these ships were released by the military to become the mainstay of the world's oil-carrying fleets, pending the completion of new postwar tonnage. Because they were so common some authorities measured tanker demand in T2 equivalent units, ie the number of these tankers needed to move the required amount of oil within the period of time allowed. The T2 tanker lasted for many years after the war in the fleets of both oil companies and independent owners. Some were still in service in the late 1960s.

After the War there was a steady growth in tanker size, much of this development being pioneered by the Greek shipowners Onassis and Niarchos who made use of what was at that time the novel method of financing ships by bank loans. They used long-term time charters from the oil majors to guarantee the cash flow necessary to meet the loan repayments and by this method their fleets grew both in size of ships and in tonnage. By the mid 1960s Greek companies owned the world's largest independent tanker fleet. In the late 1960s Hong Kong became a centre for tanker ownership and C Y Tung (Island Navigation Corp) and Sir Y K Pao (World-Wide Shipping), built up large fleets of tankers financed by Japanese interests.

So the emergence of the very large crude carrier (VLCC) was a logical, albeit rather large, step forward from the existing ships. The economic advantages were clear. The technical problems could be overcome (at least according to the experts), and it was left for the market to determine when and under what conditions these ships should be built.

The economic advantages of the larger ships had been understood for many years, but apart from technology, what had also hampered their development were port and inventory problems. The problems of ports were similar to that of the Suez Canal, already touched on.

In many ports a considerable capital investment was required to enlarge and deepen the facilities in order to accommodate these ships and there was a natural reluctance on the part of port authorities to authorise the necessary expenditure before it was clear that these ships would be built.

Unless there was a consistent demand for the cargo in quantities sufficient to require frequent and regular shipments, the inventory cost would become excessive. The economic advantages resulting from the lower unit costs of the larger ships are then more than offset by the higher inventory and port costs resulting from using larger ships and less frequent deliveries.

In the early 1960s Shell carried out a study on the economics of using a VLCC to carry oil from the Middle East to Europe – the combination of a long sea voyage, homogeneous cargo that could be rapidly loaded and discharged while the Shell operations were sufficiently large to require frequent shipments of oil in VLCCs. Thus all the preconditions were met.

The results of their studies were presented in the above graph, which indicates there would be steep reduction in costs when the ship's size was increased up to about 100,000 dwt and then a slower reduction after this. What was clear from the graph is the influence of the Suez Canal. At that time (mid 1960s) the canal could only accommodate ships of up to about 70,000 dwt fully laden on the northbound transit. Any larger ships had to carry a part cargo, with the possibility of topping up at one of the terminals in the eastern Mediterranean before proceeding to discharge in northwest Europe. The alternative to this was to transit the Suez Canal southbound in ballast and then proceed to Europe via the longer voyage around the Cape of Good Hope. The final alternative was for ships to undertake the round voyage via the Cape of Good Hope on both the loaded and ballast voyages. It was anticipated that in time the Suez Canal would be enlarged so that the larger ships would be able to transit on the loaded passage.

As a result of this and similar studies carried out elsewhere, a number of owners decided to

build the VLCCs. Shell leading with an order for over twenty tankers of what were planned to be 175,000 dwt but after the load line rules were altered they were increased to between 190,000 and 210,000 dwt. Thus by the mid 1960s tankers of over 200,000 dwt were ordered and the VLCC had arrived. The Shell vessels entered service with that group's British, Netherlands, German and French tanker operating entities, and all bore names beginning with 'M': *Marpessa* (which was lost following an explosion in 1969), *Mactra*, *Macoma* and *Marinula* are examples of the names adopted. There were variations in specification, but most were over 200,000 and not more than 212,000 dwt.

The timing of these orders was a gamble, because the tanker market was at the bottom of one of the trade cycles and freight rates were depressed – it was only the closure of the Suez Canal in 1967 that saved a number of shipowners from bankruptcy. In fact, subsequent events more than fully justified the decision to order these large ships.

For the purpose of this chapter tanker sizes are defined as:

MCC (medium crude carrier) – a crude carrier of up to 200,000 dwt.
VLCC (very large crude carrier) – between 200,000 and 299,999 dwt.

ULCC (ultra large crude carrier) – 300,000 dwt and over.

In the tanker trades dwt (deadweight) is used to describe the carrying capacity of a ship when loaded to her summer loadline. This includes fuel stores and spares as well as the cargo. In practice the cargo capacity of a tanker is always less than the stated deadweight.

Although it was technically possible to build these ships there were a number of problems with their operation, and it took a number of years before the VLCC was established as the standard tanker for the crude oil trades. Amongst the main problems that had to be overcome was the lack of ports with water deep enough to accommodate what was a major increase in tanker size. The major European and Japanese ports were eventually enlarged to take these ships but as an interim measure solutions to this problem had to be devised.

One solution was the introduction of the single buoy mooring (SBM) or single point mooring (SPM), which are mooring points at the end of a pipeline in deep water some distance from the shore. The problem of the exposed position was overcome by allowing the ship to swing so that she was always pointing into the wind or tide. In this way the mooring stresses were minimised and the ship was able

Built at a cost of 280m Norwegian kroner was the ULCC Titus, *completed in March 1976 by Nippon Kokan, Japan, for Norwegian shipowner Wilh Wilhelmsen.* Titus *has a deadweight tonnage of 380,000 and length of 355m. With the decline in popularity of tankers of this size Wilhelmsen cancelled orders for two sister-ships and these were replaced by two multi-purpose cargo vessels.* (Wilh Wilhelmsen)

An interim solution to the problem of so few ports being able to take VLCCs was lightening at sea, here being carried out by Shell's Macoma *(207,000 dwt) and the 70,000 dwt* Drupa. *The operation took 18 hours and being only 4 miles off the holiday beaches of Torbay, occasioned much environmental concern, even in 1968.* (CMP)

charge her cargo. The lightening operation was carried out close to the large tanker's final destination so that the advantages of using a large tanker for the major part of the voyage were obtained. It is a potentially hazardous operation to anchor a large tanker at sea and then moor another alongside to take off the cargo and it is a tribute to the organisation and skills of all concerned that no major spillage has occurred during these operations.

From the time of the introduction of VLCCs there were a number of ports and terminals where it would have been prohibitively expensive to dredge for the benefit of large tankers. The ports in the Baltic Sea were an example as the main problem lies in the entrance to the Baltic itself. When Gulf Oil was faced with the problem of delivering oil to their refinery in Denmark, they produced the first ULCCs and used Bantry Bay in southwest Ireland as a trans-shipment terminal. The idea was to use the 325,000 dwt *Universe Ireland* class tankers to carry the oil from the Middle East to Bantry Bay for discharge into storage tanks. Smaller tankers, in this case of 100,000 dwt, would then carry the oil from Bantry Bay

to remain on the mooring even in gale force winds although it might not always be possible to berth under these conditions.

Another solution was lightening at sea. By this method the large tanker would discharge part of her cargo into a smaller tanker while still at sea. This would reduce the draught of the larger vessel sufficiently to enable it to enter port and discharge her cargo while the lightening tanker would then proceed to port to dis-

The ULCC Universe Ireland *(325,000 dwt) docking at Bantry Bay after her inaugural voyage from Kuwait. The ship was 1135ft long and required five tugs to manoeuvre her alongside.* (CMP)

The oil cargo control room console on board the tanker Naess Scotsman *(268,235 dwt), built by Lithgows Ltd, Port Glasgow, in 1974. From this position the vessel's loading and discharge operations could be monitored and controlled.* (Lithgows)

to Gulf Oil's European refineries. Although faced with the cost of an additional terminal they avoided the problem of weather delays that were inherent in the two previously cited methods.

Another example of such a terminal is Freeport in the Bahamas where oil from the Middle East or West Africa is discharged from large tankers before being loaded into smaller tankers of about 60,000 dwt for shipment to United States East Coast ports.

It is not only in connection with harbours that these ships present problems. As already discussed, the Suez Canal provided a brake on ships trading to Europe while for ships trading to Japan, the other important area for crude oil imports, the Malacca Strait, separating Malaysia and the Indonesian island of Sumatra, has a draught restriction which prevents the passage of loaded tankers of greater than 260,000 dwt. Larger tankers are forced to use the Lombok Strait, thus adding an extra 1100 miles to the voyage.

There were also technical problems with the operation of these ships. The sheer size presented problems and various electronic aids were developed to assist with berthing – the bridge was a considerable distance from the ship's side and bow and a slight misjudgement of speed can result in extensive damage to a jetty when 250,000 tonnes leans on it. Stopping distances and manoeuvrability were problems, particularly in narrow areas such as the Dover Strait. Because of their draught these ships were confined to a fairly restricted route and in some cases unable to give way to an approaching ship.

An early problem with the VLCC was a number of then unexplained explosions which resulted in the loss of the ships. The common factor was that these ships were engaged in tank cleaning at the time. After a considerable amount of research it was decided that the most likely cause of the accident was that static electricity had ignited gas from the cargo residues. For many years tanks had been cleaned by means of high pressure jets dislodging the residues from the sides and bottoms of the tanks. With the increased size of tanks in very large ships, the pressure of the washing water was increased to ensure that the tanks were properly washed. It was thought that static electricity from these machines was responsible

for these explosions and so tank washing procedures were changed so that there was no longer an explosive mixture of air and gas in the tanks that were being washed.

There was a steady increase in the number of large tankers until the Middle East war of 1967. Once again the Suez Canal was closed and with tankers being forced to make the longer route around the Cape of Good Hope there was a shortage of crude oil tankers and a corresponding increase in freight rates. This led to increased ordering of large tankers as the Israeli and Egyptian armies settled down facing each other on either side of the Suez Canal and it looked as though the canal would remain closed for a long period.

A number of shipowners decided to build larger vessels disregarding the Suez Canal and there was a steady increase in the size of ships during this period with the average size of ship increasing from about 200,000 dwt in 1967 to about 250,000 dwt in 1973.

In 1973 there was a dramatic increase in freight rates and tanker owners enjoyed windfall profits. This in turn led to an ordering spree for VLCCs, and the construction of a number of new shipyards, large enough to build them. Large scale ordering of VLCCs in 1973 was part of a peak in the world's industrial cycle and the boom in freight rates was also mirrored in property and other booms in the industrialised countries. Among the reasons for

the large number of orders placed during this period was the general industrial growth. At the time world economies were experiencing

In the UK, and amongst the fleets of some other nations, many VLCCs were owned or managed by the oil companies. In the UK, for example, Shell, BP, Burmah, Texaco and Mobil shipping subsidiaries together controlled a large number of such vessels. Very few were in the hands of independents, and not surprisingly, several were owned by the giants P&O and Ocean Transport & Trading. Titan, *built by Gotaverken in 1972, was 230,100 dwt and sailed under the Ocean banner. In one of only a few such transactions she was sold to Mobil Oil, in 1975, and lasted for another seven years before being scrapped.* (Ocean Group)

very rapid growth, and with the price of oil in real terms at an all time low, this growth was led by oil based industry.

The United States, the world's largest oil consumer, changed from being an exporter to an importer of oil. Unlike Europe and Japan, the United States had not been an importer of oil, and in 1959, for reasons of national security its government had imposed a quota of oil imports. A limit of about 20 per cent of total consumption was imposed on imported oil, the remainder having to be met from domestic production. The result was that very little Middle East oil was traded to the USA. The industrial growth meant that United States producers were having difficulty meeting the demands of the domestic market and although oil had been discovered in Alaska the pipeline had yet to be built and so it was impossible to transport the oil. The assumption was therefore that there would be a requirement to ship large quantities of Middle East oil to the USA. That there were not the terminals to take the oil did not discourage investors – after all a tanker terminal could be built in a reasonably short time.

Another factor was the increase in productivity of the world's shipbuilding industry. The traditional European countries had maintained

The largest tanker in the world in 1968 was the Bulford *(210,822 dwt) of London's Blandford Shipping. Built by Sasebo Heavy Industries, she was an example of the Japanese domination of this sector of shipbuilding at the time.* (CMP)

their capacity while the Japanese had rebuilt their industry after the Second World War with tremendous productivity increases. The large tanker is a fairly simple ship to build and although the size is impressive it lends itself to modern prefabrication techniques and can be built in a comparatively short time. Thus the ordering spree led to an expansion of ship-building facilities which resulted in an over-capacity not finally resolved until the 1990s. Shipbuilding is also an important employer and in Europe many of the yards were in depressed areas, so they were therefore eligible for government assistance and favourable credit terms made available to owners wishing to purchase new ships.

In the early 1970s particularly, a number of banks invested in shipping for the first time. Traditionally banks have considered shipping investment as risky and therefore charged higher interest rates than for other investments, but a number considered that with the then current upturn in freight rates, shipping was a good investment. They were therefore willing to lend money without proper security. The more traditional banks have always looked for time charters which would give the shipowner guaranteed employment for the ship and thus income for a number of years, or failing this some other indication of cash flow as security before lending money for new ships. Some of the newer banks were willing to consider the value of the ship itself as sufficient security and were willing to lend money with a vessel as collateral without requiring any indication of employment. This suited many of the owners because there were then enormous profits to be made out of voyage charters, but this only ensured employment for a single voyage. As long as freight rates held up it was possible for the building cost of a VLCC to be repaid after one year. Independent owners therefore preferred to take delivery of their new ship without any prior fixtures in order to take advantage of these rates.

Another important factor was the tax situation of the owners. During this period a large number of tankers were registered in the traditional maritime countries and the owners subject to domestic tax laws. In Scandinavia, the tax systems were progressive and owners making large profits were subject to correspondingly high taxation, particularly in Norway. The only resource the owners had was to reinvest their money and there was no better investment than ships. Thus the scene was set for what turned out to be a major shipping disaster – there were more ships on order than the industry could ever hope to employ, even with

the most optimistic growth forecasts. In fact the downturn had already started, inflation was increasing and the 'Club of Rome' was issuing dire warnings on the 'limits to growth'. There were predictions that if growth in demand for oil continued at the existing rates then the world's oil reserves would be exhausted by the end of the century.

During this period OPEC (The Organization of Petroleum Exporting Countries) was gaining strength. OPEC owes its origin to the limit on oil imports imposed by the United States Government in 1959 and the decision by Exxon on 8 August 1960 to cut the posted prices on Middle East crude by 4.5 cents per barrel. This made the producers realise that the majors' policy of playing off one country against another would have to be resisted. On 9 September at a meeting in Baghdad five countries – Saudi Arabia, Iran, Iraq, Kuwait and Venezuela, who between them controlled 80 per cent of the world's exports of crude oil – decided to form OPEC and it was made clear from the start that the main enemies were the oil majors. Prior to the war of 1973 the various OPEC countries negotiated price increases and the price of oil rose from about $1.70 per barrel in 1970 to $5.19 a barrel in October 1973.

Yom Kippur and the change of economic climate

With unsustainable growth in the Western economies and a feeling of grievance amongst the oil producers the stage was set for a showdown. This was supplied by the Middle East war of October 1973.

The Yom Kippur war started by what was a brilliant attack across the Suez Canal by the Egyptian armies, which succeeded in pushing into the Sinai desert beyond. Although they were not able to maintain their position for very long it sparked off changes to the oil and tanker industries that had consequences far beyond the Middle East.

Once it was clear that Egypt was losing, the Arab producing countries asked the United States to stop supporting Israel. When the US refused, OPEC countries in the Middle East imposed cuts in oil production hoping to put pressure on Western governments to gain their support for the Arab war aims. The disruption caused by these cuts demonstrated the power of the oil producers and for the first time the OPEC members discovered the strength of their position. They used this strength to impose a fourfold increase in the price of crude oil and by January 1974 the

and this enabled them to have greater control of their oil supplies. Some governments used these companies to make barter or other deals direct with the governments of the producing countries thus bypassing the oil majors. The independent oil trader also emerged at this time; having no refining facilities themselves they bought and sold oil, frequently using the spot market in Rotterdam. The oil majors were now forced to compete on the open market for their supplies of crude oil.

The structure of the tanker market had now changed. With the higher price of oil many of the advantages of the larger ships disappeared, the inventory cost of oil was now much higher, and with oil being sold on the open market in recognised 'lots' the large tanker lost many of its advantages. In fact the million-barrel tanker was produced particularly to take advantage of the lot sizes. The United States barrel is a volumetric measure used by US companies. There are about 7.5 barrels to the tonne so a million barrel tanker has a dwt of about 140,000 tonnes and is intended to appeal to traders who deal in lot sizes of about 500,000 barrels.

In particular the ULCC was a casualty of the changing climate. These ships were ordered later than the VLCC and in late 1973 construction costs of these was much higher than the equivalent capacity in earlier VLCCs. The size of ships had grown during the 1970s and the largest to enter service was *Seawise Giant* built in 1979 and enlarged to 564,000 dwt in

price of Saudi oil, used as a bench mark for oil prices, had jumped from $5.19 to $11.65 a barrel. Now the control of crude oil production changed from the seven major oil companies to the governments of the producing countries.

The major economies went into recession, the demand for oil was cut drastically, and the market for large crude oil carriers collapsed. Tanker owners discovered that almost alone in the shipping industry they were tied to one type of cargo; not only was the VLCC suitable only for crude oil cargoes but it was tied into long haul crude oils. Over shorter distances its economic advantages would disappear.

The tanker industry found itself in a situation where there were a large number of ships on order, still to be delivered. In fact tankers ordered in 1973 were still being delivered in 1979. During 1973 a number of ULCCs were also ordered and they still had not made any

impact on the tanker market. As far as they were able owners tried to avoid taking delivery of the ships which they had ordered but the shipyards were naturally reluctant to accept straight cancellations. A number of tanker orders were converted to combination or bulk carriers and in many cases owners were able to persuade the shipyards to delay the delivery of the ships on order.

As well as increasing the price of oil, OPEC members wrested control of the supply of oil from the majors and marketed the crude themselves. Many governments, alarmed at the consequences of the oil shortages of 1973 insured against the possibility of losing their supplies of fuel again by setting up national oil companies,

1980. To gain some idea of the size of these ships, 500,000 tonnes of oil is equivalent to about 126,905,000 UK gallons, or enough petrol to take a family motor car to the moon and back six times. The ULCC was never very successful because when they were ordered shipbuilding prices had risen and their higher capital cost offset the economic advantage of their larger size. By the time they came into service freight rates had fallen to below break-even for the VLCC and even with its greater carrying capacity the ULCC could not trade profitably at these rates, far less undercut those obtained by the VLCC. A further disadvantage was that, with the increase in oil prices, crude oil was now traded in lots that were too small to provide a full cargo for them. They were forced to load and discharge in more than one port, thus losing any remaining economic advantage. By 1981 most of the major tanker ports were capable of accepting a fully-laden VLCC but there were fewer ports which could accept a fully-laden ULCC and therefore trading opportunities were restricted. The ULCC fleet never really established a trading role and most ships were laid up or used for storage and many were scrapped prematurely.

After the 1973 collapse, tanker owners were forced to trade at a loss as freight rates were just sufficient to pay the fuel and port costs leaving a little over to cover the maintenance and other operating costs. The owners who had ordered ships without fixtures were now in serious difficulties, and unable to repay construction loans. At the same time the second hand value of the ships was so low that there was no chance of selling them. The banks were then in the position of being able to repossess a large number of tankers from defaulting owners which they also had no chance of selling. The sensible alternative was to bail out the owners and allow them to continue trading with the hope that the market would recover. The owners who had fixed their ships on time charter before delivery had some respite but some of the charterers had found ways of reducing the charter rates from the pre-1973 levels, but at least those owners were still able to repay their bank loans.

Owners who had ordered the early VLCCs in 1966 had made enough money in the boom years to pay off their bank loans and were able to still trade their ships profitably but owners who paid inflated prices for ships ordered in 1973 were in difficulties. Thus by 1974–75 the tanker market was in deep depression with an excess of supply over demand of about 30 per cent or 100 million dwt.

A number of attempts were made to try and

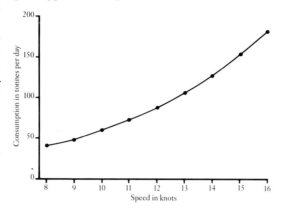

The relationship between speed and consumption for a typical steam powered VLCC

stabilise the market but the only really successful method of reducing tanker supply was slow steaming because this directly benefited the shipowner.

An effect of the increase in oil prices was that the price of bunkers rose from about $10 per tonne in 1970 to a peak of $240 per tonne in 1979. A VLCC designed in 1970 to steam at 15–16kts was consuming about 150 tonnes of fuel per day. With any ship, because of the resistance of water, a disproportionate increase in power is required in order to increase speed by a few knots, but conversely a small reduction in speed will bring about a considerable saving in fuel. The graph shows the relationship between speed and consumption for a typical steam powered VLCC of that period.

Although there were technical constraints which would prevent the large tanker from being able to use the full range of speeds, during the worst parts of the recession it was almost unknown for a large tanker to steam at her full design speed. In fact many had their engines specially modified in order that they could steam economically at slower than design speeds.

An example of the possible savings that could be achieved is:
For a round voyage of about 23,000 miles from

Kuwait to Europe, assuming the cost of fuel at $200 per tonne, the fuel costs for the voyage at a range of different speeds would be as set out in Table 4/1.

The extra running cost for the longer voyage had to be offset against the higher fuel costs but until fuel prices fell in the late 1980s, a slow steaming was the norm for VLCCs and ULCCs. This had the added advantage of reducing a considerable part of the tanker surplus.

The only other recourse open to shipowners was to lay up their ships. Lay up berths appeared close to the major trade routes and a number of tankers went straight from the builders yard to lay up and were subsequently scrapped without even carrying a cargo.

A variation on lay up was to use the surplus vessels for storage.

A result of the shortages of 1973 was that many governments increased the amount of oil which they held in reserve. In many cases there was not the storage capacity in those countries and so the immediate answer was floating storage. The larger ULCCs proved popular for this – it was about the only trade where the ULCC fleet showed any advantage over the smaller VLCC. The cost of using tankers for floating storage is higher than for the comparable land based storage because of the cost of maintaining the ships in a secure position. Large tankers have proved to be useful when temporary storage is required. Thus in the Iran-Iraq war, the Iranian Government chartered *Seawise Giant*, then the largest tanker afloat, to store oil they thought was out of range of the Iraqi air force. However, towards the end of the war it was bombed in a specially planned operation. It has since changed hands and name on two occasions. The Saudi Government also chartered tankers for storage when they were concerned that their terminals in the Gulf might be attacked.

A number of traders have shipped oil to a suitable destination, holding the tanker in a

Table 4/1: Relative Economy of Running Costs

Speed (kts)	Consumption (tonnes per day)	Days	Fuel (tonnes)	Fuel cost
8	40	120	4792	$ 958,333
9	47	106	5005	$1,000,926
10	59	96	5654	$1,130,833
11	71	87	6186	$1,237,121
12	86	80	6868	$1,373,611
13	104	74	7667	$1,533,333
14	125	68	8557	$1,711,310
15	150	64	9583	$1,916,667
16	179	60	10,721	$2,144,271

Matco Clyde *was built at Yokosuka, Japan, in 1982 to the order of Matco Tankers (UK) Ltd, a subsidiary of Mobil Oil. With two other tankers it is involved in shipping crude oil from the Beryl terminal in the North Sea to the company's refineries. Matco Clyde* can carry 100,270cu m of oil, has a length of 243.34m and a speed of 15kts. (FotoFlite)

safe anchorage for some time in the hope that oil prices would rise sufficiently to recoup the extra costs. Torbay off the coast of Devon, UK, has been used for this purpose. In practice tanker owners never made much money from chartering ships for storage but it was a better option than laying up. An exception to this was in Japan, where level land is expensive and the Japanese Government was willing to assist national shipowners and so a number of Japanese ships were chartered for long term storage. Some tankers were specially converted to be used as storage units on offshore oil fields, from where oil was pumped directly into the storage tanker. From here a specially modified shuttle tanker would transport it to the refinery.

When the VLCC was first designed, the diesel engine was not considered powerful enough and they were mostly built with steam turbine machinery. Although steam was considered more reliable than diesel, the fuel consumption was considerably higher. When fuel oil prices started to increase owners were seeking ways of reducing fuel consumption and one was to re-engine the tankers with diesel, which had now been developed sufficiently to reliably produce the power required. In many cases the power of the replacement diesel engine was less than that of the original steam engines. Savings of 30 tonnes or more of fuel per day, if the steam engine was to be replaced by a lower powered diesel engine, could be obtained from a VLCC and for many owners the savings were sufficiently attractive to justify the capital expenditure involved.

The first estimates that the slump would end between 1979 and 1984, were based on the in-dustrial growth picking up after the recession in 1974, but there were a number of reasons why this did not happen in the tanker trade.

The increase in oil prices was the spur which led to the development of new oil fields such as the North Sea, Mexico and Indonesia, all of which are closer to the major markets than those in the Middle East. Many of these countries were not members of OPEC and they tended to undercut the OPEC prices so increasing their market share at the expense of the OPEC producers. When these producers came on stream long haul crude oil was replaced with oil supplies from sources which were closer to the markets. The Suez Canal reopened in 1975 and it was quickly enlarged to take tankers of 170,000 tonnes dwt. These developments tended to favour the medium size crude carrier (MCC) instead of the VLCC.

The medium size tanker of up to 200,000 dwt became a popular size from about 1978 as the new oil fields were developed. The reason is that this size of ship was ignored in the ordering spree of the early 1970s, so there was not the same degree of overtonnaging. With the development of oil fields closer to the markets, these ships became popular because of their suitability for shorter voyages. The smaller size of these vessels enables them to use many more ports, such as those on the east coast of the USA, and also the Suez Canal that is denied to the larger VLCC.

By the late 1970s it was clear that the market was in a long-term recession and a number of attempts were made to find ways of reducing the surplus. The only serious attempt was to organise a group lay up. The concept was simple – an organisation would be specifically ini-tiated to lay up the ships and the owners would charter them at a nominal rate to this organisation. The existence of a charter was supposed to keep the ships off the market, and when enough were removed freight rates would rise to a level that would enable owners to trade their ships in service profitably. This scheme was floated in parallel with a similar idea for bulk carriers. Both schemes failed because of two obstacles.

The main problem was how to prevent cheating. With any tonnage stabilisation scheme, the shipowner who does not contribute but keeps his ships trading will enjoy the higher freight rates brought about by such a scheme and will gain at the expense of the co-operating shipowner. It was therefore necessary to find some method of preventing this from happening. This could only be achieved by co-operation with the major charterers and this would have fallen foul of the United States anti-trust laws as a large proportion of the charterers were American companies. Even if agreement should be reached amongst the shipowners and charterers, a large number of tankers at this time were technically owned by banks as the original owners had defaulted on their payments. Many of these banks were also American and so would not have been able to take part. Thus the tanker owners were left on their own to ride out the recession.

To give voice to the tanker owners, the International Association of Independent Tanker Owners (INTERTANKO) became active. First set up in London as a tanker owners forum to work out a tonnage stabilisation scheme, it was liquidated in 1969. A new association started in Norway in 1971 and had 75 per cent of the privately-owned tanker fleets as members. In 1975 it helped set up the International Maritime Industries Forum (IMIF).

The IMIF was founded in an attempt to bring the interested parties together to tackle the recession. The aim of the forum was the need to liaise with existing agencies such as the Organization for Economic Co-operation and Development (OECD) and the EEC and to impress on them the seriousness of the situation. The forum quickly extended beyond the shipowners to include banks (who lost considerable sums of money over the crisis), oil companies and owners of other types of vessel. They published a number of documents but were unable to find a method of reducing the surplus tonnage. Today the principal aim of the forum is to ensure a healthy tanker industry.

Oil pollution

The increase in the world's oil trade had the unpleasant side effect of pollution, as the tonnage of oil transported by sea increased year by year, so did the possibility of accidents. Although there was no evidence to show that the accident rate for tankers had got any worse, the sheer volume of oil being transported by sea meant that the probability of accidents was greater when this was coupled with the increasing awareness of environmental issues. This was also a feature of the 1970s and '80s, when tanker accidents assumed a greater prominence than had previously been the case. The other factor was the arrival of the VLCC and the realisation of the potential damage which could result from an oil spill following a major accident to one of these ships.

Dangers of oil cargoes

There are two major dangers concerning the transport of oil. The first danger is that of fire and explosion – always present when oil is being handled. All petroleum products give off vapours although in some circumstances, such as with fuel oils, they have to be heated first.

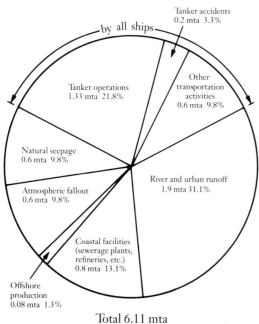

Sources of petroleum pollution and spillage
(million metric tonnes annually – mta)

by all ships

Tanker accidents
0.2 mta 3.3%

Other transportation activities
0.6 mta 9.8%

Tanker operations
1.33 mta 21.8%

Natural seepage
0.6 mta 9.8%

Atmospheric fallout
0.6 mta 9.8%

River and urban runoff
1.9 mta 31.1%

Coastal facilities (sewerage plants, refineries, etc.)
0.8 mta 13.1%

Offshore production
0.08 mta 1.3%

Total 6.11 mta

These gases when mixed with air are flammable and easy to ignite. This is why oil is such a popular fuel. Once a tanker has loaded her first cargo there will always be some gas present in the tanks and the risk of fire or explosion will remain. There have been cases of fires occurring on vessels which have been laid up for many years before being cut up for scrap even though a number of years had elapsed since the ship last carried an oil cargo.

The second danger is that of pollution. When oil is spilt at sea as a result of an accident or as part of tanker operations, the potential for destruction of marine life and damage to the coastline can be enormous. During the early 1970s there were a number of tanker casualties which, although they did not result in any oil being spilt in US waters, gave rise to concern over the possible outcome of a major tanker accident.

This concern centred around the structure of the tankers. Unlike other ships a tanker does not have a double bottom so in the event of a stranding there is only one thickness of steel between the oil and the environment.

Another problem is that of 'operational pollution'. All tankers carry sea water ballast when they do not have cargo on board. This ballast is carried in the cargo tanks and must be discharged before a new cargo can be loaded. These tanks contain residues of the previous cargo and so it is necessary to clean the tanks in order that the ballast which is discharged in the loading port does not pullute the harbour. It is, however, inevitable that some oil will enter the sea during this process.

The International Maritime Organization (IMO) is the international forum where matters concerning maritime safety are agreed. Once a new convention has been agreed it will only come into force after it has been ratified by a certain number of states. There are 134 members so it takes a long time for any convention to come into force. Because of such delays the United States Government imposed unilaterally a number of requirements for tankers trading to the US. These mostly centred around navigational equipment, and there were moves to impose a requirement for tankers to fit double bottoms but at that time they were inconclusive.

Other discussions centred around a number of developments:

Inert gas: This was a development which first appeared on tankers in the 1930s but fell into disuse. During the 1960s it was developed by BP and consists of a system where the oxygen in the ship's cargo tanks is reduced from the normal 21 per cent to 8.0 per cent, a level

The first major supertanker disaster, the grounding and subsequent destruction of the Torrey Canyon *(61,263 grt) in March 1967, introduced the world to the possibility of pollution on a hitherto unknown scale.* (CMP)

which is too low to support combustion. This was an important safety measure although initially there was some resistance from shipowners because of the cost of retrofitting on existing ships and the complexity of its operation. It requires a certain skill in its operation by the ships's crew. If the tanks are not properly inerted there could be a false sense of security.

Crude oil washing: Until then all cargo tanks had been washed using high pressure sea water to dislodge oil residues from tanks sides and bottoms. Occasionally it was heated and sometimes, usually prior to a drydocking, chemicals were mixed with the sea water to speed up the process. The advantage of using crude oil instead of sea water was that the residues in the tanks would readily dissolve in oil and could then be pumped ashore. Crude oil tank washing was designed to be carried out simultaneously with the discharge of the cargo, removing most of the residues from the tanks and so reducing the amount of washing required. It substantially reduced the potential for oil pollution and increased the amount of cargo discharged.

Washing the tanks with a flammable material (crude oil) is a hazardous operation so it can only be carried out in tanks that have been inerted. Hence there is a requirement that crude oil washing must only be carried out in port and in properly inerted tanks.

Segregated ballast tanks: With all large tankers there is some space left when the ship has been loaded with a full cargo. These spaces are connected by separate pipes and pumps for handling clean water ballast only, and this permanent ballast became a regular feature of VLCCs. The United States Government and some shipowners pressed for a requirement that all water ballast should be carried in separate tanks – so-called segregated ballast. This was supposed to eliminate operational discharges of oil and also provide a measure of protection if the tanker was involved in a collision. When a tanker is in ballast, about 30 per cent of the ship's deadweight in ballast water is needed to ensure that she is in a safe condition to put to sea. Thus by modifying a tanker for segregated ballast about 30 per cent of the cargo carrying capacity would be lost. With new tankers, the ballast spaces are positioned so as to protect the cargo tanks in the event of a collision or grounding.

The conversion of the existing fleet of tankers to segregated ballast (SGB) would have the effect of reducing its capacity by about 30 per cent. This was seen as a method of removing the tanker surplus and hence it was promoted at IMO by countries with a large number of independent tanker owners. This same measure was resisted by countries with oil company-owned ships. One of the problems which was never settled was who was going to pay the cost of the conversions? The owners certainly no longer had the sort of reserves necessary to pay for this, one estimate put it at about 5 million dollars per ship.

The outcome of these deliberations was the

The 1986-built Era, *delivered by Samsung Shipbuilding, Koje, South Korea, to R W Miller & Co Pty Ltd, Sydney, is an example of a modern crude/ products tanker. With a deadweight of 94,287 tonnes and cargo capacity of 105,660cu m, she is, together with a sister-ship, engaged in service in Australian waters and southeast Asia.* (R W Miller & Co)

International Convention for Prevention of Pollution from Ships (MARPOL). This was finally ratified on 2 October 1982 by fifteen states which collectively controlled more than 50 per cent of the world's merchant fleet and the convention came into force the following year. It took ten years from the agreement of the convention for it to come into force, hence the impatience shown by some countries over the procedure at IMO for introducing safety legislation.

These conventions were passed into the legislation of the various countries and the main requirements for the owners of crude oil tankers of over 20,000 dwt were that ships built after 1980 must have:

1. Segregated ballast in a protective location.
2. Inert gas system (IGS).
3. Crude oil washing.

Existing ships had a number of options but it came down to:

1. Inert Gas System (IGS).
2. Either segregated ballast or crude oil washing.

The requirements for products tankers, particularly if they were less than 20,000 dwt, were less demanding. Almost all owners went for the cheaper crude oil washing alternative so these rules did little for the tanker surplus. In fact they probably made it worse by encouraging owners to retain existing ships. Any new ships would have been required to have segregated ballast tanks, and therefore their carrying capacity would be less than that of a comparable existing tanker. It was in an owners interest to hold on to existing tonnage. These new measures certainly reduced operational pollution but there remained the problem of major tanker accidents.

The loss of *Torrey Canyon* (61,623 grt) in March 1967, *Amoco Cadiz* in 1978 and the grounding of *Exxon Valdez* in 1989 demonstrated that tanker accidents would still occur and even with the best regulated ships it was the human element that presented the greatest problems. All these tankers had the latest safety equipment, they all grounded on coastlines of countries which had the resources to fight pollution and yet in each case this was not controlled and led to immense environmental damage. When it is considered that tankers carrying over double the amount of oil which escaped from these ships frequently pass vulnerable coastlines it can be seen why the operation of oil tankers is so tightly regulated.

The stranding of *Exxon Valdez* off Valdez, Alaska, renewed the discussion about tanker safety, particularly the fitting of double bottoms or even double hulls. There is talk of the United States Government introducing requirements for tankers trading to that country to be fitted with some of these features in advance of any IMO requirement.

The future

The tanker surplus has finally come to an end and in the early 1990s tankers were trading profitably. The question which now needs to be answered is what will happen to the tanker fleet? As Table 4/2 shows, the majority of large tankers were ordered during the 1973 period and will need replacing in the near future. With the uncertainty over any new requirements for ships trading to the USA and the high cost of new buildings shipowners are adopting a wait and see attitude to ordering new tonnage. The only hope is that a possible shortage of VLCCs in about five years time does not lead to a repeat of the 1973 situation.

Table 4/2: Tanker fleet as at 1 April 1991 (Number of vessels and total deadweight tonnes)

Year	No.	10–79,999 dwt	No.	80–89,999 dwt	No.	90–99,999 dwt	No.	100–109,999 dwt	No.	110–149,999 dwt	No.	150–199,999 dwt	No.	200–249,999 dwt	No.	250–299,999 dwt	No.	Over 300,000 dwt	No.	Total dwt
71	302	10,030,430	16	1,333,737	14	1,373,977	7	730,311	18	2,234,432	6	947,945	8	1,781,347	8	2,152,274	0		0	379	20,584,453
72	43	1,267,449	0	0	3	291,581	0	0	7	878,338	2	320,426	7	1,581,281	13	3,379,227	0		0	75	7,718,302
73	71	2,156,231	6	512,348	1	98,969	0	0	17	2,173,134	0	0	17	3,947,487	23	6,275,883	0		0	135	15,164,052
74	64	2,228,265	20	1,715,816	6	574,938	1	109,468	30	3,914,748	2	342,262	16	3,718,393	54	14,581,376	7	2,293,072	200	29,478,338
75	100	3,090,072	35	3,021,999	5	460,742	2	207,603	50	6,568,196	5	789,908	20	4,718,155	43	11,676,886	20	7,017,948	280	37,551,509
76	99	3,183,159	20	1,724,647	14	1,328,432	2	209,498	28	3,681,417	17	2,728,785	19	4,442,743	37	9,936,929	25	9,833,614	261	37,069,224
77	62	1,999,151	3	251,235	6	555,425	0	0	17	2,222,714	15	2,379,789	1	228,276	6	1,608,148	19	7,080,883	129	16,325,621
78	47	1,835,947	5	415,799	3	287,433	0	0	6	802,843	8	1,357,418	2	458,716	3	814,907	5	2,125,466	79	8,098,529
79	45	1,774,952	12	1,012,265	0	0	5	518,281	2	252,634	5	843,306	0	0	3	828,128	3	1,310,522	75	6,540,088
80	74	2,946,855	24	2,037,724	5	471,144	2	216,676	0	0	3	519,397	0	0	1	279,688	2	758,843	111	7,230,327
81	113	4,826,372	19	1,615,770	4	383,677	1	101,832	1	119,990	1	163,647	1	224,738	2	529,832	1	360,700	143	8,326,558
82	129	4,449,266	9	757,963	1	99,800	0	0	3	405,013	1	180,377	0	0	1	290,085	0	0	144	6,182,504
83	84	3,009,258	5	427,754	1	98,200	0	0	4	514,018	0	0	0	0	1	290,085	2	645,358	97	4,984,673
84	69	2,751,482	0	0	0	0	0	0	3	364,023	1	163,647	1	238,465	0	0	0	0	74	3,517,617
85	72	2,446,904	12	1,043,904	5	464,933	1	107,800	0	0	0	0	1	239,781	1	285,090	0	0	92	4,588,412
86	71	2,438,106	18	1,536,098	2	189,130	4	421,596	1	122,472	0	0	6	1,410,060	3	774,492	0	0	105	6,891,954
87	56	2,114,516	14	1,200,532	1	94,287	2	209,283	4	504,360	1	153,500	0	0	2	930,995	2	522,164	84	5,729,637
88	55	2,025,762	7	583,950	1	96,551	5	524,115	9	1,178,945	0	0	3	725,004	7	1,830,419	0	0	87	6,964,746
89	44	1,536,578	6	500,754	9	861,464	1	100,047	17	2,245,008	0	0	4	958,494	10	2,605,565	2	609,329	93	9,417,239
90	39	1,510,493	5	423,069	10	963,259	7	709,726	7	933,224	2	305,052	3	718,819	11	2,980,270	0	0	84	8,543,912
91	8	292,958	0	0	5	480,096	0	0	2	244,155	1	153,500	0	0	2	560,000	0	0	18	1,730,709
Total/ dwt	1,647	57,914,206	236	20,115,364	96	9,174,038	40	4,166,236	226	29,359,664	70	11,348,959	113	26,322,754	231	62,201,448	86	32,035,735	2,745	252,638,404

Chemical carriers

A trade which has developed from the oil industry is the transport of liquid chemicals by sea. Early chemical tankers were little more than product tankers which specialised in the chemical trade but over the years a number of factors have emerged, not least that of safety, which led to the development of the specialised chemical tanker.

The carriage of liquid chemicals by sea in a tanker presents hazards additional to those which are associated with the carriage of petroleum cargoes. The need to protect the ship's crew and the environment from the consequences of an accident is one of the factors which led to the emergence of the specialised chemical tanker. In addition to the risks associated with the carriage of oil, some chemicals carried are liable to ignite spontaneously in the presence of oxygen; they must therefore be blanketed with an inert gas at all times. This has led to the need for sophisticated fire precautions and fire-fighting equipment for ships which carry such chemicals. Some chemicals will react with others carried in the same tanker or even with the steelwork of the tanker itself so it is necessary to prevent them from coming into contact with each other or with the steel of the tanker's hull.

Many chemicals carried are poisonous and special precautions are therefore required for their carriage, including the use of protective clothing and breathing apparatus by crew members involved in handling the cargo, special stowage arrangements to keep them away from living quarters, and prevention of leakage in the event of an accident.

Over the years the requirements by the chemical industry for the carriage of cargoes by sea has become more demanding. The development of improved analytical techniques has meant that shippers are expressing contamination requirements in terms of parts per million instead of parts per thousand and hence the tanks must be cleaned to a very high standard before shippers will allow a cargo to be loaded. Even then there are stringent requirements concerning the previous cargoes that have been carried before a shipper is prepared to consider loading a cargo into that tank. These requirements for cleanliness have posed a challenge for both builders and operators of chemical tankers.

A parallel trade to that of the liquid chemicals is the trade in edible oils, although not possessing the hazards associated with some liquid chemicals the purity and inspection standards are similar so they can be carried in the same type of ship although clearly they must be separated from chemicals that might be harmful.

Built at the Moss Rosenberg Shipyard in Norway in 1970 was the chemical tanker Bow Gran, *owned by AS Rederiet Odfjell, a leader in the transportation of chemicals. The vessel has a cargo capacity of 8874cu m including four segregated cylindrical tanks on deck.*

The chemical tanker Stolt Australia *is engaged on voyages in Australian coastal waters. Built in 1986 by Mitsubishi, Shimonoseki, it is owned by De Uyeno (Bermuda) Ltd, a subsidiary of Uyeno Unyu Shokai KK, of Japan, and flies the Australian flag. Its international background is complicated further as its managers are Howard Smith Industries Pty Ltd and its operators Stolt-Neilsen Australia Pty Ltd. The latter company is associated with Stolt-Nielsen Inc, USA, controlled by Stolt-Nielsen of Norway and British Petroleum Co Ltd, UK. Such complicated backgrounds are not uncommon and reflect diverse international investments, particularly in the oil and related industries.* (Howard Smith Industries)

Construction requirements

The requirements for the construction and operation of chemical tankers come from two directions. Those concerned with safety and pollution come mainly from IMO but some states set additional requirements for ships entering their waters. The requirements for the care of the many different cargoes are set by the shippers which are the chemical and food industries (in the case of edible oils).

Safety and pollution requirements

IMO (International Maritime Organisation) has laid down a set of rules for the construction of chemical tankers, and these must be followed if a ship is to be given a certificate allowing it to carry liquid chemical cargoes on international voyages.

The rules which govern the design, construction and operation of chemical tankers relate among other things, to their ability to survive damage to the hull in the event of collision or grounding.

Under the rules type I tankers are built to the highest standards, whilst types II and III have less demanding requirements imposed upon them.

The position of the cargo tanks is also specified for each of the three types of ship with the tanks being divided into independent tanks, which do not form part of the hull and integral tanks which are part of the hull. Type I tanks must be separated from the outer hull by empty spaces or other tanks and must be located in areas where damage is unlikely to occur. Type II tanks must also be separated from the hull by other tanks or by void spaces while type III tanks can be next to the hull. Thus ships are likely to have type I or II tanks in the centre with type III tanks at either side.

The rules on survivability and tank location mean that ships of type I and II are required to have double skinned hulls and bottoms while type III ships have a single hull. Thus the only cargoes which an oil product tanker is allowed to carry are those which can be carried in type III tanks.

The MARPOL (Prevention of Pollution from Ships) rules are concerned with the discharge of polluting substances into the sea, and therefore relate to the construction of the tanks themselves. The tanks are specially designed so that the cargo can be readily drained in the discharge terminal, leaving the minimum cargo residues behind to be removed by tank washing which always follows discharge. The MARPOL rules are also concerned with the cargo handling and tank washing procedures to ensure that they are carried out in a safe manner and that the possibility of any cargo or residues causing any pollution is minimised. Under MARPOL, cargoes are classified into four different categories with category A cargoes being the most harmful, category B and C cargoes are progressively less harmful and category D present a 'recognisable' hazard. These categories relate to the pollution hazard and the permissible concentration of residues in any slops which may be discharged into the sea. For example residues from class A cargoes may not be discharged into the sea under any circumstances.

Requirements for protection of the cargo

The very high standards of quality control required by shippers for the carriage of chemicals and edible oils means that there are two other features which distinguish some chemical tankers from other ships:

Pump and pipeline arrangements

A conventional tanker will have up to four cargo pumps and they are connected to a pipeline system so that any pump may be used to discharge cargo from any one of the ship's tanks. Thus there is always the possibility of a cargo being contaminated by residues from a previous cargo which may remain in the pumps or the pipelines or by traces of oil leaking from another tank. In practice, if the proper procedures are carried out, any quantities remaining are so slight that they do not normally cause any problems.

With the chemical tanker, however, very much higher standards of purity are required and practically no contamination is permissible. To prevent this possibility each tank is fitted with its own pipeline and pump leading directly to the shore connections.

Tank coatings

The need to thoroughly clean the cargo tanks prior to loading a cargo and the corrosive action of some chemicals means that the inside of the tanks on chemical tankers has to be coated. The most popular but also the most expensive coating used is stainless steel, other coatings in use include zinc silicate, epoxy resins and various types of rubber. It is important that the owner takes care of the tank coatings as the loading of an unsuitable cargo or loading at too high a temperature can damage the coatings and lead to damage to the steelwork or contamination of cargoes.

Structure of the fleet

The chemical tanker fleet can be divided into the following main types:

General chemical tankers are the most common type, ranging from highly sophisticated ships which run on regular routes offering what is almost a liner service to simpler chemical/ product carriers. The larger ships will have up to fifty separate tanks with different coatings capable of carrying types A, B and C cargoes. Simpler types of ship built for less demanding trades have less sophisticated equipment and will not be able to carry the same range.

There are a number of chemical tankers dedicated to a single product, an example being the phosphoric acid tanker. Such tankers are simpler and less expensive than the general tanker but the lack of alternative trades if employment proves difficult in the chosen trade limits the numbers of these ships.

Chemical/products tankers are designed to carry petroleum products and chemicals, they can generally carry types B and C cargoes but are more expensive to build than the ordinary products tanker.

Chemical/lpg tanker: chemicals are carried in the form of gas as well as liquid so there is a limited requirement for this type of ship.

Trade patterns

Trades for these specialised carriers form a complicated pattern, with the chemical and the edible oil trades forming distinct sectors although the tankers are capable of carrying both types of cargoes provided that the rules on compatibility can be met.

Liquid chemicals

Most of the world's chemical industry is found in the major industrial countries, the United States, Europe and the Far East with Japan being responsible for the greatest capacity in that area. The large proportion of the seaborne

The world's first liquefied gas carrier was Methane Pioneer *which was converted from a US-built standard type cargo ship in 1958. Built at Duluth, on Lake Superior, in 1945 by W Butler (Shipbuilders) Inc, the vessel's cargo holds were replaced by tanks with a total capacity of 5125cu m. Under the ownership of British Methane Ltd, a company in which the British Gas Council had an interest, the vessel was again converted in 1960 to test the carriage of lng. The success of these tests, carried out with Algerian lng and using a plant at Canvey Island, on the River Thames, saw the ordering and building of larger purpose-built carriers for the trade.* (FotoFlite)

trade in liquid chemicals is between the United States and Europe, intra-Europe, the United States and the Far East and the Middle East to western Europe.

Many of the liquid chemicals which are transported by sea are petrochemicals mostly obtained from petroleum feedstocks, and hence the oil companies have a major share in the chemical industry.

Many oil producing countries are turning to refining in order to take advantage of the higher prices that can be obtained from selling oil products instead of crude, resulting in increased production of petrochemicals in the Middle East for export, particularly to Europe. In addition to the petrochemicals, other important cargoes are sulphuric acid, phosphoric acid and caustic soda. North Africa is an exporter of phosphoric acid, mainly to Europe, with Moroccan and French shipowners very much involved in this trade.

Oils and fats

The varying climates world-wide and the wide range of products brings about a complicated trade pattern for oils and fats. The main trade routes are North America–Latin America; North America–Asia; Latin America–Asia; intra-western Europe; western Europe–Asia; Asia–western Europe; Asia–North America and intra-Asia. The important cargoes in seaborne trade are palm oil, soya bean oil, animal oils and fats, which includes tallow and grease. Although the numbers of vessels involved in edible oils and similar trades is relatively low, it is a well-established trade which owes much of its development to the Unilever Group subsidiary Palm Line Ltd, London. Palm Line carried palm oil and other 'edible' oils, not only in tankers, some purpose-built or converted, but also in the deep tanks on its general cargo vessels.

Molasses, an extract of sugar, is another important cargo, it is not really part of this group, as it is not used for human consumption. It therefore does not require the same standard of carriage care. It is a useful cargo as it is easy to prepare tanks before loading and it does not leave any residues which could cause difficulties when cleaning for other cargoes. The trade pattern of molasses is the reverse of some of the other cargoes and so it forms a convenient backhaul cargo for chemical tankers.

The breakdown of cargoes for the chemical tanker trade in 1987 was:

Organic chemicals 37 per cent;
Inorganic chemicals 22 per cent;
Vegetable/animal oils 32 per cent;
Molasses 9 per cent[1]

Liquefied gas carriers

It is only possible to carry gas at sea in a liquefied form, the ratio of the volumes between liquid and gas being about 1 to 600. Therefore to carry gas at sea would require so much space that it would not be remotely economic. The gasses can be liquefied prior to shipment, either by cooling or by pressure, as in a domestic refrigerator, or by a combination of both.

The seaborne trade in liquefied gas can be divided into two main sectors: liquefied natural gas (lng) consisting of about 80 per cent methane and carried at −162 °C, as it is impossible to liquefy methane by pressure alone; and liquefied petroleum gas (lpg) consisting of propane and butane. Many ships will also carry ammonia and other chemical gasses. These cargoes may be liquefied by pressure, or by cooling (typically −55 °C) or by a combination of both.

1. H P Drewry shipping consultants.

The relative densities of gas are comparatively low, around 0.5–0.6, and the capacity of the ships is therefore measured in cubic metres, as the cargo which they can carry is limited by space rather than by weight. A 125,000-cubic metres lng carrier has a total deadweight of about 70,000 tonnes and a 55,000cu m lpg carrier has a deadweight of about 40,000 tonnes.

Liquefied natural gas

Liquefied natural gas (lng) is derived from natural gas with most of the impurities removed. It normally consists of about 80 per cent methane and some ethane and propane. As a liquid it has a density of 0.474 and as a gas it is lighter than air so any leaks will escape upward and should not present a hazard to the ship. Lng can be found with oil, in which case it is known as associated gas or independently, when it is known as unassociated gas. The gas found associated with oil contains impurities and is therefore more difficult to purify.

The ships

The carriage of methane by sea was first undertaken in 1960 by the appropriately named *Methane Pioneer*, a converted cargo vessel, built in the United States during the Second World War. The experimental voyages she made between Algeria and Canvey Island on the Thames were successful and brought about the construction of large vessels purpose-built for the trade. There is now a flourishing trade out of Arzew, Algeria, and many other locations, particularly Indonesia and Malaysia.

Methane can only be liquefied by cooling to around its boiling point of – 162 °C. This requires a special type of ship as at this temperature, mild steel which is used in the construction of a ship's hull, would fracture. There are various types of methane carrier in use but a feature of all the designs is the importance of providing insulation between the cargo tanks and the ship's hull. Temperature detectors are provided to give advance warning of a breakdown in the insulation.

To protect the ship's hull, tank types are divided into types A and B. Type A tanks are those attached to the hull and therefore both primary and secondary barriers are required to guard against leakage tanks. Type B tanks are free standing and as any liquid leaking from a tank would not come into contact with the hull, only one insulation barrier is required.

The tanks can be free standing (type B), an example of which are the spherical or prismatic tanks. The tank structure is such that it is free to expand and contract as the temperature changes between that of the very cold cargo and the ambient temperature after the cargo has been discharged. As this type of tank is clear of the hull, secondary insulation is not required, a drip tray beneath the tank being considered sufficient to prevent any liquid from reaching the hull. Examples of this are the Kvaerner–Moss design of spherical tank. The other main type is the membrane tank, which is attached to the ship's hull and is therefore a type A.

Liquefied methane has a relative density of about 0.5 and therefore as it is important to maximise the tank volume, spherical tanks are not as efficient as membrane tanks in this respect. To avoid having to cool down before

Malaysian International Shipping Corporation owns five large carriers which transport lng from a terminal at Bintulu, Sarawak, to Japan. Built in France in 1981, Tenaga Dua has a gas capacity of 130,000cu m and is typical of the large generation lng carriers conceived in the 1970s. In this 1982 FotoFlite picture she is at the Canvey Methane Terminal, situated on Canvey Island in the Thames Estuary, undertaking gas equipment trials before sea trials and other operational testing.

loading, it is usual to leave a small amount of cargo in the tanks after discharge to maintain the temperature when the ship is in ballast with no cargo on board.

Boil off

During the voyage the cargo will boil thus giving off vapour. Up to now it has not been considered feasible to reliquefy this gas on board ship. The choice is therefore whether the gas should be allowed to escape or made use of as a fuel for the engines. Most lng carriers have steam turbine machinery and boilers to take advantage of this fuel. This procedure can give rise to disputes as to whether and how the fuel should be paid for.

The trades

Liquefied natural gas is mainly used as a domestic fuel or for power generation where its purity makes it popular on environmental grounds. It is also used for industrial purposes and as a raw material for the chemical industry.

The trade of lng is in two forms – natural gas by pipeline and liquefied natural gas by sea. Where it is possible to transport the gas by pipeline it is considerably cheaper because costs of liquefaction and gasification are avoided. Thus most trade in natural gas is by pipeline in the United States and Europe where much comes from the former Soviet Union.

The sea trade in lng is therefore restricted to routes where it is not possible to build a pipeline and there are only about sixty-five lng carriers, some of which trade in lpg.

Gas projects

The bulk of the lng trade is by project, consisting of a long term contract to buy and ship gas, with typically twenty years needed to justify the cost of building the gas plants, terminals and ships. Ships will then be specially built or chartered for the specific project, leaving very little scope for spot market trading. The difficulty as far as the shipowner is concerned is that in many cases it is necessary to place orders for the ships before the project has been finally agreed. In some cases falling oil prices have led to the cancellation of the project, leaving the ships without employment. A number of projects have also been suspended after running for a few years, again leaving the ships without employment. However, to partly remedy this a number of carriers have been designed to carry lng and lpg and are able to switch trades.

Liquefied petroleum gas (lpg)

The two main lpgs, propane and butane, can be used separately or as a mixture. They are pro-duced (a) by separation from natural gas at the gas field; (b) removal from the crude oil when it is 'stabilised' for transport; (c) as a byproduct of crude oil refining. They can be readily lique-fied by pressure or by cooling for carriage by sea, and it is also possible to reliquefy the boil off and return it to the cargo. Lpg is used as a fuel, and an important market is the production of bottled gas. There are also applications for electricity generation and as chemical feedstock. One company noted for the carriage of its own lpg is the Danish concern Kosangas, now part of the J Lauritzen group, which founded much of its postwar business on the supply of bottled gas to domestic users in Denmark.

Ammonia

Ammonia is a chemical gas which is chiefly used for the production of fertiliser. It has a boiling point of −33.4°C and a density of 0.583.

Other chemical gasses

Other chemical gasses which are carried by lpg carriers are the olefines ethylene, propylene, butadiene and vinyl chloride monomer (VCM). These are used in the chemical industry as feedstocks.

The ships

Liquefied petroleum gas carriers are similar to products tankers in that they are designed to be able to carry a number of different gasses at the same time. A few ships are able to carry oil and/or chemicals as well as lpg. The carriers are constructed to carry their cargo in three different ways:

1. Fully pressurised vessels: The cargo tanks on these are cylindrical or spherical and because they carry the cargo at ambient temperature there is no need for liquefication arrange-ments. The drawbacks with these vessels are:
(i) the shape of the containers prevents the best use being made of the cargo spaces;
(ii) the weight of the tanks is high, thus reduc-ing the cargo capacity. For these reasons these are usually small ships, generally less than 2000 cubic metres, although there are some larger.
2. Semi pressurised/refrigerated carriers: These are able to transport the cargo at lower

This partial cutaway drawing of Northwest Snipe *shows one of the four independent Moss type spherical tanks installed. Each of these has a capacity of 31,934cu m and the lng is carried at a temperature of −163°C. The tanks are 39.46m in diameter and made of aluminium alloy with insulation of polystyrene foam covered with aluminium foil.* Northwest Snipe *is one of a series of similar vessels which is transporting lng from Withnell Bay, on Western Australia's remote Burrup Peninsula, to Japan. The lng is created by cooling natural gas to −160 °C, the temperature at which it changes from gas to liquid and 1/600th of its original volume. It is carried on board in this form and converted back to its natural gas state at the discharge terminal. (Alsoc)*

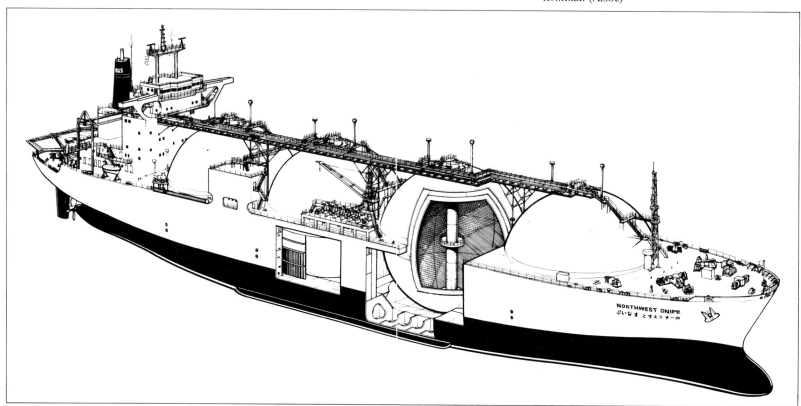

One of the most prolific builders of gas carriers is the German shipyard of Jos L Meyer, at Papenburg, which in 1982 delivered Tycho Brahe *to Hamburg shipowner Friedrich A Detjen. With a capacity of 15,000cu m of lpg,* Tycho Brahe *was chartered into the French-controlled Gazocean group, owners and operators of a large fleet of gas carriers. (FotoFlite)*

pressure than fully-pressurised ships, thus allowing the tanks to be of lighter construction. On these ships some of the tanks are designed to carry fully-refrigerated cargoes. In general ships of this type have a capacity of between 2000–15,000cu m although there are some larger ships.

3. Fully-refrigerated carriers: These are the largest with a capacity of up to 81,000cu m, and the majority in this class have a capacity greater than 20,000cu m. These must have primary and secondary barriers with inert gas in the spaces between the tanks, and will also be fitted with a refrigeration plant so that any boil off can be returned to the cargo.

The main trade for the large ships is from the Middle East to Japan with other trades from North Africa to Japan and southern Europe. The long distance trades in ammonia are Caribbean to western Europe; Ukraine (Black Sea) to the United States, and the Middle East to Far East.

J Strange

Typical products tankers since 1945

Ship	Flag	Built	By	GRT DWT (Oil capacity m³)	Length (oa) × breadth × depth × draught Feet–Inches Metres	Tanks	Engines	Speed	Remarks
ESSO AVONMOUTH	UK	1945	Sun SB, Chester, Pa	10,724 16,451 (141,200)[1]	523–6 × 68–3 × 39–3 × 30–2 *159.56 × 20.8 × 11.96 × 9.2*	26 tanks	turbo/electric 1 steam turbine 7240shp; 1 electric motor 6000shp	14.5kts	ex-US; T2 type
LUCERNA	UK	1952	Smith's Dock, Middlesborough	11,292 16,677	529–0 × 69–10 × 38–0 × 29–10 *160.93 × 21.29 × 11.58 × 9.1*	—	1 Hawthorn Leslie diesel 5500bhp	13kts	
CUAUHTEMOC	Mex	1967	IHI, Tokyo	10,086 17,482 (19,644)	475–0 × 70–0 × 38–9 × 30–7 *144.79 × 21.34 × 11.79 × 9.32*	24 tanks	1 IHI/Sulzer diesel 7200bhp	13kts	
CIELO DI SALERNO	Ita	1974	Italcantieri, Castellammare di Stabia	18,161 29,912 (37,308)	579–5 × 85–2 × 45–6 × 35–11 *176.61 × 25.96 × 14.48 × 10.93*	20 tanks	1 GMT, Trieste, diesel 10,000bhp; 1 shaft	15.5kts	
GALP LEIXOES	Pt	1983	Viana do Castelo	13,589 18,732 (21,610)	537–2 × 76–11 × 41–8 × 28–0 *163.73 × 23.44 × 12.7 × 8.54*	15 tanks	1 Harland & Wolff/B&W diesel, 7040bhp	14kts	
OKTAVIUS	Swe	1986	Uddevallavarvet, Uddevalla	14,937 23,050 (25,287)	519–4 × 86–9 × 45–0 × 32–10 *158.3 × 26.45 × 13.72 × 10.0*	14 tanks	1 Uddevalla/ B&W diesel 7480bhp	14.5kts	
KAPITAN KOROTAYEV	SU	1988	Brod Uljanik, Pula	10,948 17,400 (20,502)	496–6 × 73–8 × 40–0 × 29–7 *151.34 × 22.46 × 12.2 × 9.0*	18 tanks	1 Uljanik/ B&W diesel 7450bhp	15.1kts	
IVER EXPLORER	Ne	1991	Brod Uljanik, Pula	22,733 40,077 (45,043)	577–5 × 105–4 × 49–6 × 36–10 *176.0 × 32.1 × 15.1 × 11.23*	6 tanks; 12 wing tanks 16 cargo pumps 5440 t/hr	1 Uljanik/ B&W diesel 10,645bhp	14.3kts	oil/ chemical

Notes: [1] Barrels capacity.

Typical crude carriers since 1945

Ship	Flag	Built	By	GRT DWT (Oil capacity m³)	Length (oa) × breadth × depth × draught Feet–Inches Metres	Tanks	Engines	Speed	Remarks
BULKPETROL	Lib	1948	Welding Shipyards, Norfolk, Va	15,794 30,011	629–8 × 84–2 × 43–9 × 34–9 *191.92 × 25.66 × 13.33 × 10.8*		2 General Electric steam turbines 17,600shp; 1 shaft	16.5kts	
VEXILLA	UK	1955	Cammell Laird, Birkenhead	20,776 32,287	659–9 × 84–6 × 46–3 × 36–0 *201.08 × 25.75 × 14.10 × 10.97*		2 Cammell Laird steam turbines 14,500shp; 1 shaft	16.5kts	
UNIVERSE LEADER	Lib	1956	National Bulk Carriers, Kure	51,400 85,515	854–9 × 125–5 × 61–3 × 47–0 *260.52 × 38.22 × 18.67 × 14.32*		2 General Electric steam turbines 21,175shp; 1 shaft	15kts	
UNIVERSE APOLLO	Lib	1959	National Bulk Carriers, Kure	72,133 114,356	949–9 × 135–5 × 67–6 × 50–9 *289.48 × 41.28 × 20.57 × 15.47*		2 General Electric steam turbines 27,500shp; 1 shaft	15.5kts	
MACOMA	NeA	1968	IHI, Yokohama	104,302 209,995 (247,488)	1066–3 × 155–0 × 80–5 × 62–2 *325.08 × 47.22 × 24.52 × 18.95*	13 tanks	2 Mitsubishi steam turbines 28,000shp; 1 shaft	15kts	
GLOBTIK LONDON	UK	1973	IHI, Kure	238,207 483,933 (599,253)	1243–0 × 203–7 × 118–1 × 92–6 *378.88 × 62.06 × 36.0 × 28.2*	21 tanks	2 IHI steam turbines 45,000shp; 1 shaft	14.75kts	
TEXACO SPAIN	UK	1974	ASTANO, El Ferrol	140,264 274,088 (335,200)	1129–9 × 176–1 × 86–8 × 67–3 *344.33 × 53.68 × 26.42 × 20.5*	13 tanks	1 Bazan/Kawasaki steam turbine 32,000shp; 1 shaft	15.5kts	
BATILLUS	Fra	1976	L'Atlantique, St Nazaire	275,267 553,662 (677,325)	1358–11 × 206–10 × 114–10 × 93–6 *414.21 × 63.05 × 35.0 × 28.5*	37 tanks	4 Atlantique/ STAL-LAVAL steam turbines 64,800shp; 2 shafts	16.5kts	
ISUZUGAWA MARU	Jap	1987	Kawasaki HI, Sakaide	141,181 238,505 (291,032)	1033–7 × 185–9 × 98–5 × 64–0 *315.04 × 56.62 × 30.0 × 19.52*		1 Kawasaki/B&W diesel 22,800bhp; 1 shaft	15kts	
BLOOM LAKE	Pan	1991	Hitachi Zosen, Nagasu	156,215 281,794 (324,509)	1076–3 × 187–1 × 101–0 × 69–0 *328.04 × 57.04 × 30.8 × 21.03*	12 tanks 3 cargo pumps 17,100 tonnes/hour	1 Hitachi/B&W diesel 20,610bhp; 1 shaft	14.9kts	

Typical liquified natural gas carriers since 1958

Ship	Flag	Built	By	GRT (Cargo capacity m³)	Length (oa) × breadth × depth × draught Feet–Inches Metres	Tanks	Engines	Speed	Remarks
METHANE PIONEER	UK	1945	W Butler SB, Duluth	5058 (5125)	338–9 × 50–4 × 41–0 × 23–6 *103.25 × 15.34 × 12.5 × 7.18*	—	1 Nordborg diesel, 1700bhp; 1 shaft	11.5kts	Converted from general cargo vessel 1958
METHANE PRINCESS	UK	1964	Vickers-Armstrong, Barrow	21,876 (27,400)	621–1 × 81–9 × 58–5 × 35–1 *189.31 × 24.92 × 17.81 × 10.70*	9 tanks	2 Vickers/Pametrada steam turbines, 13,750shp; 1 shaft	17.25kts	

Ship	Flag	Built	By	GRT (Cargo capacity m³)	Length (oa) × breadth × depth × draught Feet–Inches Metres	Tanks	Engines	Speed	Remarks
HASSI R'MEL	Alg	1971	CNIM, La Seyne	31,420 (40,109)	654–8 × 96–2 × 60–11 × 30–6 *199.55 × 29.32 × 18.57 × 9.3*	6 tanks	2 Blohm & Voss/ STAL-LAVAL steam turbines, 16,250shp; 1 shaft	16kts	
BEN FRANKLIN	Fra	1975	La Ciotat, La Ciotat	80,071 (120,152)	894–11 × 134–8 × 84–8 × 36–5 *272.78 × 41.05 × 25.81 × 11.10*	6 tanks	2 l'Atlantique/ STAL-LAVAL steam turbines, 33,600shp; 1 shaft	19kts	lng/lpg
TENAGA SATU	Mly	1979	France-Dunkerque, Dunkirk	68,085 (130,000)	920–8 × 136–8 × 90–8 × 38–6 *280.63 × 41.64 × 27.61 × 11.73*	5 tanks	2 Alsthom-Atlantique/ STAL-LAVAL steam turbines, 45,000shp; 1 shaft	20kts	
KOTOWAKA MARU	Jap	1984	Kawasaki HI, Sakaide	97,788 (122,695)	921–11 × 145–0 × 82–0 × 37–10 *281.01 × 44.21 × 25.02 × 11.52*	5 tanks	2 Kawasaki steam turbines, 40,000shp; 1 shaft	19.25kts	
NORTHWEST SANDERLING	Aus	1989	Mitsubishi HI, Nagasaki	105,010 (128,270)	892–5 × 155–1 × 86–11 × 37–4 *272.0 × 47.27 × 26.5 × 11.39*	4 tanks	2 Mitsubishi steam turbines, 23,300shp; 1 shaft	18.5kts	

Typical liquified petroleum gas carriers since 1960

Ship	Flag	Built	By	GRT (Cargo capacity m³)	Length (oa) × breadth × depth × draught Feet–Inches Metres	Tanks	Engines	Speed	Remarks
SHELL MURACHI	Ven	1950	J L Thompson & Sons, Sunderland	7012 (1643)	423–10 × 62–9 × 21–6 × 18–7 *129.17 × 19.12 × 6.55 × 5.65*	—	2 Smith's Dock triple expansion steam engines, 4200ihp; 2 shafts	12kts	Converted 1960 to lpg with cylindrical tanks in central cargo tanks. Also carried 10,300m³ oil
JOYAMA MARU	Jap	1965	IHI, Nagoya	29,489 (46,548)	649–9 × 95–4 × 63–9 × 36–2 *198.03 × 29.06 × 19.41 × 11.02*	4 tanks	1 IHI/Sulzer diesel, 12,000bhp; 1 shaft	15.75kts	
LINCOLNSHIRE	UK	1972	Swan Hunter SB, Hebburn	19,799 (30,724)	613–0 × 88–2 × 50–6 × 32–1 *186.85 × 26.88 × 15.4 × 9.78*	3 tanks	1 Doxford diesel, 15,000bhp; 1 shaft	17.25kts	lpg/ ammonia
GAS AL KUWAIT 1	Kuw	1978	La Ciotat, La Ciotat	43,604 (72,121)	758–2 × 114–3 × 73–2 × 41–8 *231.10 × 34.83 × 22.31 × 12.71*	4 tanks	1 CCM Sulzer diesel, 26,800bhp; 1 shaft	16.5kts	
ISOCARDIA	UK	1982	Harland & Wolff, Belfast	39,932 (59,725)	689–0 × 103–2 × 70–5 × 34–1 *209.99 × 31.45 × 21.47 × 10.4*	5 tanks	1 Harland & Wolff/ B&W diesel, 20,500bhp; 1 shaft	17kts	
JOYAMA MARU	Jap	1986	Mitsubishi HI, Nagasaki	47,533 (80,863)	739–10 × 118–3 × 73–2 × 37–1 *225.51 × 36.05 × 22.3 × 11.31*	8 tanks	1 Mitsubishi/ Sulzer diesel, 18,600bhp; 1 shaft	17.5kts	
GAS ARIES	Lib	1991	Mitsubishi HI, Nagasaki	44,493 (76,000)	754–8 × 120–3 × 66–11 × 35–7 *230.0 × 36.65 × 20.4 × 10.84*	—	1 Mitsubishi diesel, 16,800bhp; 1 shaft	15.5kts	

5

Passenger Ships: Ferries and Cruise Ships

ACCORDING to the *Oxford Companion to Ships and the Sea* a ferry is

a vessel designed for the transport of persons and goods from one place to another on a regular schedule of sailings. They can vary from small boats across rivers and estuaries (sometimes with a chain across the bottom by which they are hauled over, either by hand or with the chain operated around a winch) to large specially built ships with roll-on/roll-off facilities for cars, lorries and trains.

This is however only one authors' definition and it is difficult to make a clear distinction as to when a ship should be described as a ferry. Criteria which could be used are length of the voyage, frequency of sailings, number of vessels on the particular run, carriage of passengers, freight, or both.

Lloyd's Register helpfully defines a ferry as 'a ship specially designed and constructed for the carriage of passengers and/or vehicles on a regular scheduled service of short duration'. It also defines a passenger ship as 'a ship specially designed and constructed for the carriage of more than 12 passengers', and a roro cargo ship as 'a ship specially designed and constructed for the carriage of vehicles, and cargo in pallet form or containers, and loaded/unloaded by wheeled vehicles'.

In the early postwar years Frank Bustard & Sons Ltd commenced the Transport Ferry Service, providing a regular service between Tilbury (London) and near Continental ports. The company's initial fleet consisted of a number of former LCTs built in the UK and whose principal cargoes consisted of military vehicles and supplies. In the late 1950s the former landing craft were replaced by new purpose-built ferries and expansion of services in the 1960s brought about the introduction of further vessels. One of these new vessels was Gaelic Ferry *(built 1963, 2760 grt), which joined* Bardic Ferry *(1957),* Ionic Ferry *(1958),* Cerdic Ferry *(1961) and* Doric Ferry *(1962) and was followed by* Europic Ferry *(1967) on services linking Tilbury with Antwerp and Rotterdam and Preston with Northern Ireland, carrying vehicles, continers and passengers. (Atlantic SN Co)*

Many present day ferries can be placed in all three of the categories described, making it virtually impossible to draw a clear boundary between ferries and other vessels which operate on what could be described as ferry routes, such as roro vessels with accompanying drivers.

According to ISL Shipping Statistics (Institute for Shipping Economics and Logistics) there were 2657 ferries in January 1991 operating world-wide which were over 300 grt. The definition used for this classification was that of Lloyd's Register.

Nevertheless, using these definitions as a starting point, the following areas will be explored to the extent possible in this chapter:

– the first forms of ferry traffic;
– modern ferry development and design;
– different types of ferries;
– ferry traffic routes;
– operational aspects of ferries;
– the safety and security of ferries.

The first forms of ferry traffic

The use of boats to ferry passengers across water barriers goes back to prehistoric times. In this account only 'ship' ferries are detailed. It appears that the first ships performing ferry functions were a number of train ferries, the oldest around 1840 across Lake Huron and around 1890 across the Kattegat between Sweden and Denmark. Later on some of the train

ferries on the Dover-Dunkirk route had a few garages to accommodate the small number of cars that could be carried across. In 1923 the wooden hulled *Motor Princess* owned by Canadian Pacific Railways was capable of carrying forty-five drive-on vehicles, and in 1930 the Danish *Heimdal* of about the same capacity entered service across the Great Belt. *Kronprinsessan Ingrid* entered the Frederikshavn-Gothenburg route in 1936, and a year later the first of the *Peter Wessels* on the Frederikshavn-Larvik line.

In the early days it was usual for cars to be loaded and discharged by cranes in a lift-on/lift-off style operation. The first British, true drive-on cross-channel ferry came in 1939 on the Stranraer to Larne route, as *Princess Victoria*. However, it was not until 1952 that the first purpose-built roro car ferry, *Lord Warden*, with a capacity of 1000 passengers and 100 cars was introduced by British Railways on the English Channel sailings. It is believed that the Belgians were the first with their converted steamer *London–Istanbul* to load up to 100 cars and 200 passengers through four roro ramps. These were all on the starboard side at different heights, in order to cope with tidal changes.

The roro concept as we know it today was boosted by the use of ramps in the landing craft of the Second World War. Nevertheless it was not until about the mid 1960s that these principles were put into full commercial prac-

A typical Baltic ferry of the 1960s was Fennia, *built in 1966 for Svea Line of Sweden. She was built for service between Sweden and Finland and carried a maximum of 1200 passengers and 200 cars. The size of ferries on this route has increased steadily and by the early 1990s had reached almost 60,000 grt.* (FotoFlite)

tice and the first roro ferries appeared on the English Channel and on Scandinavian routes.

Although there are distinct disadvantages to the concept as far as design and broken stowage is concerned, the high speed of terminal throughput and short cargo handling time in relation to the actual sailing time has made the roro ship by far the most popular type of ferry. Another reason for the enormous development in roro ferries has been the increase in private car ownership from the late 1950s onwards. The size of the ferries has grown roughly parallel to the growth in private car ownership as roro handling was by far preferred to the previous lift-on/lift-off handling of the precious motor cars. Simultaneously freight traffic could also start to benefit from the new way of cargo handling as no reloading of cargoes was required for the sea leg of the transport.

Modern ferry development and design

The length of the ferry passage and the route will obviously dictate the design criteria and the facilities required. A thirty-minute daytime crossing will not necessitate very elaborate accommodation but at the same time will not provide very high sales revenues which are possible on an eight-hour trip. Night time crossings require hotel type services which can prove quite profitable, while international traffic creates the possibility of duty free sales – one of the reasons for the increase in capacity on the trans-Baltic routes.

All trades have been seen to develop in different ways depending on national characteristics and potential passengers. In the Baltic the ferry excursions have become a way of life, sailing directly out of densely populated cities such as Stockholm and Helsinki. The English Channel traffic on the other hand exists mainly for the purpose of getting from one country to another and sails from more remote ferry ports, for example Newhaven and Dieppe where passengers must travel in order to board a ferry. This affects the development in designs.

The 1970s saw a sudden and dramatic jump in ferry size from the 4000–5000 grt range to 12,000 grt and over, which were the norm by the end of the decade. On the English Channel there are now ships up to 27,000 grt, and in the

UK-continent trade in the southern North Sea, vessels of up to 39,000 grt operate for North Sea Ferries and Olau Line. Seakeeping in heavy weather, weatherproofing the ship, passenger comfort by reducing the rolling and pitching, avoidance of cargo damage and ability to maintain a schedule in any kind of weather are of the utmost importance here.

Illustrating the growth of ferries owned by one well-known operator on the English Channel routes Townsend (later Townsend-Thoresen, now merged into P & O Ferries) are the following examples:

Name	Built	Grt	Passengers	Vehicles
Free Enterprise	1962	2606	670	120
Free Enterprise III	1966	4657	1200	350
Pride of Dover	1987	26,433	2290	650

Although not all that spectacular, flexibility of design is given top priority. One operator requires that twenty-three different berths in twelve ports must be serviceable by each vessel in order to reach optimum operational flexibility and efficiency.

The new tonnage measurement convention of 1969 which came into force in 1982 allowed owners to either use the new measurement or the old one until 1994. The new measurement system resulted in a larger gross tonnage for existing vessels. All vessels built after 8 July 1982 had to be measured according to the new rules and therefore appeared larger as far as gross tonnage was concerned. Although this does give a false impression regarding the sudden increase in ferry size, the ships are indeed

getting larger all the time, but the gross measurement is certainly more 'generous' than before.

The growing demand for greater capacity has led to much consideration in the design stage, and extensive model testing has become useful in order to ensure passenger comfort and fuel economy. Various types of body forms have been experimented on as larger propellers became necessary but at the same time vibrations had to be kept to a minimum. Safety elements have become a subject of their own and great care is paid to them.

Baltic ferry designs differ from vessels used in other regions due to a number of limitations and requirements:

– need for large bow and stern ramps;
– ice conditions and operations without ice-breaker assistance;
– safety standards/stability requirements;
– restricted to 6.7 metres draught;
– strong winds affecting berthing;
– difficult routes through archipelagos;
– small ports and harbours;
– tight operating schedules on day and night crossings.

Nevertheless ferries were growing in size, especially in this area, so power had to be increased, and as the draught is limited vessels had to grow upwards and athwartships. Large areas of glass in the superstructure were allowable because of the relatively sheltered areas of operation and seakeeping characteristics did not really present many problems. In the archipelagos lower environmental-disturbance wave patterns were required, but at the same time higher standards of comfort were set in order to stay competitive.

The 1972-built Free Enterprise VI, *owned by Townsend Car Ferries Ltd, and operating in the Townsend Thoresen grouping, was 5049 grt when new, and carried 1200 passengers and 310 cars between Dover and Calais/Zeebrugge. To extend its usefulness it was lengthened and widened at Bremerhaven in 1985 with a view to increasing the car and freight vehicle capacity.* (Townsend Thoresen)

Baltic ferry growth can be illustrated from the vessels of one particular operator:

Year	Cars	Passengers	Berths
1961	175	1200	292
1972	146	1000	400
1975	287	1200	163
1979	510	2000	1314
1985	600	2500	2372

Modern ferry design procedure is very much the reverse of traditional priorities. It begins at the passenger or customer end and the market then sets the standards for naval architects to work from. The 'cruise ferries' are probably the best example, showing how the need to include aspects of entertainment have considerably influenced the design.

The 'super ferry' philosophy has led to fierce competition with owners striving to stay at the top of the market and this had led to the premature sale of less extravagant but nevertheless good vessels. In this context it is notable to see the enormous amount of Mediterranean and sub-tropical ferries which have been built to the highest ice class! Greek owners in particular have quickly purchased many highly-rated vessels from northwest European and Scandinavian owners over the few years while the 'super ferry' war has been raging.

In the English Channel the main aim of the design has been to provide a swift, comfortable crossing in the shortest possible time. Very little price competition has resulted in a low passenger preference for a particular company and the departure time and duration of the crossing have usually been the most important elements for passenger choice.

Mediterranean ferry trades have been more varied; development, being influenced by oper-

ating subsidies, and absence of duty free sales, has never taken a great leap forward.

In the East, Indonesian and Philippine inter-island trades have been handicapped in their development by a lack of capital for newbuilding. Only recently have there been a few newly-built additions to a predominantly second-hand tonnage usage.

The necessity to use the lower hold space for cargo has resulted in a number of new designs, whereby the engine rooms are moved to the outer sides of the lower hold, creating a cellar deck in the middle which can be used for roro cargo. This considerably improves vessel stability and consequently allows a more flexible use of the higher-located cargo spaces.

For some time the growth of the so-called 'fast ferries' has been curtailed, due to limitations in production techniques. The boom in this field over the last few years has been at least as spectacular as with the more conventional ferry vessels and it seems the end is not in sight yet. Caught under the heading 'dynamically supported craft' there are many designs and types: catamarans, trimarans, hydrofoils, SWATHs (small waterplane area twin hull), hovercraft, all capable of carrying passengers, cars, trucks and coaches, either exclusively or in combinations.

There are already new designs in swaths featuring a capacity of 500 passengers and 150 cars at speeds of 37kts and jumbo catamarans for 1200 passengers and 275 cars at fully laden speeds of up to 45kts.

Whatever may be the criteria or limitations one thing is sure – gone are the days when a ship, the ports, a schedule, and a car deck were the only requirements for a ferry service.

Greek inter-island ferry operators have long been purchasers of redundant ferries and small passenger liners. Here, the former Baltic ferry Marella *(built 1970) is named* Alcaeus, *destined for Greek islands service with her new owners Maritime Co of Lesvos. Previously owned by SF Line of Mariehamn, Åland Islands, this vessel, with accommodation for 176 berths and 824 deck passengers, was engaged in the trans-Baltic routes from Sweden to Finland, via Mariehamn. On this route several operators have competed for the lucrative onboard sales from supermarkets and liquor stores.* (FotoFlite)

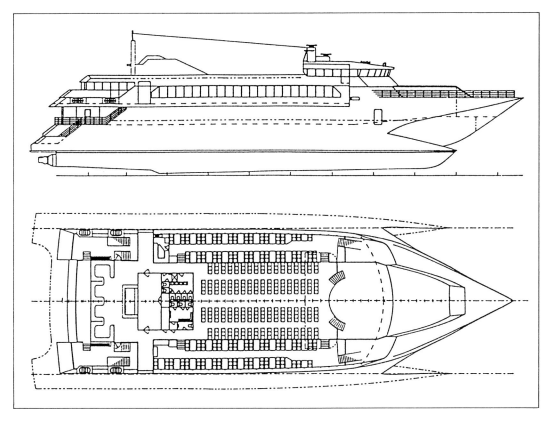

The plan and profile of the Hoverspeed Ltd SeaCats
Hoverspeed France and Hoverspeed Great Britain
which operate between Dover and Calais. Both have a
capacity of 383 passengers and 84 cars. They were built
by International Catamarans Tasmania, of Hobart,
in 1990.

Ferry types

The high speed ferry

In the 1970s high speed craft such as hovercraft and hydrofoils, using mainly aircraft technology, were very expensive to build and operate, but during the 1980s came a rapid expansion of the types and numbers built. The reasons for this expansion were developments in technology of welding aluminium, improvements in engines which were able to provide cost effective propulsion, and the dramatic rise in the leisure industries in the developed world.

The designs are mainly catamaran-style and built of aluminium, but recently glass reinforced plastics have been used as an alternative, and as for propulsion a new trend is the use of waterjet pumps instead of propellers. However the high-speed craft do not comply with all normal safety of life at sea (SOLAS) requirements but should meet standards of the IMO Code of Safety for Dynamically Supported Craft. This code uses two criteria, construction and area of service; the philosophy being that if the construction requirements are not fully comprehensive there should be proper readily-available rescue services in the area of operation. Now some of the new designs do not comply with these rules either and new legislation is being drafted to cover the new phenomena.

A recent addition is the 3000 grt, 74m Sea-Cat which is intended to replace the English Channel hovercraft. One advantage over the hovercraft is the reduced noise levels which will allow a 24-hour service. This is of course a distinct advantage over the night-time service restrictions which apply to hovercraft. SeaCat is able to carry 383 passengers and 84 motor cars. The new SeaCats *Hoverspeed France* and *Hoverspeed Great Britain*, built for Sealink's operating subsidiary Hoverspeed, were built in Australia for the English Channel service, in which they will have a normal speed of 35kts. Two new vessels, also building in Australia, will carry 600 passengers and measure 4500 grt. Furthermore, SeaCat's all-weather capability should mean an improvement over the limitations of the hovercraft.

The rail ferry

One of the oldest special types of ferry, which up to only comparatively recently retained its exclusive nature, is the rail ferry. The first appeared some 150 years ago maintaining a service across Lake Huron; and at the turn of the century well-established services existed across the Kattegat, linking Denmark and Sweden.

The basic design of rail ferries has been more or less the same over the years, but developments have seen the introduction of 'combination' carriers, with capacity not only for rail wagons, but also for road vehicles and passengers.

One problem encountered with rail ferries is the keeping of rails on shore aligned with those on deck. Another major consideration has been the matching of rail gauges on international routes to ensure the system is universal.

Excluding rail carrying barges, there are about 120 rail ferries in operation world-wide, being either rail-only, rail-truck or rail-truck-passenger ships.

The Norwegian company Westamarin AS, of Mandal, have designed the successful type 4200S high-speed passenger catamaran Mirage *suitable for ferry services. The vessel was built in 1991 by Oskarshamns Varv, Sweden. This vessel has a service speed of 35kts and propulsion is provided by two 2000kW diesels. Passenger capacity is for 408, with 304 seats in the main deck lounge and the remainder in the upper deck lounge; gross tonnage is 497.* (Westamarin)

The former Sealink train ferry Speedlink Vanguard, *owned by a UK associate of Stena AB, of Sweden, was built in the Netherlands in 1973 as a vehicles roro ferry. Following a few years operation in New Zealand, she was lengthened in 1977 and converted to a rail ferry in 1980. With a length of 142.27m, she can carry twenty-four freight wagons on deck. In 1989 she was re-converted to a vehicles roro ferry, with limited passenger accommodation and in 1992, after several changes of name, was operating between Caen and Portsmouth. (FotoFlite).*

As far as designs are concerned there are just a few alternatives. Unlike car ferries, with their slanted ramps, trains on rail ferries cannot cope with steep slopes. Therefore if multi-deck ships are used, upper and lower decks are reached by elevator platforms. Single, double and even triple rail deck ships have been constructed, and in order to move wagons transversely either a lateral transfer system or a movable rail platform is used.

As a matter of comparison the Danish-owned *Lillebaelt* of 1872 had just 38m of track and the 1990-built *Railship III*, owned in Germany, has 2000m.

Important rail ferry traffic routes are:
- Denmark-Sweden and Denmark-Norway Sweden-Poland
- Germany-Sweden and Germany-Finland (longest train ferry route in world)
- Southern Italy-Sicily
- Russia-Bulgaria and Romania-Turkey (across Black Sea)
- Siberia-Sakhalin
- Japan inter-island
- Canadian East Coast–the Maritime Provinces
- British Columbia regional and to Alaska

- US West Coast–Alaska (mainly towed barges)
- Between North and South islands of New Zealand
- Great Lakes (declining in importance).

The United Kingdom to France route has never developed very well, but has been recently gaining importance in view of the expected Channel Tunnel competition. New computer-controlled ferry berths have been constructed at Dover and Dunkirk, and the new ships which will service the route will offer advantages for the transportation of hazardous cargoes, carried in special compartments, as they will not be allowed to be carried through the tunnels. These vessels are designed to carry some 30–45 rail wagons.

Used on what have probably been the best-developed rail ferry runs anywhere – Germany to Denmark and Germany to Sweden – are so called multipurpose ferries capable of carrying foot passengers, private cars, road freight vehicles, passenger railway coaches, and rail freight wagons.

Southern North Sea ferries

The ultra-modern *Olau Hollandia* and *Olau*

Britannia, built in 1989 and of 33,336 grt, are the largest ferries on the southern North Sea route with a total of 1642 berths each.

The operational profile has played a major role in the design, with a daytime crossing of eight hours and at night time a ten-hour crossing, making two service speed profiles necessary, together with appropriate accommodation for day and night passengers.

The engine-room has been designed for attended operation only, resulting in simpler machinery and control equipment, and the restricted sailing routes and the constant short distance from the coast justified only six lifeboats with ample additional raft space available.

In these vessels no two spaces are the same or of the same colour, making it easy to distinguish different parts of the vessel. There are very few corridors, which are regarded as lost spaces, and passengers have to pass through one compartment to get to another. The vessels have four cargo decks and bow and stern

General arrangement of the 1987-built ferries Norsea *and* Norsun, *built for P&O and Hollandse Vrachtvaart Maats respectively, partners in North Sea Ferries and operating between Hull and Rotterdam/Europort.* Norsea *(31,785 grt) was built by Govan shipbuilders, UK, and her sister was a product of Nippon Kokan at Yokohama. Both are 179m in length, and with a total main engine power of 26,100 bhp, are able to carry 1250 passengers and 850 cars (180 trailers) at 18.5kts. (The Motor Ship)*

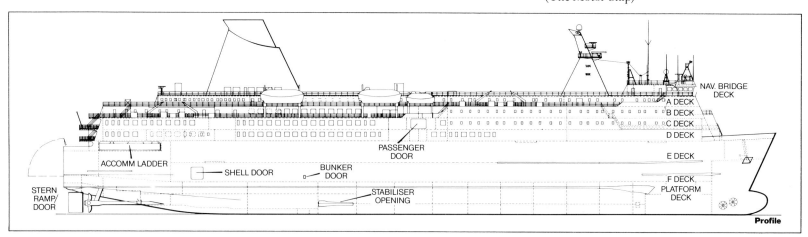

Entering service in 1985 for the Silja Line Service linking Sweden and Finland was the 33,829 grt Svea, one of a newer generation of superferries introduced on this highly competitive route. Owned by Svea Line (Finland) AB, and under Swedish flag, Svea has accommodation for 2000 passengers. Her four Wartsila/ Pielstick diesels produce a total 35,890 bhp and a service speed of 22kts. (Wartsila)

ramps which are operational to an elevation/ slope of eight degrees. In stowed position the ramp forms the forward watertight seal and is backed up by a watertight door at the collision bulkhead.

Built by Schichau Seebeckwerft AG, at Bremerhaven, these two new vessels are more than double the size of their 14,981 grt predecessors, whose names they perpetuate. The twin-screw vessels, which have four Polish-built Sulzer diesel engines with a total 57,600bhp, have an upper service speed of just over 21 kts.

English Channel ferries

Pride of Calais and *Pride of Dover*, built in 1987, and of 26,433 grt, are capable of carrying 2290 passengers, 700 cars or 102 trucks of 15m length at 22 kts. These are typical of Dover Strait ferries which are intended to withstand any tunnel or fast-ferry competition, and therefore maximum operational efficiency and reliability are vital. On the Dover–Calais route the intention is five round trips each day, seven days a week, for fifty weeks of the year.

A number of new features appeared in these ships, including four point embarkation, updated life-saving appliances (including four marine escape slides), void spaces in way of the engines are now incorporated in the engine rooms, and the double bottom is extended up the ships' side to the lower deck, thus creating a part double skin.

The vessels have ten decks and vehicle access is two tier, two lane loading and discharging through bow and stern doors. There are only some forty-five double-berth cabins for use if the vessels are switched to services other than Dover-Calais.

Like the Olau vessels described above, *Pride of Calais* and *Pride of Dover* were built in Germany, also by Schichau, at the Unterweser shipyard in Bremen. They have 31,400bhp Sulzer engines.

The super cruise ferry

One of the most recent and most spectacular entries on the Baltic Sea scene is undoubtedly *Silja Serenade*, described as a cruise ferry. With its 58,376 grt and 2500 passenger capacity, this can certainly be labelled a jumbo, offering high quality accommodation and a broad range of entertainment.

By incorporating a central longitudinal atrium 140m long, 8m wide and five decks high, within the vessel it has been possible for 80 per cent of all cabins to have windows. Of the total of 952 cabins, 750 have windows, and all 2500 passengers have cabin berths.

The atrium, called a promenade, is covered by a skylight to increase the amount of natural light coming in.

Entertainment facilities, besides the usual restaurants, discos and shops, include the largest 'children's world' afloat, a show lounge, casino, nightclub with panoramic view lounge, swimming pools with water-slides, jacuzzis, steam baths, saunas with access to the sun deck, and conference rooms which can be converted into a ballroom for 650 people. The cargo capacity is 450 cars or 60 trailers on two decks and there are anti-heeling tanks to make cargo operations easier.

The ship is equipped to the highest safety standards prevailing and the atrium has extra protection: it is isolated from the rest of the vessel; has television monitors; fire insulated walls, floors and ceilings, a mechanical smoke exhaust system and fire and smoke detectors. Furthermore lifeboats, liferafts and inflatable evacuation platforms, increased engine-room safety, environment-friendly protected fuel tanks, improved sewage treatment and garbage and waste disposal all add to an improved operational safety standard. The ship's machinery consists of four main engines, two auxiliary engines, a stern thruster, two bow thrusters and two controllable pitch propellers.

Silja Serenade and her sister-ship Silja Symphony (58,376 grt, 2426 passengers and 450 cars) were built by Masa Yards, Turku, for the Silja Line Service between Stockholm and Helsinki and represent another step forward in the ferry-cruise concept. The development of these vessels has resulted in a new feature, the 'promenade'. This atrium area is in the very centre of the vessel with all main activities located around it. Another objective of this advanced design was to create an environment satisfying the needs of various passenger categories, and this has resulted in passengers' freedom to choose between several restaurants, shops, entertainment facilities and other activities. (Kvaerner Masa Yards)

Operating on the Dover-Calais service of P&O Ferries since 1987 is Pride of Dover *(26,433 grt), built at the Vegesack shipyard of Schichau-Unterweser AG. Like her sister-ship* Pride of Calais, *this vessel accommodates 2290 passengers and their cars and transits the Dover Strait at 22kts. The three Sulzer CCM diesels totalling 31,400 bhp, drive three shafts. (P&O)*

Ferry traffic routes

English Channel routes

The realisation of the Channel Tunnel project will have an effect on Dover Strait ferry traffic. To what extent, however, can only be guessed. Traffic routes to the north of Ramsgate and to the south of Portsmouth are likely to survive, but if the same will hold for the services between these boundaries remains to be seen.

Traffic through Dover is expected to decrease by half when the tunnel is in full operation but there will still be a need for the ferries to continue service alongside it. Probably all foot passengers will go via the tunnel, about half of the motor cars and coaches but only one-third of the freight. All hazardous cargo is banned from the tunnel, and as statistics indicate that about one-fifth of all international road and rail freight consists of hazardous cargo, this adds up to a substantial amount which will still have to use ferry services.

The introduction of fast ferries in the Dover Strait is viewed as another possible way of competing with the tunnel, and the limitations of the hovercraft can probably be overcome by the new types of vessels. However, even though the alternative tunnel is available, it is thought that the possibility of a passenger rest

The 3715 grt twin-screw motor ferry Ailsa Princess, *was built in 1971 for the British Rail service linking Stranraer with Larne, Northern Ireland. Like many ferry operators British Rail's Sealink subsidiary transferred vessels from one route to another for operational reasons and in 1982* Ailsa Princess *underwent a £280,000 refit to improve passenger accommodation and for alterations to bow and stern ramps allowing the carriage of heavy lorries. This was prior to transfer to the Weymouth-Cherbourg service on which Sealink introduced freight roro facilities. (FotoFlite)*

period, compulsory or voluntarily will prove a distinct advantage of the ferry crossing.

Public opinion regarding travel by ferry will be a dominant factor. The tragedy of *Herald of Free Enterprise* and the non-introduction of generous modern (safe) new tonnage but conversions of second-hand pure freight roros, certainly does not add to a positive public opinion.

Baltic routes

On the Sweden-Finland trade new tonnage is being introduced by competitors Slite and Viking, and the new generation of cruise ferries seems to be moving westward to Sweden-Germany. Further developments are soon expected in the Baltic due to the changed political situation in the former Eastern-bloc countries.

Another new development likely to increase in importance in the future is the introduction of high-speed vessels, catamarans and hovercraft, into the Baltic. The shortest routes are the most likely to be served first and these would probably include Sweden to Åland, Gotland and Finland.

Regional routes

Around the United Kingdom there are over 110 ferry routes ranging from very short to intermediate crossings and employing very small to medium-size vessels. If the regional ferry wants to compete with bridges, tunnels, and longer auto routes, there has to be a distinct advantage for the passengers. The facilities provided both on board and ashore are becoming more important in the competition, and the fast catamaran is probably one of the strongest new elements in the regional ferry survival race.

One example of this is the Tilbury (Essex) to Gravesend (Kent) route, once operated by

three steam passenger ferries and two car ferries. Upon the opening of the Dartford Tunnel (5 miles up river) in the early 1960s, the car ferries were soon withdrawn and the steam passenger ferries were replaced by new diesel-driven vessels. Reductions in passenger traffic over the years have brought about a corresponding reduction to one passenger-only ferry on the service and this is now rapidly nearing the end of its economical career.

The service was one which was sold by British Rail (Sealink) to Sea Containers in a controversial take-over a few years ago, but was not of interest to Sealink's new Swedish owners when they bought the group from Sea Containers and it has changed hands again. The new owners, White Horse Ferries Ltd, in 1992 acquired a high-speed catamaran feeling that this was the only alternative to complete withdrawal of the service.

Japanese routes

Although mainly domestic, the Japanese ferry trade can hardly be neglected in the context of this book. The growth and designs have not been as spectacular as in Europe, but an industrialised maritime nation consisting of a large number of islands is of course bound to have a substantial amount of ferry traffic.

The Japanese ferry routes include some of the longest in the world. Since many major cities and towns are located on the coasts and are surrounded by difficult countryside, the ferries form an important means of transport. (There is great similarity here with the Norwegian coastal routes.) The only serious competition is from air transport and especially the first class passengers are trading ferry travel for air travel.

Figures from 1990 show that in Japan there were more than 820 owners running 2400 vessels on 1300 routes, and of course most of these are very small craft on short routes across harbours or estuaries. Of these, however, there are 190 car ferry operators with 510 vessels on 260 routes. Of this number 375 are of less than 3000 grt.

Unlike the European trades the main income is freight transport at around 75 per cent, compared with passenger fares at only 19 per cent and the on board sales without the benefit of international duty free only a mere 6 per cent of the revenue. However a change of philosophy is becoming apparent in trying to attract more domestic passengers away from train and air travel and to increase tourist trades and operations to mainland China and Korea. A part of this attraction could well be the introduction of high-speed vessels such as

catamarans. Japan is no stranger to this type of ferry as a very successful catamaran roro service has been running in Tokyo Bay for some years.

Operations, safety and security

Operations

Ferry operations are heavily associated with the tourist industry, which in turn is very much seasonal. As a result the ferry industry finds itself facing rather unwelcome peaks and troughs. The traditional summer peak capacity is found hard to satisfy. Winter trough capacity utilisation on the other hand is hard to come by even though various alternative markets are tried. Some ferries are diverted to regions which then experience a seasonal peak, some are used for semi-cruising purposes, while others may act as floating accommodation if such a role presents itself. Obviously maintenance, surveys and docking will take place in the slack periods and probably sailing frequencies reduced, and if all else fails the need might arise to lay-up a vessel for a period of slack time.

The major operators of the Baltic are continually ordering larger and more sophisticated ships. The new orders can be justified by inventive marketing approaches, competition, excellent vessel designs and the alcohol policies in the countries involved. However many feel that the sensible level of size and design has been reached if not passed already. Special events, discount fares, shipboard conferences and other attractions have provided off-peak utilisation at quite an acceptable level in this region.

Mediterranean traffic is even more peak season orientated and operators here are very much in favour of the cheaper conversion of roro freighters to car/passenger ferries instead of newbuilding.

Due to high revenues from on board sales in shops, bars, restaurants and duty free shops, fares have been traditionally very low in Baltic ships compared to other routes. However as the joining of the EEC comes closer there will have to be a change in pricing strategies. Furthermore 1992 might see the possible abolition of intra-European duty free which is seen as profitable but also a means of minimising passenger fares.

In about 1970 the number of cross-Channel ferry services could be counted on one hand. In 1990 there were twelve routes served by eight companies. The introduction of the Channel Tunnel is regarded with mixed feelings by the ferry operators. Freight volumes are rising and

it is thought that a short comfortable crossing might very well compete with any type of transport through a tunnel. Improving documentation clearance might also be seen as beneficial while fleet expansion programmes and updating of existing terminals and ports seem worthwhile.

Obviously operational costs, depending on so many factors, are very operator and region orientated. An impression of the cost percentages for a cross-Channel ferry operation in 1989 is given as follows:
Administration and advertising 20 per cent
- Crew 30 per cent
- Insurance/stores/repairs 15 per cent
- Fuel 15 per cent
- Port dues 20 per cent.
As crew costs take up a considerable percentage, a somewhat deeper investigation seems justified.

Immediately the many different schedules and philosophies for crewing become apparent. In general it can be said that operations are quite intensive so a fresh, alert crew is a necessity at all times. This can be achieved in a number of ways:
- With a high relief frequency, and short terms of duty, a normal size crew will do, but there is a need for two or three full crews on a rotating relief schedule. Two to three days on, three to six days off is a possibility.
- With a low relief frequency, longer periods of duty, a larger crew will be needed on board, but the size and number of relief crews can be smaller. Two weeks on two weeks off are known to be used in such cases.

A number of local factors come into the picture, very much depending on standards of employment common in a fleet, a company or a country. On a continuous service the situation is comparable with other forms of shipping, but on a daytime service there are various ways of counting duty times. Sometimes the crew remains on board, and on many regional routes the crew simply goes home at night. There is not a standard which can be considered as universal.

One fairly common practice is that, due to the large number of arrivals and departures, berthings and unberthings, most of the ferry operators prefer their masters to perform own pilotage activities, therefore reducing time, effort and costs.

The trend of polyvalent or integrated crews in order to cut costs does not apply to ferries. The intensity of the operations requires often even an increase rather than a decrease of the number of staff on board, although this by no means excludes polyvalent trained staff from

crewing the ferries. The benefit of crew cost reduction will just not be possible on this type of intensive operation.

Depending on the type of ship and sailing time there will then be other crew departments next to the ship operational crew:

– catering personnel for restaurants and bars;
– hotel personnel for passenger accommodation;
– shop personnel for stores, banks, casinos, etc.

Shoreside cleaning gangs and containerised handling of stores and waste make a crew of 200 possible on the new super vessels in the Baltic serving some 2500 passengers with 450 cars. However on a regional Netherlands route with one-and-a-half hours daytime crossings, and consequently no cabin accommodation a maximum of 1700 passengers and 120 cars are served by just seven crew and fourteen catering staff.

Safety

The sea is always dangerous, and whilst many ships are lost from year to year, the most extensive reporting and concern relating to marine casualties is focused on ferries. Because of the very large numbers of people travelling on ferries safety is clearly of prime importance. The roro vessels in particular have come under major scrutiny following casualties the most widely publicised probably being the loss of *Herald of Free Enterprise*. The most serious casualties in recent years are listed in Table 5/1.

Ironically, it is not the number of deaths, but the region where the disaster occurs and the wealth of the countries involved, which seem to be the criteria used to start procedures for the improvement of ferry safety and the protection of passengers. After the *Herald of Free Enterprise* disaster leaving Zeebrugge in Belgium, a number of new safety measures started to come into force on roro ships and in particular on roro passenger ships, to which category most of the present-day ferries belong. The new rules requirements include bow door indicators, continuous physical or television surveillance of vehicle spaces, and improved emergency lighting lasting at least three hours in public spaces. The measures will be in force immediately on new ships and gradually phased in on existing ships.

Furthermore, stricter stability requirements are coming into force giving better survival chances for the ship, taking into account the worst possible conditions such as all passengers on one side of the vessel, launching of full lifeboats and excessive wind forces. Stricter design criteria will probably come into force at a later

Table 5/1: Serious Ferry Losses 1960–92

Name	Date	Location	Fatalities
Midori Maru	19 Aug 1963	Japan	122
Pioneer Cebu	16 May 1966	Philippines	431
Pioneer Leyte	23 Oct 1966	Philippines	81
Wahine	10 Apr 1968	New Zealand	51
Nam Yung Ho	15 Dec 1970	South Korea	323
Fatshan	16 Aug 1971	Hong Kong	80
Toe Aye	21 Feb 1973	Burma	171
Don Juan	22 Apr 1980	Philippines	1000
Tampomas II	27 Jan 1981	Indonesia	431
Juan	17 July 1981	Philippines	57
European Gateway	19 Dec 1982	Felixstowe	6
Dona Cassendra	21 Nov 1983	Philippines	168
Venus	28 Oct 1984	Philippines	137
Dona Josefina	24 Apr 1986	Philippines	194
Herald of Free Enterprise	6 Mar 1987	Zeebrugge	193
Dona Paz	20 Dec 1987	Philippines	4386
Dona Marilyn	24 Oct 1988	Philippines	150
Scandinavian Star	9 Apr 1990	North Sea	156
Moby Prince	11 Apr 1991	Mediterranean	140
Nawa Prateep III	9 Mar 1992	Thailand	about 80

stage eliminating bow doors completely, introducing watertight transverse bulkheads in the cargo spaces and formalising operational procedures and management ashore.

Security

Drunken soccer fans, passengers going overboard in suspicious circumstances, suspected arson . . . these are a few of the most highlighted security risks that can or have taken place on ferries. Some governments are now considering the introduction of mandatory security precautions as the public is demanding protection, not only from incompetence and mechanical failure, but also from criminal or terrorist acts of violence.

Security of ferry operations will be more difficult to control than for instance airline traffic due to the higher volume and frequency per unit. Security should be seen in its entirety: the type of passenger; checks and searches; a secured area around the vessel itself, on board precautionary measures. Measures too strict however, could cause dalays, military style control and checks and extra costs. These are all rather unfavourable elements which no one is seeking. The approach considered is therefore of a more preventive nature, such as the introduction of video cameras and surveillance, the locking of unused spaces, special locks and keys only to be used by ships' personnel, and safety routes and emergency exits made accessible with modern control equipment.

Other equipment to improve safety of operations includes remote draught reading devices coupled to a loading and stability computer which then supplies information about capacities, stability, ships strength during cargo operations, etc. However all the equipment and procedures are only as reliable as the people that are operating and implementing them.

Captain Steven Cross

Cruise ships

Historically stretching a point, cruising has existed since the first time Cleopatra ventured on a lavish barge and travelled down the Nile. Cruises involve the transportation of pleasure-seeking travellers on ocean voyages offering one or more glamorous ports of call. A clear emphasis of modern cruise ship operations is the marketing of sea, sun, sand and service, rather than on a pure transportation function which was characterised by former passenger liners. Thus, the principal objectives promoting patronage aboard cruise ships today are 'sunlust' and 'wanderlust'. 'Wanderlust' – a human desire to visit new places and cultures – has always been at the forefront of the rationale for vacation travel, while 'sunlust' – an urge to escape the temperate climates, especially those of the winter season – has become ever more important in holiday marketing and is the major impetus for the development of large-scale cruise operations.

A history of cruise shipping

The idea of embarking passengers on a sea voyage for pleasure, rather than simply for transportation, is usually credited to Arthur Anderson, one of the founders of Peninsular & Oriental Steam Navigation Company (P&O). In 1835, Anderson proposed an imaginary cruise from England to the waters of Iceland and the Faeroe Islands, and suggested a potential for future cruising under the warm Spanish sun during the cold winter months. As early as 1844, P&O offered occasional cruises to the Mediterranean Sea. In 1881, the first passenger ship capable of a round the world voyage, the steamer *Ceylon* (2376 grt) began her service. Other noteworthy pioneers of cruise operations during the latter 1800s and early part of

the present century included the first cruise from the United States on the wooden-hulled paddle-wheel steamer *Quaker City* (built 1854, 1900 grt), to the Mediterranean in 1868. As a matter of additional interest Mark Twain was on this first 'cruise' and it inspired him to write *Innocents Abroad*.

Later the Orient Line of London, in association with the Pacific Steam Navigation Co, was the first regular line operator to offer a true cruising programme. With its near-sister vessels *Chimborazo* (3847 grt, built by John Elder & Co, Glasgow, 1871) and *Garonne* (3860 grt, built by Napier, Glasgow, also in 1871) cruises to the Norwegian fjords were made in 1889 and eventually to Mediterranean regions in 1893.

Hamburg-Amerika Line, under the guiding genius of Albert Ballin, sent its *Augusta Victoria* (built 1889, 7661 grt) on a Mediterranean cruise rather than have her sail half-empty on her regular transatlantic route during the winter season of 1891, and in 1895 another Pacific Steam/Orient vessel *Lusitania* (built 1871, 3877 grt) made a sixty-day luxury cruise to the West Indies, Madeira, Tenerife and the Azores.

Of special significance, *Prinzessin Victoria Luise* (4409 grt), which was the world's first vessel purpose-built for cruise service made her first cruise in 1901 and became an instant success. Unfortunately this vessel was wrecked after being stranded on an uncharted reef off Jamaica in January 1907. She was replaced

The first vessel built specially for cruising was Prinzessin Victoria Luise, *seen here at Hamburg when about to depart on her first cruise in January 1901. Although her career was short, being wrecked off Jamaica in 1907, the commercial success of the vessel was such that the owners, Hamburg-Amerika Line sought an immediate replacement. Victoria Luise was built at the Hamburg shipyard of Blohm & Voss and carried 200 passengers. (Hapag-Lloyd)*

In the early 1990s, the introduction of large cruise vessels combined with a world recession may see the disposal of older vessels which become increasingly uneconomic. One such vessel is Carnival Cruise Lines' Carnivale (18,953 grt) which was built in 1956 as Canadian Pacific's Empress of Britain, and still retained much of its original lines in the 1990s. After a time as Greek Lines' Queen Anna Maria, this vessel joined the Carnival Cruise fleet in 1975, three years after they had purchased another Canadian Pacific vessel, Empress of Canada, latterly in service as Mardi Gras. (Carnival Cruise Lines)

quite promptly by a second-hand vessel, but the steamer *Victoria Luise* (16,703 grt), the former Hamburg-Amerika express liner *Deutschland* (built 1900), was refurbished and entered continuous cruise service in 1911.

From this early beginning, vessels that provided cruises primarily served a very limited clientele compared to liners built for transportation functions. On occasion, either because of low bookings or situations where some vessels could only be regularly employed on their dedicated routes on a seasonal basis, opportunities existed to deploy passenger liners from fixed shuttle routes to cruise trades. Cruising, much like passenger ship operations, was disrupted during both World Wars. Although the Depression of the 1930s negatively influenced passenger travel, Prohibition greatly promoted cruising. Many liners of the time were pressed into cruise service to maintain their operations, and 'booze cruises' became very popular.

Not connected with the 'booze cruise' market, but possibly the best-known cruise vessel of the 1930s, was Blue Star Line's *Arandora Star*. Built by Cammell Laird at Birkenhead, she was one of five sister-ships completed during 1926–27 for Blue Star's refrigerated cargo and passenger service from London to South America. Delivered in June 1927, exactly two years later she emerged from Fairfield's

shipyard at Govan following a five-month conversion to a cruise vessel. Apart from increasing the passenger capacity from 164 (as built) to 400 (cruising), all her refrigeration equipment was removed, and her gross tonnage went up from 12,838 to 15,501.

Arandora Star had a very successful cruising career. With a white hull and green band on the sheer, she became known affectionately as 'the chocolate box', carrying the rich and famous. Her last cruise was made in 1939 and during her ten years in this role, she made 124 cruises; one to the Baltic, one to the Indian Ocean, six to the West Indies, twelve to the Canaries, but by far the most popular were to the Mediterranean and the Norwegian fjords (fifty-six and forty-four respectively). Alas, after being taken on government service, she became a war loss in 1940.

The modern era of cruising, the 'Initial Stage', began in the late 1950s and early 1960s when air transport first displaced Atlantic liners as the major mode for travel between the United States and Europe. Once again,

shipowners redeployed their vessels into the cruise trades to generate needed revenues. Vessels which were not designed specifically for cruising, and many were not air conditioned and had minimal open deck space, were converted to what was for them an entirely different role. On many vessels passenger complement was reduced due to the necessity of offering only a two-class system and the need to find space for additional on-board facilities. Representative vessels of this stage that are still in service include the sister-ships, *Independence* (built 1950, 20,220 grt) and *Constitution* (built 1951, 20,269 grt), which originally operated between New York and Mediterranean ports. These vessels were built in the United States and sailed under the banner of American Export Lines at a speed of 20kts and carried 1000 passengers. After a brief spell with the C Y Tung Group of Hong Kong they are back under the United States flag and are the only US-registered large cruise ships still in service. *Constitution* and *Independence* currently operate in the protected intra-

Requisitioned for Government service in September 1939, Arandora Star was torpedoed and sunk by a German U-boat less than one year later. However, during the 1930s she became one of the best-known and most popular cruise vessels afloat, following conversion from a regular line passenger/cargo vessel in 1929. Built in 1927, she was the last of three sister-ships completed by Cammell Laird, Birkenhead, for Blue Star Line Ltd, London, then owner of a substantial fleet of refrigerated cargo vessels. The three sisters were ordered in 1925, at a cost of £303,300 each excluding refrigeration equipment, and commissioned during 1926–27. Originally carrying 164 passengers, the post-conversion complement of Arandora Star was 400, and tonnage was increased from 12,838 grt to 15,501 grt. (Harold A Ball)

Hawaiian Islands trades for American Hawaii Cruises Inc, San Francisco, carrying a maximum of 900 passengers and offering cruises of seven days duration.

Mardi Gras, the first vessel owned by Carnival Cruise Lines, was the former *Empress of Canada* built in 1961. This 18,261 grt ship is a vintage ocean liner that was converted for warm-weather cruising in 1972. She is 650ft in length with a beam of 87ft. The vessel has a passenger capacity of 906, and cruises at 21kts. Although *Mardi Gras* began her cruise service in the seven-day market out of Miami, she currently is deployed in the growing three-and four-day market providing cruises to the Bahamas, while home ported in Port Canaveral, Florida.

Funtastica, operated by a United States company, is another good example of a former liner that has received a second life as a cruise ship. Built in 1944 as a troopship, she was converted for commercial passenger service in 1956. This 800-passenger ship also provides service in the short-term duration market, with cruises to the Bahamas. The vessel which up to 1992 was better-known under one of her former names, *Emerald Seas*, is 18,927 grt, 622ft in length with a beam of 75.5ft, and cruises at 18kts.

Meridian, the refurbished Italian liner *Galileo Galilei* (built 1963) which provides seven-day cruises to the Caribbean and Bermuda, carries 1106 passengers at 24kts. This 30,440 grt vessel is presently operated by Chandris Celebrity Cruises. She was under the Chandris Lines flag from 1984 to 1989 and was named *Galileo*.

Britanis was built in 1932 as the Matson liner *Monterey*. Whilst under Matson ownership she was renamed *Matsonia* (1956) and *Lurline* (1970). This vessel, with its classic liner styling, is only one of a handful of two-funnelled ships still in service. She, like many of the older ships still operating, undertakes short cruises, including two-day cruises to the Bahamas and five-day cruises to the western Caribbean.

All six of the above ships were built prior to the emergence of today's modern cruise indus-

P&O Steam Navigation Co changed in the 1960s from a regular line carrier, notably UK-Australia, to a cruise operator, and through new building or acquisitions its fleet of cruise vessels increased steadily in the 1970s and '80s. In 1984 the fleet was augmented by the arrival of Royal Princess *(44,348 grt), built by Wartsila at Helsinki. Based on the United States market, this streamlined vessel carries 1250 passengers and has a speed in service of 20kts. The four Wartsila/Pielstick diesels drive two shafts and have a combined 31,543 bhp. (Wartsila)*

try, and have all undergone extensive refurbishment through the years. Their past and present financial success has led cruise ship owners to construct purpose-built cruise ships to meet the growing demand for cruising as a holiday option. The design of ships specifically dedicated to cruising ushered in the next epoch of the modern cruise industry, the 'first generation'.

The majority of the first generation cruise vessels were operated by new entrants into the industry, rather than existing ocean transportation companies, but exceptions to this general rule were the operations of P&O, Cunard, and Chandris Lines. Scandinavian and European companies provided the impetus for exploring the Caribbean market from the United States East Coast. This legacy is still alive today in the form of such cruise lines such as Norwegian Caribbean, Royal Caribbean, Royal Viking and Holland America. Other 'new kids on the block' included the United States companies of Carnival Cruise Lines and Princess Cruises.

Examples of the first generation cruise ships, that were expressly constructed for cruising include *Ocean Princess*, formerly *Italia* (built 1967), which has been utilised, first through charter, to pioneer United States West Coast cruising on the Mexican Riviera and to Alaska. The ship measures 8469 grt, with a length of 438ft and breadth of 77ft. She can carry 500 passengers and sustain a speed of 19kts. This cruise ship operates under the livery of Princess Cruises and provides service to the Caribbean and South America.

Triton, previously *Sunward II* and *Cunard Adventurer* (built 1971), which provides cruises in the Caribbean. The vessel, operated by Epirotiki Lines, of Greece, is known for its

sleek profile with a raked bow. She is of 14,110 grt, has a passenger capacity of 696, and a cruise speed of 16kts.

Princess Cruises' *Pacific Princess* (built 1971), of 'The Love Boat' fame, and *Island Princess* (built 1972) both cruise world-wide. These sistership, with their sleek lines, are both about 20,000 grt, 550ft in length and have a beam of 80ft. They operate at a speed of 20kts, and can each carry 626 passengers.

Westward (built 1972), *Royal Odyssey* (built 1973), and *Sunward* (built 1973), are a trio of vessels built by the Finnish shipyard of Wartsila, that provide world-wide service, mainly from San Francisco. These cruise ships have accommodation for 725 passengers, and operate at a cruising speed of 21.5kts.

The first generation cruise ships were smaller and more intimate than their liner predecessors and were able to carry less than 1000 passengers. Their major new design feature, in addition to the necessity of shipboard amenities favourable to cruising, was a sleeker image that was very similar to the European ferries of the mid-1970s. Industry-wide success, resulting from increasing demand for cruise services, created problems for the industry, since available tonnage suitable for conversion was limited. The immediate solution to this problem was to 'stretch' (increase carrying capacity) existing ships by adding hull midsections.

By the early 1980s, growth in the demand for cruising along with the associated need for new capacity encouraged the cruise lines to order new, larger vessels. These, the 'second generation', approached in passenger capacity the scale and size of the large former transatlantic liners.

Royal Caribbean Cruise Line operates the 37,584 grt
Song of America *which was built by Wartsila at*
Helsinki *in 1982.* Song of America, *based on the US*
cruise market, carries 1577 passengers and has a total
crew of 500. (Wartsila)

Typical second generation cruise ships include *Tropicale* (built in Denmark in 1981), the first Carnival Cruise Lines new vessel, which is generally regarded as the 'prototype' in this era. She measures 22,919 grt, and operates at 20kts in the United States West Coast to Mexico market. Her passenger capacity is 1400, and she has a length of 672ft and beam of 86ft.

Sky Princess, previously Sitmar Cruises' *Fairsky* (built 1984), which has a passenger complement of 1400, and operates in both the Caribbean and Alaskan markets. She is 43,692 grt and has an overall length of 789ft.

Holland America's 33,930 grt *Nieuw Amsterdam* (built 1983) which provides service to the Caribbean, Alaska and the Mexican Riviera. This vessel has a long, squat, angular profile and operates at service speeds of 22kts. She can carry 1350 passengers.

Royal Princess (built 1984), Princess Cruises' 44,348 grt vessel which provides Mediterranean itineraries and trans-Canal (Panama) cruises. At full capacity, she can carry 1260 passengers at speed of 22kts.

Carnival Line's sister-ships *Jubilee* (built 1986) and *Celebration* (1987) are of 47,262 grt and can carry 1850 passengers. They were designed for the clientele of unsophisticated Middle America to provide a Las Vegas-type experience at sea, while cruising the Carib-

bean. They are 748ft in length and their beam is 28m.

Song of America (built 1982), a Royal Caribbean Cruise Line entrant, is 703ft long, and 93.2ft wide. She provides seven-day excursions to the Caribbean, operating at 21kts, and can accommodate 1577 passengers. Her gross tonnage is 37,584.

Noticeable trends of the second generation vessels are the maximisation of the number of outside cabins because of their premium rates. Also, there has been shift away from steam turbines for propulsion, in favour of slow-speed diesels due to lower operating fuel costs. An extremely high passenger cruise industry satisfaction rate, of greater than 90 per cent, promoted growth and encouraged shipowners to

order even larger cruise ships in the early 1990s. These 'mega-ship generation' vessels approach and even exceeded 2000-passenger capacities.

The numerous mega-ship generation is typified by vessels such as Royal Caribbean's *Sovereign of the Seas* (1988), which was the first of this class, along with two other vessels *Monarch of the Seas* (built 1991) and *Majesty of the Seas* (built 1992). These ships can carry the largest berth-passenger complements afloat, ever, at 2673. They are the biggest cruise ships ever built, at 73,192 grt and, except for *Norway* (the ex-transatlantic liner *France*) which is 1035ft, and the 963ft *Queen Elizabeth 2*, their 874ft hulls are the longest currently in service. Their beams are very wide at 106ft. All three ships are dedicated to the seven-day Caribbean cruise market, *Sovereign* out of Miami, *Monarch* departs from San Juan, and the home port for *Majesty* has yet to be determined.

The most striking feature, other than sheer size, has been the inclusion of multi-deck atriums on the mega-ship generation vessels. This characteristic, along with exterior boxy designs and luxury hotel-type interiors has led many cruise patrons to remark that these ships are destinations unto themselves. In addition to the mainstream categories of vessels described

The 1992-built cruise ship Majesty of the Seas *(73,937 grt) arriving off Miami.* Majesty *has joined* Monarch of the Seas *(1991) and* Sovereign of the Seas *(1987) on US-based cruise programmes for their operators Royal Caribbean Cruise Lines AS, Oslo. Built by Chantiers de l'Atlantique, St Nazaire,* Majesty of the Seas *carries 2767 passengers and has thus the largest capacity of any cruise ship afloat.* (Royal Caribbean Cruise Line).

above, the past decade has seen the emergence and the proliferation of smaller-sized luxury vessels capable of carrying over 100 but less than 500 passengers. Examples of these ships include: Cunard's *Sea Goddess I* and *Sea Goddess II*; Delfin Cruises' *Delfin Caravelle* and *Delfin Clipper*; Renaissance Cruises' *Renaissance I–IV*; and Seabourn Cruise Line's *Seabourn Spirit* and *Seabourn Pride*.

Early in 1992, P&O announced that in April 1995 it would take delivery of the first cruise vessel to be custom-built for the United Kingdom market. Costing £200 million, with a gross tonnage of 67,000 and a passenger capacity of 1975 in 900 cabins, the new vessel will operate primarily out of the United Kingdom and is to be specifically equipped to undertake world cruises. It will have an operating speed of 24kts, just a little more than *Canberra*, which has become a popular vessel on the United Kingdom cruise scene. The new 852ft vessel is being built to meet the demands and growth in the British cruise market, which has expanded at an annual rate of 15 per cent since the mid-1980s.

Final comments pertaining to cruise ship evolution should not overlook potential future projects of ships on the drawing board that even exceed the mega-ships in size. Two possibilities into the future are *Phoenix World City*, at 250,000 tons with the ability to carry 5600 passengers and the smaller 160,000-ton *Ultimate Dream*.

The appeal of cruising

The increasing popularity of cruise holidays is directly related to understanding its value and affordability. As an all-inclusive package, the price of a cruise includes accommodation, meals, daytime activities, night-time parties and entertainment, plus transportation to and from the ship. With the exclusion of beverage service and gratuities, the total cost of the vacation can be computed prior to departure.

It was not many years ago that cruising was perceived as an option for only the very old and very wealthy. This situation has changed; the average cruiser is getting younger. Between 1980 and 1990 the average age of a cruise passenger declined from 58 to 48, and about 30 per cent of all passengers today are less than 30 years old. A false image of cruise passengers is that they are retired persons, with both the time and income to permit an at sea vacation; in fact many of those who cruise have annual incomes in the $25,000 bracket. Mass marketing and the economies of scale provided by large cruise ships has made cruising a viable choice for families, couples and single people.

There clearly are cruises and ships to cater to every whim and pocket. In general, younger age groups take shorter cruises, while more expensive, longer cruises attract an older crowd. Cruise ships may be differentiated based on a price classification or per diem cost per passenger, assuming double occupancy. Three classes of cruises can be distinctly identified:

1. Standard quality, sometimes referred to as 'standard' or 'contemporary', which offers rates of between $175 and $225 per person day (ppd);
2. Premium quality, often called 'intermediate' or 'moderate', at rates from $250 to $275 ppd;
3. Luxury or 'upscale', which costs $300 or more ppd.

In addition to ppd pricing, the duration of the voyage affects the total cost of the cruise. Thus,

One of the leading forces behind the postwar development of the international cruise industry was the USSR. From modest beginnings with just one vessel, its involvement in the cruise market got underway in earnest in the 1960s, and was soon to cover world-wide operations. Many of the earlier vessels also ran on regular line services, but eventually the USSR acquired purpose-built cruise vessels, two later examples of which were Kareliya *(left) and* Gruziya, *both 13,251 grt, carying 504 passengers, and built in Finland in 1975–76. They have been owned throughout by the Black Sea Shipping Co, Odessa, and following the break-up of the USSR were reported as flying the Russian ensign. In this FotoFlite picture they are at the Port of London's Tilbury passenger landing stage in 1982.*

there are cruises that can meet the needs of most customers. Once on board ship, a passenger can partake in the many activities offered aboard or simply relax and soak up the rays of the sun. The meals, three in the dining room, a midnight buffet, morning and afternoon teas, the option to dine at breakfast and lunch in a casual atmosphere on deck, plus twenty-four-hour room service in the cabin, make cruising a gastronomic delight. If special diets are required, for medical or other purposes, most ships will make arrangements to please.

Itineraries and cruise ports

Vessel operating speed, embarkation ports, voyage durations, and the spatial pattern of cruise ports govern the bounds of cruise ship itineraries. The cumulative effect of these factors not only determines itinerary planning, but also sets limits to itinerary options. With the preference replacement of diesel power for propulsion, cruise ships operate at slower speeds than passenger liners which had usually,

In the 1980s and '90s there has been a trend towards sail and sail assisted vessels, not only in cargo carrying vessels, but in the cruise trade also. Built at the van Langerbrugge shipyard at Gent, Belgium, is Star Flyer, *a 2298 grt barquentine-rigged auxiliary passenger ship. Equipped with a Caterpillar diesel engine of 1380 bhp, she is operated by Star Clippers, of Miami, and is owned by White Star Clippers SA, Luxembourg.* Star Flyer, *which has 36,000sq ft of sail, carries 180 passengers on seven- and fourteen-day cruises from St Martin.* (Star Clippers)

although not entirely, favoured steam. This change was encouraged by rising energy prices and a desire to reduce operating costs. Although slower transit speeds may prevent the implementation of certain potential itineraries, the rapid movement of cruise vessels is not as vital as it was, for example, to transatlantic movements. The location of embarkation ports, relative to destination ports, along with vessel speed and the number of days allocated to complete each round-trip voyage also impacts the number of ports that can be visited. The norm in most popular cruising areas, on a seven-day voyage, is three to four different ports of call, while on the growing three- and four-day market only one or two may be visited.

The Caribbean is the most favoured cruising region in the world. A combination of all-year-round mild climate and easy accessibility by air

Often referred to as the flagship of the German fleet is the cruise vessel Europa (33,819 grt), *built at Vegesack in 1981 for Hapag-Lloyd AG. The serried ranks of sundecks aft give a clear indication of one of the principal attractions of cruising.* (Hapag-Lloyd)

transport from the large United States population centres in the east and Midwest provide the perfect conditions for cruise holidays. Physical distance to and within the Caribbean, with the islands in reasonable close proximity to each other and their different attractions and cultures, has led to the growth of Miami and Port Everglades as embarkation ports and their self-awarded titles of the cruise capitals of the world. In the Caribbean, the longest trips between ports are around thirty-six hours, and usually ports of call are only an overnight voyage apart, allowing for cruises of two, three, four, five and seven days.

Cruise ports, based on their operational characteristics, may be classified into three categories – ports of embarkation (sometimes referred to as home ports), ports of call, and all-purpose ports. Ports of embarkation provide facilities for the loading and unloading of cruise passengers and their baggage. They must be in close proximity to other forms of transportation, capable of handling a great amount of people at one time, and able to provide a pleasing environment. Easy transport access to the port from an airport is essential, because many cruise passengers join the cruise ship via scheduled air services as part of an air-sea package. These packages furnish reduced or even free air transportation with the pur-

chase price of a cruise ticket. With the introduction of the 2000 plus capacity cruise vessel, the embarkation and disembarkation a vast number of passengers within a few hours on the same day creates a severe logistical problem that only few ports can accommodate.

Ports of call service cruise ships and their passengers *en route* for usually only a portion of the day, but on occasion a port stay may be longer. These ports usually offer something beyond the convenience of berthing the vessel. Access to an area possessing either a landmark of historical importance or an exotic or foreign culture are prime requirements, in addition to possessing a good climate. A key requisite of the port of call is that the land transport infrastructure, including taxis and buses to take passengers from the ship to inland area of interest, must be adequate. The influx of new, larger vessels to the cruise market will undoubtedly create opportunities for new cruise itineraries, and in turn, new ports of call to whet the appetites of repeat cruisers. However, the mega-ships will also present difficulties to both ports and places with rudimentary transport systems.

All-purpose ports are a hybrid of ports of call and ports of embarkation. These ports embark and disembark cruise passengers in addition to servicing cruise vessels *en route*. Their existence is attributable to the development of the fly-cruise holiday, which allows passengers to join the cruise ship at an overseas port without incurring increased transport costs. They also are established when cruise itineraries involve round-the-world service but individual cruise segments are sold. Although the provision of facilities to process passengers is a necessity, less extensive facilities than for major ports of embarkation are required. These ports frequently have many of the amenities of standard ports of call; their emergence is of relatively recent origin, with the ports of San Juan and Montego Bay, in the Caribbean, functioning in this manner. They also provide expanded services to ports of call which cannot be visited within a weekly voyage from the traditional south Florida embarkation ports.

Cruise ship markets and marketing

Demand for cruise services has grown from one and a half million passengers in 1980 to four million passengers in 1990, representing only a 2 per cent penetration of the specialised leisure holiday market. Even of greater significance is the fact that only about 6 per cent of the United States and Canadian population has ever taken a cruise, and North American clientele compose about 84 per cent of the world cruise market. In addition, the cruise industry, over the past decade, has been the fastest growing segment of the travel industry. Thus, a latent market, with its tremendous growth potential, is the principal rationale for the optimism that currently prevails within the cruise industry. Recent additions of newbuildings and cruise ships on order support this position.

The cruise ship operations market may be viewed from two vantage points – regional berth availability, and market share by company. During the 1987–88 cruise season, available berths (passenger capacity) for Caribbean

cruising (45,145) was almost double its nearest competitor, the Mediterranean/Black Sea (26,314). The Caribbean market, thus recorded over 35 per cent of the world market; followed by the Mediterranean/Black Sea (almost 21 per cent), Alaska (over 12 per cent), Mexico and Panama (over 11 per cent), Australia (slightly under 10 per cent), northern Europe (over 8 per cent), and Hawaii (almost 2 per cent). Figures for the United States market share by cruise line for 1991 revealed that Royal Caribbean captured the largest share with 14.2 per cent with the addition of its mega-ships. Other major operators included: Carnival Cruise Lines (13.0 per cent), Princess Cruises (11.2 per cent), Norwegian Cruise Line (7.6 per cent), Costa Cruises (6.9 per cent), Cunard (5.3 per cent), and Holland America Line (5.2 per cent).

As a result of increasing competition within the cruise industry, as well as the desire to capture a larger share of the total holiday market, cruise companies will have to differentiate their products by niche marketing. Such market segmentation will follow several structures, that are neither exhaustive nor mutually exclusive; these include:

1. A geographical marketing orientation, focusing on the attraction of patronage from a well-defined market region.
2. A theme marketing emphasis, catering for the common interests of passengers; for instance bridge or other card game cruises, mystery-solving cruises, Octoberfest cruises and sports personality cruises.

3. An itinerary marketing approach, providing cruises to distinct overseas marketing areas; for example the Caribbean or Mediterranean or out-of-the-way places infrequently visited by tourists.
4. Time constraint marketing endeavouring to attract clientele for a specific duration, encompassing short cruises of one day to 'nowhere'; three- to four-day excursions; medium cruises spanning seven to fourteen days; and long cruises exceeding more than two weeks.
5. A socio-economic marketing effort directed towards an identifiable section of the population; for example young newly affluent Americans.

Present and future trends in cruise shipping

The modern cruise industry is barely over thirty years old. From a struggling beginning, it has adapted to an ever-changing holiday marketplace. The industry has grown from five hundred thousand passengers in 1970 to over three and a half million in 1990, and projections are that it will serve ten million passengers by the year 2000. Airlines, once the enemy, are now the allies of the cruise industry, transporting passengers to and from the port of embarkation. The cruise industry has now entered a mature economic phase, by becoming more streamlined, through mergers and consolidations. Five major companies, Carnival, Cunard, Kloster, P & O and Royal Caribbean, control the lion's share of the

The shape of the future – the twin-hulled cruise vessel Radisson Diamond *(354 passengers), in 1992 the largest SWATH ever constructed. Built by Finnyards Ltd, Rauma, Finland, the $125m vessel has attracted world-wide attention with its two underwater hulls in which the engines are located. The twin-hull design gives excellent sea-keeping and further stabilisation is provided by four computerised fins. The engine vibration level was found on trials to be one-tenth of that in conventional cruise vessels. Because of the vessel's relatively wide breadth (32m) on 20,400 grt, it was possible in designing the passenger accommodation to combine the best features of large and small cruise ships. The vessel is based at San Juan, Puerto Rico, and will undertake Caribbean cruises for its owners, Diamond Cruise OY, of Helsinki.* (Finnyards OY)

cruise market. Orders for new cruise ships – the mega-ships – involve an ability to carry more than 2500 passengers, and require investment exceeding $200 million each. Undoubtedly the cruise market is dominated by United States demand. Although cruises to the Caribbean continue to remain most popular, several interesting industry-wide trends have emerged in the late 1980s early '90s. These include:

1. The opening up of the Japanese market, and particularly, the potential of southeast Asia as a cruise region.

2. The growth in demand for luxury cruising on small vessels.

3. The vibrant growth of the Alaskan market.

4. The growth in the market for exploration and other speciality cruises, including such non-standard vessels as sailing ships and submarines.

5. The trend toward shorter cruises, especially the three- and four-day markets.

The above trends may erode the move toward further consolidation within the industry but nevertheless, the cruise industry remains optimistic that its wide variety and choice of products will continue to bode well for the future. The question whether or not a revolution or an evolution has occurred in the cruise shipping industry can be answered, based on the historical facts versus measures of technological change, in favour of an evolution, since cruising has been around for a long time.

Bruce E Marti

Typical rail ferries since 1945

Ship	Flag	Built	By	GRT DWT	Length (oa) × breadth × depth × draught Feet–Inches Metres	Route	Engines	Speed	Remarks
FYN	Dmk	1947	Burmeister & Wain, Copenhagen	2,941 830	353–9 × 56–7 × 20–10 × 13–1 107.83 × 17.25 × 6.35 × 4.0	Denmark/Kattegat	2 B&W diesels, 4350bhp; 2 shafts	15kts	260.4m track 30 wagons/ 110 cars, 1200 pass
HELSINGOR	Dmk	1955	Helsingor Skibs, Helsingor	1123 640	262–6 × 42–5 × 17–3 × 11–9 80.02 × 12.93 × 5.26 × 3.58	Denmark/Kattegat	4 B&W diesels, 2100bhp driving 4 generators connected to 2 electric motors each 550shp; 2 shafts	11kts	76.15m track 8 wagons/ 55 cars, 500 pass
ASA-THOR	Dmk	1965	Nakskov Skibs, Nakskov	3544 2240	431–11 × 58–1 × 23–0 × 14–9 131.65 × 17.71 × 7.01 × 4.5	Denmark/Kattegat	2 B&W diesels, 7840bhp; 2 shafts	17kts	412.67m track 40–50 wagons; 12 pass
GEROI SHIPKI	SU	1978	Brod Uljanik, Pula	10,096 12,889	604–4 × 87–10 × 49–11 × 24–3 184.21 × 26.78 × 15.22 × 7.4	Iliychevsk–Varna (Black Sea)	2 Uljanik/B&W diesels, 17,600bhp; 2 shafts	20kts	1650m track 108 × 14.7m wagons
GARIBALDI	Ita	1982	Cant Nav Riuniti, Palermo	5570 4311	479–0 × 63–0 × 25–0 × 18–8 146.01 × 19.21 × 7.62 × 5.7	Southern Italy– Sicily	2 GMT diesels, 12,000bhp; 2 shafts	19kts	80 × 10.6m wagons, 12 pass; 24 TEUs
ARAHURA	NZ	1983	Aalborg Vaerft, Aalborg	7583 2457	486–9 × 67–3 × 38–9 × 18–0 148.37 × 20.5 × 11.82 × 5.5	New Zealand (North Island– South Island)	4 Wartsila diesels, 22,270bhp driving 4 generators connected to 2 electric motors each 4555shp; 2 shafts	19kts	60 wagons; 1085 pass + vehicles
NILS DACKE	Swe	1988	Schichau-Seebeckwerft, Bremerhaven	24,745 8900	581–4 × 87–0 61–9 × 20–0 177.2 × 26.5 × 18.83 × 6.1	Trelleborg– Travemünde	4 MAN/B&W diesels, 20,130bhp; 2 shafts	20kts	910m track 75 wagons, 500 cars (100 trailers), 300 pass
RAILSHIP III	WG	1990	Schichau-Seebeckwerft, Bremerhaven	20,500 10,000	622–4 × 70-11 × 44–0 × 19–0 189.7 × 21.6 × 13.4 × 5.8	Travemünde– Hanko (Finland)	2 Wartsila diesels, 22,150bhp; 2 shafts	19kts	2000m track

Typical ferries in European waters since 1945

Ship	Flag	Built	By	GRT (Passengers)	Length (oa) × breadth × depth × draught Feet–Inches Metres	Route	Engines	Speed	Remarks
English Channel/North Sea									
HALLADALE	UK	1944	A & J Inglis, Glasgow	1572 (400)	301–7 × 3675 × 17–6 × 10–10 *91.91 × 11.14 × 5.33 × 3.29*	Dover–Calais	4 Parsons steam turbines, 6500shp 2 shafts	17.5kts	Converted frigate 1949 – cars
FREE ENTERPRISE II	UK	1965	Werf Gusto, Schiedam	4011 (1000)	354–9 × 60–4 × 31–9 × 13–3 *108.13 × 18.39 × 9.68 × 4.05*	Dover–Calais	2 J & K Smit/MAN diesels, 7700bhp; 2 shafts	19kts	– cars
ST NICHOLAS	UK	1982	Gotaverken Arendal, Gothenburg	17,043 (2100)	488–11 × 91–10 × 52–10 × 20–1 *149.03 × 28.0 × 16.11 × 6.13*	Dover–Calais	4 Wartsila diesels, 26,000bhp; 2 shafts	20.5kts	700 cars
KONINGIN BEATRIX	Ne	1986	Van der Giessen – de Noord, Krimpen	31,189 (2100)	531–0 × 90–7 × 60–9 × 20–4 *161.85 × 27.63 × 18.52 × 6.2*	Harwich–Hook of Holland	4 MAN-B&W diesels, 24,348bhp; 2 shafts	21kts	500 cars
NORSEA	UK	1987	Govan Shipbuilders, Govan	31,785 (1250)	588–7 × 83–2 × 58–9 × 20–3 *179.41 × 25.35 × 17.91 × 6.18*	Hull–Europoort (Rotterdam)	4 Wartsila/Sulzer diesels, 16,100bhp; 2 shafts	18.5kts	850 cars
PRIDE OF CALAIS	UK	1987	Schichau- Unterweser, Vegesack	26,433 (2210)	556–6 × 92–10 × 45–3 × 20–1 *169.63 × 28.3 × 13.8 × 6.12*	Dover–Calais	3 CCM Sulzer diesels, 31,400bhp	22kts	650 cars
OLAU HOLLANDIA	WG	1989	Schichau- Seebeckwerft, Bremerhaven	33,336 (1720)	541–4 × 95–1 × 62–1 × 21–4 *165.0 × 29.0 × 18.93 × 6.5*	Sheerness– Vlissingen	4 Zgoda/Sulzer diesels, 57,600bhp; 2 shafts	21.3kts	575 cars
PRINS FILIP	Bel	1991	Boelwerf SA, Temse	24,000 (1200)	536–1 × 88–7 × — × 30–2 *163.4 × 27.0 × — × 9.2*	Ostend–Dover	4 Jugoturbina/Sulzer diesels, 28,720bhp; 2 shafts	21kts	600 cars
Baltic									
FINNHANSA	Fin	1966	Wartsila, Helsinki	7820 (1400)	441–0 × 65–11 × 36–9 × 18–10 *134.42 × 20.1 × 11.21 × 5.74*	Helsinki–Lübeck	2 Wartsila/Sulzer diesels, 14,000bhp; 2 shafts	20kts	
VIKING 5	Fin	1974	Jos L Meyer, Papenburg	5286 (1200)	386–5 × 56–7 × 19–8 × 15–5 *117.79 × 17.25 × 6.0 × 4.7*	Sweden–Finland	2 Bolnes diesels, 11,000bhp; 2 shafts	19.5kts	About 250 cars
FINNJET	Fin	1977	Wartsila, Helsinki	25,042 (1790)	698–2 × 80–2 × 48–7 × 22–0 *212.81 × 24.44 × 14.81 × 6.7*	Helsinki– Travemünde	2 Pratt & Whitney gas turbines, 75,000shp and 2 Wartsila diesels, 15,500bhp; 2 shafts	30.5kts	374 cars
SVEA	Swe	1985	Wartsila, Helsinki	33,829 (2000)	551–3 × 90–8 × 47–5 × 21–4 *168.03 × 27.64 × 14.46 × 6.51*	Sweden–Finland	4 Wartsila/Pielstick diesels, 35,890bhp; 2 shafts	22kts	350 cars
BIRKA PRINCESS	Fin	1986	Valmet OY, Helsinki	21,484 (1500)	469–0 × 82–6 × 45–3 × 18–4 *142,95 × 25.15 × 13.8 × 5.6*	Sweden–Finland	4 Wartsila diesels, 23,930bhp; 2 shafts	18kts	80 cars
SILJA SERENADE	Fin	1991	Masa Yards, Turku	58,376 (2656)	666–1 × 104–9 × 68–11 × 23–4 *203.03 × 31.93 × 21.0 × 7.12*	Sweden–Finland	4 Wartsila diesels, 44,300bhp; 2 shafts	21kts	450 cars

Typical cruise vessels 1889–1992

Ship	Flag	Built	By	GRT (Passengers)	Length (oa) × breadth × depth × draught Feet–Inches Metres	Cruising area(s) etc	Engines	Speed
CHIMBORAZO	UK	1871	John Elder, Glasgow	3847 (164)[1]	384–0(bp) × 41–4 × 35–4 × – 117.04 × 12.59 × 10.76 × –	Norwegian fjords 1889	1 John Elder compound steam engine, 550ihp; 1 shaft	13kts
PRINZESSIN VICTORIA LUISE	Ger	1900	Blohm & Voss, Hamburg	4419 (200)	407–6(bp) × 47–2 × 27–0 × 20–1 135.94 × 14.33 × 9.14 × 6.12	First purpose-built cruise vessel	2 sets Blohm & Voss quadruple expansion steam engines, 3600ihp; 2 shafts	15kts
ARANDORA STAR	UK	1927	Cammell Laird, Birkenhead	15,501 (400)	535–0 × 68–3 × 42–6 × 28–1 163.07 × 20.81 × 12.95 × 8.56	Converted from cargo/ passenger 1929	4 Cammell Laird steam turbines, 2078nhp; 2 shafts	16kts
CARONIA	UK	1948	John Brown, Clydebank	34,183 (580)[2]	715–0 × 91–5 × 53–3 × 31–7 217.93 × 27.87 × 16.23 × 9.62	Atlantic service and cruising	6 John Brown steam turbines, 35,000shp; 2 shafts	22kts
CANBERRA	UK	1961	Harland & Wolff, Belfast	44,807 (1702)	818–6 × 102–6 × 41–6 × 32–9 249.49 × 31.25 × 12.65 × 9.99	World-wide	2 AEI steam turbines, 88,200shp driving 2 generators each 32,200kW connected to 2 electric motors 42,500shp; 2 shafts	27.5kts
MARDI GRAS	Pan	1961	Vickers-Armstrong, Newcastle	18,261 (1240)	643–6 × 86–10 × 48–0 × 29–0 198.13 × 26.45 × 14.64 × 8.84	Converted from passenger liner *Empress of Canada* 1972	6 Vickers steam turbines, 30,000shp; 2 shafts	20kts
SUN VIKING	Nor	1972	Wartsila, Helsinki	18,559 (880)	563–3 × 78–10 × 46–7 × 20–8 171.69 × 24.03 × 14.2 × 6.3	Caribbean	4 Wartsila/Sulzer diesels, 18,000bhp; 2 shafts	21kts
ROYAL PRINCESS	UK	1984	Wartsila, Helsinki	44,348 (1260)	757–6 × 96–6 × 63–5 × 26–4 230.89 × 29.42 × 19.33 × 8.02	Caribbean	4 Wartsila/Pielstick diesels, 23,200bhp; 2 shafts	20kts
ECSTASY	Lib	1991	Masa Yards, Helsinki	70,367 (2634)	855–0 × 103–6 × 44–5 × 25–10 260.6 × 31.53 × 13.52 × 7.85	Caribbean	6 Wartsila/Sulzer diesels, total 57,425bhp driving 4 generators connected to 2 electric motors each 19,033shp; 2 shafts	18kts
MONARCH OF THE SEAS	Nor	1991	Ch de l'Atlantique, St Nazaire	73,937 (2766)	880–4 × 105–10 × 31–10 × 24–9 268.32 × 32.25 × 9.7 × 7.55	Caribbean	4 Alsthom–Atlantique/ Pielstick diesels, 27,837bhp; 2 shafts	21.25kts
RADISSON DIAMOND	Fin	1992	Finnyards, Rauma	18,400 (354)	420–0 × 103–0 × – × 26–0 128.01 × 31.39 × – × 7.92	Caribbean; largest twin-hulled vessel	– 2 shafts	12.5kts

Notes:
[1] Normal line service 72 1st, 92 2nd and 265 3rd class passengers.
[2] Normal line service 580 1st and 350 3rd class passengers.

6

Short-Sea and Coastal Shipping

COASTAL shipping might best be described, quite literally, as any shipping which occurs around a coastline. This does not imply limits on distance or vessel size and while such traffic may well be domestic for one country, especially an island state such as Britain, it is not necessarily so. Short-sea shipping is even less clearly defined. It can be taken to mean shipping within 'seas' as distinct from oceans, or between islands or groups of islands which are not separated by great distances. A recent study of European short-sea trade adopted an arbitrary one-way route of less than 1500 miles as a convenient guideline.

Many governments impose more precise definitions on short-sea trading and these differ from country to country. The purpose of establishing boundaries is to set 'safe' levels of operating standards on ships in the defined regions. For example, the United Kingdom Merchant Shipping Regulations of 1985 (Regulation 2(1), Schedule 2) defined the requirements for vessels trading in a 'limited' zone and 'extended European waters'. Short-sea may be taken to include these areas combined although some might question the inclusion of the area southwards from Cape St Vincent to Dakar in West Africa.

Coastal and short-sea vessels

If there are problems in providing a satisfactory definition of short-sea trading areas defining the vessels employed in these trades is even more difficult. It has been suggested that ships in this sector can be distinguished from deep-sea shipping 'because of their somewhat different functions and because of the different economic environments in which they normally operate'.[1] However, as the following survey will show, the distinction is often far from clear and there exists a wide array of designs, some of which are unique to coastal and short-sea trades but many of which could equally well operate, and often do, in deep-sea trades.

Ships working specifically in European coastal and short-sea trades are usually classified into groups according to their gross registered tonnage (grt). The group, or 'paragraph' as it is commonly called, determines the minimum manning and safety requirements to which vessels in each group must adhere – minimum crew size, crew qualifications, ship freeboard, type of navigation and safety equipment. These requirements will relate to the area in which the vessel will operate. Different paragraphs have been adopted by different nations, each with its own ideas about standards of safety. The reservation of domestic trade for national flag ships, known as cabotage, serves to emphasise regional paragraph characteristics.

Provided that they meet the requirements of the regulatory authority, the maximum size ships operating in coastal and short-sea trades will be determined mainly by the nature of the trades concerned and by the physical constraints imposed by seaways and ports rather than legal restrictions. For example, large deep-sea vessels of 60,000 dwt carrying capacity have recently been used to carry granite chips from western Scotland to the Thames and over the shorter distance to Liverpool.

With the great geographical diversity of the world's coastlines and archipelago regions and the peculiarities of local trades it is hardly surprising that there is a matching variety of vessel types employed. For example, the coastal junks of China and the island trading vessels of Indonesia are greatly varied in style and size. The vessels operating on United States domestic trades, including Alaska and Hawaii are hardly different from trans-oceanic vessels and the United Kingdom east coast trade in coal produced the distinctive 'flatties' or 'flat iron' colliers. These vessels, usually about 2900 dwt had squat superstructures and collapsible masts,

---

1. A D Couper, *The Geography of Sea Transport* (Hutchinson, 1972).

A familiar sight throughout northwest Europe before the 1980s but less so now with the emergence of low profile vessels, is the traditional two hatch/single hold motor coaster of which Mary Coast *is typical. Built in Appingedam, Netherlands, in 1961, the vessel changed hands several times before being purchased by D J Goubert Shipping Ltd, of Guernsey. At 386 grt and with a maximum hold capacity of 783cu m, Mary Coast had two wooden hatches of 11.5m × 4.5m and a single hold 29.9m in length. Her 220 bhp diesel engine gave a speed of 8.75kts. (FotoFlite)*

The short-sea trader Speciality was built in 1951 for Britain's largest coastal/short sea operator F T Everard & Sons Ltd. Speciality, was of 1570 grt and 1850 dwt, and is representative of the medium-sized short sea trader of the 1950s. Built at Grangemouth, she was equipped with a Newbury diesel and had a service speed of 10kts. In postwar years, apart from shipowning, Everard has owned within its group shipbuilders and repairers, road haulage, engine makers, and other industries. (F T Everard & Sons)

and sometimes funnels, to allow navigation under Thames bridges to riverside electricity generating stations and gas works. They had a shallow draught which also allowed them to seek shelter in small ports when sea conditions were too rough. Some of these colliers were self trimming, some had cargo handling gear and others did not but in their day they were some of the 'most advanced vessels on the coast'.[2]

Mainly with reference to northwest European trades, the following analysis will highlight key developments in the design of coastal and short-sea vessels since the 1950s and explain the background to such developments.

The 1950s

The ending of the Second World War and the subsequent rebuilding programmes in Europe

Mergers and buyouts will give future historians much to write about, this being as true of the coastal shipping industry as any other sector. In the 1970s, Booker Bros of Liverpool, then controllers of coaster owner S William Coe & Co, bought the old-established family concern Metcalf Motor Coasters Ltd, London, together with a fleet of coastal tankers and general cargo vessels. These companies were later merged within the Booker group to become Coe, Metcalf Shipping Ltd, operationally headquartered in Liverpool. In 1984 when Booker, then Booker McConnell plc, was winding-up its shipowning interests, the Coe, Metcalf entity and its fleet was sold to Barrow-in-Furness owner James Fisher & Sons PLC, under whose banner the fleet still operates. One vessel which has been through all these changes is the motor tanker Frank M (1819 dwt), built by Burntisland Shipbuilding Co in 1965. (Alan Sparrow)

and other regions affected by hostilities sparked off one of the greatest economic booms in recent history. The shipping industry was a main beneficiary with the rebuilding of national fleets but also with transporting the materials needed in first the rehabilitation and later the expansion of infrastructure and industry.

During the war many vessels had been lost, those that survived had a backlog of maintenance and lack of new construction meant an ageing fleet. In the immediate postwar period

there were still a number of steam vessels of dated design and sailing schooners and barges were still a relatively common sight at some ports. John Masefield's 'Dirty British coaster with a salt-caked smoke stack' was still around. Most vessels operating in coastal trades were general cargo, single-deck ships, sometimes divided into a number of holds. However, during the 1950s the shelter-deck ship became more fashionable – this was able to provide the ship owner with a higher cubic capacity in the same gross tonnage but the availability of the second deck was increasingly useful for a growing diversity of cargoes. Netherlands and German shipowners were to the fore in introducing the shelter-deckers.[3]

Typically, the vessels of the time had a well flared shape with high forecastle and superstructure (either midships or aft), fairly high

2. *Ibid*, p194.

3. S Ovrebo, *Short-Sea and Coastal Tramp Shipping in Europe* (Institute for Shipping Research, Bergen, 1969).

funnels (especially the steamers) and fixed masts usually with cargo handling derricks. They were mostly very seaworthy craft, rarely held up by bad weather but with considerable top hamper (superstructure, masts) could be less stable when light particularly if they did not have adequate ballasting. The average size of the vessels in the General Steam Navigation Company's fleet, then one of the largest coastal and short-sea operators, was in 1950 about 950 grt with a range from 276 to 2385 grt. Many of the vessels operating only in coastal trades were much smaller. These vessels could serve ports both large and small and the smaller of them could penetrate to some inland ports. They carried the whole range of cargoes – timber, forest products, steel, bagged commodities and vehicles – and were able to handle the cargo themselves when shore facilities were not available.

With the economic boom many of the older prewar vessels were replaced by more efficient ships. There was an increased need for materials to be delivered in larger parcel sizes as economies of scale came to dominate the thinking of industrialists and ship owners. There was a trend towards industrial relocation in larger units with large areas of land for plant and stockpiles and this was to gather momentum in the 1960s and 1970s. There was the emergence of what became known as Maritime Industrial Development Areas (MIDAs) in which large scale basic industries (oil refining, petrochemicals, iron and steel, power generation) were associated with dedicated port facilities. Rotterdam, Antwerp, Dunkirk, Marseilles, and possibly less dramatically the estuaries of the Tees, Humber, Thames and Severn in Britain became concentrations of such port-related industries.

The 1960s

The 1960s saw new opportunities develop for coastal and short-sea shipping and good freight rates encouraged the replacement of older vessels with higher capacity, more efficient tonnage and marine architects produced designs which maximised the revenue earning carrying capacity, the deadweight tonnage (dwt), on dimensions (grt) which maintained small ship characteristics and access to smaller ports. The

A typical European-built motor coaster of the 1960s was Anton Held, *named after its owner, of Haren/Ems, Germany. Delivered in 1967 from the Cassens shipyard at Emden with a gross tonnage of 299.96 and deadweight of 468,* Anton Held *was often used in timber trades, having a very useful 733.5cu m capacity.*

shelter-deck ship characterised this trend. Adoption of more efficient designs by some owners clearly put pressure on others but not all could afford to follow the trend. It is important to note that at this time there were many one-ship, family companies in which the vessels often served as the family home and it followed that most of the vessels were 'one-off' buildings with a great variety of size and design reflecting the requirements of individual owners. Small companies found it more difficult to finance newbuildings and the Swedish coastal fleet, for example, was virtually eliminated by a combination of high operating costs, fierce competition and unattractive or inadequate ship financing schemes. Even the small, wooden motor vessels which worked the timber trade to Denmark all but disappeared by the late 1960s.

Increasing ship size in deep-sea trades favoured concentration of cargo handing at a smaller number of ports readily able to accommodate the larger vessels with feeder services to smaller coastal and inland ports. This clearly favoured short-sea shipping and despite the growing competition from road and rail transport, shipping was still the cheapest mode for most bulk cargoes (china clay, oil products, aggregates, grain) and also some general cargo especially when in large quantities and in standardised form (semi-bulk cargoes such as timber, forest products and steel). Shipping was most competitive where it could capitalise on economies of scale not available to the land transport modes.

During the early 1960s there was an associated increase in ship deadweight and growing efficiency in cargo handling with more cargo stacked on wooden pallets and simple, efficient ship cranes in place of the more complex derricks for cargo handling. By the mid-1960s the postwar boom had peaked, industrial growth slowed down, freight rates fell, labour costs were rising and in some trades there was excess

tonnage. It became critical for the ship owner to reduce his costs to the minimum.

Reducing crew costs became a main strategy and owners found it cost effective to put more money into the ships – 'capital has been substituted for labour where this is possible'.[4] But this had to be achieved within the framework of the regulatory paragraphs for particular trades and the skill of the marine architect was required to produce ships that would carry more but on dimensions which would not take them into a higher cost paragraph. Shipowners ordered vessels as close to the paragraph ceiling as possible and hence the large number of vessels at 499 grt. It has been suggested that the freight rate differential between a 1599 grt and 1600 grt vessel could be as high as 20 per cent as a consequence of the additional costs for crewing and meeting other regulatory requirements.[5] As far as possible water and air draughts were not increased so that access to smaller ports was not limited and capacity was increased by greater lengths and beams.

In the 1960s many small ships were still being built but the general design was changing. Single, box-type holds became common, the vessels had less flare to their shape, the general profile was 'flatter' even when a raised forecastle and superstructure remained a feature and steel hatch covers replaced the traditional hatch boards and canvas cover. A vessel such as *Anton Held* (built 1967, 299 grt) had a traditional hull form but a single hold and an air draught with mast lowered of only 4.25m which allowed the vessel to trade inland to Dortmund and Bethune. Such a vessel was probably less seaworthy than one of traditional design but was more flexible and lower cost in use.

---

4. *Ibid*, pp36–7.

5. Z De Jong and R. Tollenaar, *European Coastal Fleets* (Netherlands Maritime Research Institute, Rotterdam, 1985), p11.

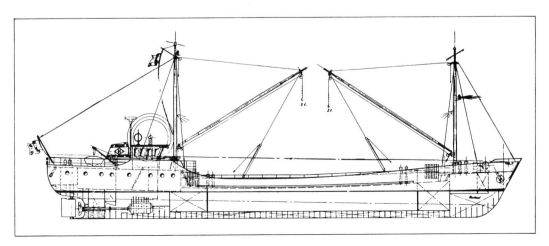

The last half of the 1960s saw revolutionary developments in cargo-handling technology including the advent of containerisation and rapid growth in roll-on/roll-off traffic. These changes were to affect deep-sea and short-sea trades alike. The nature of the trade was also changing. Although bulk cargoes still predominated the movement of general cargo gained in significance. Much of this was high value manufactured goods which was suited to container and roro methods. In Europe, trade between the partners in the Economic Community was growing very rapidly and Britain's trade was increasingly with its European neighbours and less with its colonial possessions and dominions. Between 1969 and 1986 United Kingdom deep-sea trade dropped from 51.7 to 30.9 per cent of the total while short-sea trade rose from 48.3 to 69.1 per cent. The short-sea sector was becoming increasingly important as direct trade between European neighbours flourished and as transshipment resulted in feeder movements.

Tankers apart, the coastal and short-sea vessels of the early 1960s, whether operating 'liner' (fixed port services) or on a tramping basis were essentially general purpose carriers able to take the great variety of commodities which characterised short-sea trades. As time went on even these general purpose vessels were to change dramatically in size and design and a variety of completely new cargo-carrying technologies were introduced.

General purpose vessels

Many ships were designed or modified to carry containers, roll-on/roll-off traffic, refrigerated cargoes (either in containers or in trailers) and palletised goods. However, costs were still ris-

---

6. Ovrebo, *op cit*, p17.

7. *Ibid*, p8.

8. *Ibid*, p16.

9. *Ibid*, p30.

ing, freight rates remained low and competition from road and rail transport increased. Many vessels were reaching the end of their operational lives with insurance and maintenance costs eating into profits. Replacement ships needed to be more efficient and with lower operational costs and a number of governments provided incentives in the form of tax reductions or building subsidies. This led to over-capacity and protectionist policies of cabotage served to limit access to vessels of non nationals.

Many ships became more specialised being 'particularly constructed to transport and handle one single commodity or group of commodities with particular efficiency, both with respect to cargo quantity and quality'.[6] As a consequence of the introduction of more specialised vessels the general purpose shelter-decker became less popular in short-sea trades. As with all such changes there was something of a transition period as the older designs were phased out and the new designs became dominant. Thus, as shelter-deckers declined they were replaced with vessels able to carry efficiently a mix of cargoes. A late example of this was *Dangeld* of 1969, a 932 dwt vessel with two large holds, refrigerated capacity and side doors to facilitate the handling of pallets by fork-lift trucks – a combination well suited to the Whitstable-Esbjerg service operated by Rochester shipowners Crescent Shipping.

The use of side doors and fork lift trucks was also becoming popular in the forest product trades especially in paper pulp, kraft liner and newsprint from Scandinavian countries – a roll-on stowage method sometimes called 'sto-ro'. As container shipping gained in popularity so many purpose-built container vessels were introduced into short-sea trades often operating with ferry-type regularity between fixed ports. An example would be the Parkestone Quay, Harwich-Zeebrugge container link started in 1966.

In 1966, the bulk of the United Kingdom coasting and short-sea vessels were in the 500–

1500 grt range but with a few as large as 5000 grt and as many as 126 below 500 grt.[7] Between them, Belgium, Finland, France, Portugal and Spain had only 300 short-sea vessels whereas West Germany and the Netherlands had 608 and 593 paragraphers of less than 500 grt and a further 484 and 310 non-paragraphers below that limit.[8] Not surprisingly, these two countries were also the main builders of smaller vessels and the 'Dutch' or 'Groningen' vessels became a generic type. It could be shown that not only was the average size of newbuildings increasing but that within each smaller size group the average tonnage was tending towards the typical paragraph size limits eg, 199 grt, 299 grt, and 499 grt. This reflected the ship owners attempt to get the most out of the particular paragraph size.

In Britain during the 1960s many smaller coal-fired electricity generating stations closed, there was concentration on much larger plant on estuarine sites, and all the coal ('town') gas works were closed. There was a great reduction in the coastal coal trade and the dry cargo fleet was halved to 400,000 grt. This, together with increasing imports of cheap American and Australian coal, usually via mainland European ports, led to the use of much larger 'colliers' and the demise of the 'flatties'. In the coal trades vessels of 7000 dwt and above became common (eg 12,000 dwt vessels from northeast England to the Thames) and this was because of the nature of the trade, the commodity and the voyage characteristics rather than paragraphing considerations. The coal was needed in large quantities, it was easily handled and economies of scale could be achieved by using larger vessels and without greatly increasing port time costs. The effect of distance on size was also apparent with Polish coal transported to Denmark in vessels of about 4000 dwt and to western Europe in 8000-tonners.[9]

Another possible advantage of using larger vessels is that they can be transferred to deep-sea trades if demand and freight rates in short-

The merchant fleet of the Soviet Union expanded quite dramatically in the 1950s, '60s and '70s and numerous vessels were part of large series production. The 1970-built Krasnoborsk *(2723 grt) was one of twenety-nine similar vessels of the Bereznik class, in which there were minor variations.* Krasnoborsk *was built by Hollming, at Rauma, Finland, and was highly suited to the Baltic timber trade and is pictured here with such a cargo from Finland. As is common with most Soviet vessels her hull is ice-strengthened. Her cargo handling gear consists of eight 5-ton derricks and cargo capacity is 4785cu m. (L Schofield)*

British east coast colliers were affected by the change to North Sea gas and the conversion of some power stations to oil fuel, whereupon the demand for coal rapidly declined, as did the collier fleet. Bulk carriers suitable for coal were introduced, gradually became larger, until in the mid 1980s, Sir Charles Parsons (and two sister-ships) were introduced. These 'giants', at 22,530 dwt, were built for Bishopsgate Colliers Ltd, and service the coal-fired power stations of National Power. (Nigel Cutts)

sea trades should fall off. This serves to blur the distinction between short- and deep-sea vessels.

By 1970 the single decker 'workhorse' of short-sea bulk tramp trades had an average of 1500 dwt tonnes, about twice the size of the same vessels ten years earlier. Size continued to grow and by the early 1980s newbuildings were close to the 1599 grt limit thereby increasing the dwt to about 3000 tonnes.[10] The rise of specialised vessels has meant that fewer multi-deck and shelter-deck vessels have been built and the total in operation has declined.

The European short-sea fleet under 1600 grt has remained at about 9.3 million tonnes but this conceals increases in the fleets of countries such as Greece, Cyprus and the former Soviet Union and decreases under the British and German flags. In fact, to reduce operating costs many West German vessels were re-registered under the Cyprus flag and some British owners are now 'flagging out' to the Bahamas and other flags. So great were the pressures on the short-sea operators that they have pressed for relaxation of the paragraph requirements to reduce costs.

In 1968 Norway and West Germany allowed 1600 grt vessels to operate on coastal routes under the same rules as smaller vessels and in 1970 the Netherlands introduced new paragraphs based on length and 246ft in particular, with any vessel under the length operating on

coastal routes with the same manning levels irrespective of gross tonnage.[11] This effectively allowed larger vessels to ply coastal trades without the cost penalties that would otherwise have applied. During the 1970s Spain, West Germany and the Netherlands introduced further relaxations in paragraphing with the result that vessels of 3000–6000 grt could be found in some short-sea trades. This trend was assisted by advances in engineering, design and equipment reliability which allowed un-manned engine-rooms, higher levels of automation and easier navigation.

Naval architects also continued to produce designs in which ever higher deadweight was achieved against gross tonnage. There was a

resultant decline in the number of smaller paragraphers, especially 499 grt, and an increase in the number at 1599 grt and what have been called the 'mini-bulkers' came to dominate in short-sea trades. This was reflected in port statistics. For example, at the small port of Mistley on the Stour river inland from Harwich, the average shipment per vessel rose from 141 tonnes in 1967 to 218 tonnes in 1975, 540 tonnes in 1980 and to 980 tonnes in 1986. Similarly, at the port of Perth on the Tay, the average shipments rose from 610 tonnes in 1979–80 to 1022 tonnes in 1986–7.

The new designs also changed dramatically the relationship between gross tonnage, as an influence on operating costs, and deadweight, a measure of earning potential. In the 1950s and 1960s the gross/deadweight tonnage ratio was usually in the order of 1:1.1–1.4 but by the late 1980s, when the whole basis of tonnage measurement was changed for newbuildings, ratios

10. De Jong and Tollenaar, op cit, p10.

11. D Tinsley, Short-Sea Bulk Carriers, (Fairplay, 1984).

The mini-bulker Sea Avon (1102 grt) discharging at the London terminal of her owners Freight Express-Seacon Ltd. Sea Avon was built in 1977 at Tokushima, Japan, and has capacity for 2545cu m of bulk cargo. She has one hold 43.9m in length, and one hatch measuring 40.5m × 10.3m. (D Hilling)

of 1:2.25 and exceptionally 1:3.9 could be found. In Britain the family firm of F T Everard & Sons Ltd was in the forefront of the paragraph movement. In 1977–8 they introduced *Speciality* and *Stability* which on 1599 grt had a deadweight of 4554 (a ratio of 1:2.84) and in 1984–5 they introduced the *Selectivity* class of 799 grt and 2415 dwt (a ratio of 1:3.0).

The end of the 1970s and early 1980s saw continued over-supply of short-sea tonnage and this grew worse as economic depression deepened. In West Germany and Denmark, tax incentives to encourage newbuildings were abandoned and British owners, without any such tax advantages, were hard-pressed to replace tonnage – that some, like Everard did so, was a measure of their high level of managerial ability. British operators' costs were also rising in relation to those of West Germany and the Netherlands. Not surprisingly, the British fleet was ageing in comparison with its competitors especially in the larger size ranges.

In order to gain maximum cargo carrying space in most of the newbuildings the engine-rooms are compact and placed well aft – the use of 'rudder propellers' of the Schottel type has assisted in this. The box hull and hold is now almost universal but does not always make for attractive looking vessels.

The river-sea ships

As ships increase in size so the number of ports that they can use will decrease as smaller coastal ports and inland ports become inaccessible to them. It was to counteract this trend that

12. *Ibid.*
13. *Ibid*, p41.

shipowners started to introduce vessels which had full sea-going capability but dimensions, especially in respect of water and air draught, which did not exclude them from smaller ports. Such vessels were in effect refinements of the mini-bulker type and the generic name now used for them is low-profile or river-sea ship. In the 1960s the Soviet Union led in the introduction of such dual-capability vessels which allowed the integration of improved navigation on inland waterways such as the Volga with short-sea hauls. As time went on river-sea ships became a common sight on the Rhine, Seine, Rhone, and many of western Europe's larger waterways and they allow inland ports such as Basle, Duisburg, Liege, Paris, Brussels, and Gainsborough and Selby in the United Kingdom to provide direct links with overseas trading areas. A high proportion of the vessels serving smaller coastal ports such as Teignmouth or the Cornish china clay ports are now of the river-sea type.

In the early 1980s most river-sea ships were in the 1500–1700 dwt range which was considered the optimum for such ships.[12] However, others have since been built to larger dimensions which may restrict their access to smaller ports, coastal or inland, but does allow them to compete more effectively on a wider range of short-sea and even deep-sea routes. For example, Seacon has a number of ships of between 2700 and 2900 dwt, the largest still able to reach as far inland as Duisburg on the Rhine. The paragraph changes allow such vessels to sail with a crew of five or six.

The river-sea ship concept has been described as 'an open-ship . . . of a single box-like, obstruction-free hold and maximum-width hatchway, and with restricted draught above and below the waterline'.[13] The box

hold allows easy handling of a great variety of cargoes – grain, ores, coal, fertiliser, scrap, steel, bagged goods, forest products and they are often dimensioned to take containers in the hold and on the hatch covers, and provide great operational flexibility. These craft are invariably gearless and dependent on shore cargo-handling equipment.

Another feature of this type of vessel is the ability to 'take the ground' at tidal berths which, with the fast handling of cargo from the box hold often allows them to depart on the tide after they arrive. Key builders of such ships in Britain include Cochrane of Selby (builders of, for example, *Stridence* and *Turbulence* in 1983) and Yorkshire Dry Dock of Hull (for example *Hoo Venture* for John I Jacobs PLC, chartered to R Lapthorn of Rochester, and *Hoo Creek*). On the Continent some of the main yards include Hermann Sürken (many of whose ships have retractable wheel houses), J J Sietas and Hugo Peters all of West Germany, Nordsjovaerft of Denmark, and Ferus Smit and Bijlsma in the Netherlands.

In 1972, two ships, *Auberg* and *Osenburg* (488 grt) were built at the Danube river Tito yard in Belgrade for West German owners. These ships were early examples in which the profile was lowered by retracting the wheelhouse hydraulically, in this case by a scissor lift mechanism. Together with Cochrane of Selby, the Tito yard illustrates the fact that smaller, inland yards could participate in the construction of such ships. In 1973 *Cargo Liner I* was built at the Kramer & Booy yard at Kootstertille in northern Holland; her hydraulically retractable bridge reducing her air draught to 4.5m. This device has now become commonplace and gives the ships maximum flexibility in serving a wide range of inland and coastal ports.

Well known in river-sea ship trades are companies such as Seacon, which in 1973 merged with Freight Express and developed a range of services but with specialisation on steel trades out of the Ruhr; Rhein-Maas und See (RMS), of Duisburg, Germany, which in the 1960s formed a partnership with Paal Wilson,

The unusual and unattractive lines of Ladoga-106, *built for Northwestern River Shipping Co, now of Russia, in 1989, are seemingly a successful formula as a large number of these vessels, going back to* Ladoga-1 *in 1972, have been constructed in Finnish shipyards, for service throughout northwest Europe. Rauma-Repola, Finland, produced this vessel and several sister-ships of 1835 grt with a total cargo capacity of 3040cu m. The upper deck hatch covers are hydraulically-operated and are strengthened for the carriage of containers.*
(Rauma Yards)

The low air-draught short-sea trader Sea Este, *built by J J Sietas KG Schiffswerft, Hamburg, in 1982 for Heinrich Hauschildt, West Germany. The wheelhouse and masts can be lowered enabling the vessel to navigate under bridges on inland waterways and canals. Low air draught vessels are now commonplace in northwest Europe, with the majority in German, Netherlands, UK and Danish fleets.* (Seacon)

Norway, to link Rhine ports with Norway but has since expanded to become one of the largest operators and managers of river-sea tonnage. Union Transport which in 1973 turned from chartering to owning river-sea ships and Pohl & Co, formed in 1974 and originally largely concerned with shipping Scandinavian forest products to waterside inland locations in the rest of Europe. A recent study of river-sea ships lists nearly six hundred such vessels and this maritime technology comes closest to providing the links and integration which a Single Market will require after 1992.[14]

In the 1980s and '90s a large number of roro ships, many of over 10,000 grt, have entered service on routes in northwest Europe and Scandinavia. Typical of these is Solano, *owned by a subsidiary of leading Finnish shipowner Oy Henry Nielsen AB, Helsinki. Built at Rauma in 1984,* Solano *(8996 grt), carries roro and pallet cargo and particularly paper products. Her Wartsila oil engines of 7750 bhp give a service speed of 16kts.* (Nigel Cutts)

Fleet development

The contribution of the different ship types to national fleets varies significantly. For example, in 1984 West Germany had 56 per cent of the European fleet of vessels in the 101–499 grt range amounting to some 1300 ships, mainly single deckers and involved widely in the trades of other countries, eg United Kingdom trade which is open to all comers. West Germany also controlled about 50 per cent of the vessels in the 500–999 grt range, 1000 grt being a main paragraph of the German regulations. Most of these were also single deckers.

The Netherlands has a large number of ships between 500 and 1600 grt, again most of them

14. M Heinemann and C Cheetham, *Modern Rhine-Sea Ships* (Fairplay, 1987, revised 1990).

Arrangement plans of low air-draught vessels produced by German shipbuilder Hermann Surken, of Papenburg. Typical of the general design, hundreds of which have been produced by shipbuilders in northwest Europe, the vessel has transom stern, bulbous bow, and single hold which can be completely opened by means of folding hatches. The Surken type is 499 grt, 1555 dwt, and has a length of 74.9m, and a maximum cargo capacity of 2351cu m. (Hermann Surken)

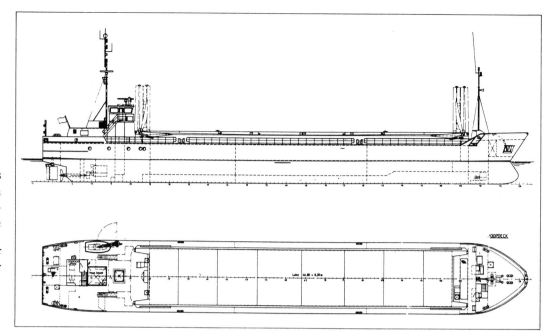

are single deckers,[15] and this reflects changes in 1982 whereby gross tonnage replaced length as the main determinant of paragraphs and allowed the building of larger, more competitive ships for short-sea trades. Another characteristic of the Dutch fleet is the small number of specialised ships – this reflects the policy of Netherlands owners and agents who act as exclusive brokers for their vessels and operate them largely in the 'tramp' rather than the 'liner' trades in which the more capital intensive and more specialised ships find their niche. However, this does not necessarily mean that all their contracts are short term and owner-shipper relationships often develop and lead to longer-term contracts, sometimes as long as six years.

West Germany in contrast showed more enthusiasm for specialised ships for container, roll-on/roll-off and refrigerated traffic. In 1983 RMS introduced medium air draught roro ships to link Duisburg, London, Boston (Lincolnshire) and Goole. The initial ship, *Laila*, was 997 grt with 2352 dwt on a length of 300ft, beam of 44ft, water draught of 15ft and air draught of 34ft and she was followed by several others of similar dimensions (eg *Rolf Buck*, *Linda Buck* and *Anke S*).

15. De Jong and Tollenaar, *op cit.*

16. *Ibid.*

Denmark has one of the youngest fleets of vessels in the 500–1599 grt range with only 15 per cent over ten years of age in 1984[16] and about 75 per cent of the vessels being shelter and multi-deck type. This reflects the much greater involvement of Danish owners in trades with a more international, even non-European flavour. Ships of 1600–3000 grt belong mainly to eastern and southern European countries. The former Soviet Union does not have paragraph rulings comparable with western European countries and this means that they are able to operate ships of 3000 grt with a 3500 dwt – in western Europe a ship of this deadweight capacity would be of 1600 grt or less.

Over 80 per cent of western European new-buildings are in the 1600 grt plus range and most are of the mini-bulker or low-profile type. However, these are often, especially at the lower end of the size range, capable of serving smaller ports with restricted draughts but also able to move out into deep-sea trades as demand requires. An example of such a vessel was North British Maritime's *Norbrit Faith*. Another significant change has been away from the one-off designs which characterised much of the building in the 1960s and an increasing emphasis on 'series' building of both mini-bulkers and low-profile ships. Greater standardisation clearly reduces construction costs and well known series ships are the Rauma (Finland) yard 'Ladoga' ships for Russian owners, the Damen (Gorinchem) 996 grt 'Combi' coasters and Yorkshire Dry Dock's 1400 dwt 'Yorkshire' coaster.

While standardisation reduces construction costs it is sometimes necessary to design vessels for particular routes or commodities. For example, an improved Saimaa Canal was opened in 1968 providing access to southeast Finland through the Russian port of Vyborg. This is an important timber producing area and vessels are designed to transit the locks which are 82m × 11.8m × 4.2m (269ft × 38ft × 13ft). Access to the Lake Vanern timber producing area of southern Sweden is by way of the Trollhätten Canal (87m × 12.5m × 4.6m). In 1989 the 2150 dwt hybrid carriers *Shuttle Goteborg* and *Shuttle*

The mini-bulker Norbrit Faith, *owned by North British Shipping Ltd, Hull, and built by its associate company Cochrane Shipbuilders Ltd, Selby, was one of two such vessels built in 1982–83. With a gross tonnage of just under 1600, these vessels were equipped with two 10-ton cranes, a single cargo hold with one hatch and were able to carry 70 TEUs or 3048cu m of bulk cargo.* (Cochrane Shipbuilders)

Karlstad were introduced primarily for forest products which could be rolled on and off by a stern ramp but which could also carry containers and oil products in bottom tanks – hence they were known as COB (container-oil-bulk) carriers. Vessels intended for winter trading in the Baltic or Russian north are constructed to relevant 'ice class'.

With a great demand for aggregates and rock in southeast England which can only be satisfied from outside the area, UK based Civil & Marine in 1988 took delivery of a 3200 dwt low-profile vessel to which had been fitted a self-discharging conveyor system. While initially used for aggregates from Dunkirk to the Thames the vessel could also be used for any granular or powder cargoes. More recently the Foster-Yeoman aggregates company has used 27,000 and 75,000 dwt self-dischargers for moving granite chips from waterside quarries at Glensanda in western Scotland to the Isle of Grain in the River Medway. Jebsen Thun Beltships (JTB) a Norwegian-Swedish partnership is taking delivery of a number of self-dischargers in the 4300–9700 dwt range for intra-European trades. Proposals to develop, a large quarry in Bantry Bay, southwest Eire, will also create a demand for large bulk carriers in short-sea trades. The self-discharging vessels reduce port time and are flexible in use but the 20–35 per cent additional cost of the shipboard equipment must be covered by very intensive vessel use.

In addition to these developments, all of which derive in degree from traditional ship design and cargo handling there is also a range of completely new technology that now impinges on coastal and short-sea shipping. These will now be considered.

Tug-barge systems

In the United States, exceptionally high crew costs stimulated the adoption of systems in which regulatory requirements could be satisfied with smaller crews. In particular, a tug, for which the crew was only one-quarter to one-third that of a conventional ship, could be used to tow a crew-less cargo-carrying barge. As on inland waterways this could be done either by towing the barge(s) on a line astern or by pushing. With sufficiently powerful tugs the barge could be as big or even bigger than many conventional vessels – units of 40,000 dwt are not uncommon in United States domestic trades for petroleum products, coal and mineral ores and they can be loaded to a higher load line than would be possible for a conventional ship.

In the 1960s line-towed barges were introduced in American domestic services to Alaska, Hawaii, the Virgin Islands and Puerto Rico and in Britain Laxey Towing used them from Liverpool to the Isle of Man, although on a much smaller scale. However, line towing is inefficient from a propulsive point of view and manoeuvrability is difficult and just as push-tow systems have been developed on inland waterways so more elaborate designs are now found in sea-going tug-barge systems.

The seaworthiness of a tug-barge combination clearly depends on the character and strength of the linking mechanism and safety requires that the two can be speedily separated if the need arises. The first fully-integrated tug-barge (ITB) system, CARPORT, was designed in 1951 by Hugh Macmillan of Cargo Carriers Inc (Minneapolis) and George Sharp Inc, of New York, for use between the southern states of the United States and the Caribbean. The tug fitted like a wedge into a notch in the stern of the barge, sitting on the bottom of the notch and secured at tug deck level by structural overhangs. The difficulty of separating the tug and barge and the fact that in practice the two were not separated led to a US Coast Guard ruling that the system could not qualify for full manning reductions. Nevertheless, the system remained in operation until the mid-1970s. The CARPORT system was not patented and was adopted and modified by other designers. For example, in the late 1960s Breit designed units for the Ingram company in which an hydraulic ram allowed the tug and barge to 'mate' and also uncouple easily. At sea the shallow notches and loose cable connections of the first generation ITBs proved unsatisfactory and the rigid connections became favoured.

There have been numerous rigid coupling systems some of which allow the tug to pitch, roll and heave independently from the barge (for example the Seapushtow system of Lunde, 1966, and the Sea Link system of Glosten, 1964) and others which allow the tug only to pitch independently of the barge (eg the Artubar system developed by E H Fletcher and installed in some Japanese units in the 1970s). The Breit-Ingram designs introduced in the early 1970s (eg on *Martha R Ingram*) was accepted by the US Coast Guard as a tug and unmanned barge and this reduced costs and led to renewed interest in ITB systems.[17] With improved linking systems larger barges could be used. The 'Lumberjack' system introduced in 1974 to carry paper and fuel oil for the Philippines newspaper industry had 1700 dwt; the Catug (catamaran) system introduced by Seabulk Tankers in 1974–75 had barges with a 40,000 dwt and the *Presque Isle* designed for use on the Great Lakes had a dwt capacity of 50,000 tonnes.

The ITB system has continued to attract interest with new designs entering service in the original area of use, the United States, but also

---

17. A Traill, *Inland Waterways – The Maritime Link* (International Cargo Handling Coordination Association, London, 1988).

A typical coaster container vessel, the 2213 dwt Bell Rover, *with other vessels of the Bell Lines fleet maintains regular services between ports in Ireland, the UK, and northwest Europe. One of a series built at Kagoshima, Japan, dating from the mid-1970s, the vessel was originally registered under the ownership of Scotstoun Shipping Co Ltd, Glasgow. In this FotoFlite picture the vessel is carrying a deck load of 62 TEUs, 8 short of its maximum. A further 52 TEUs can be stowed in the hold.*

ramps, placed one on each side
sist of one section and are hydr

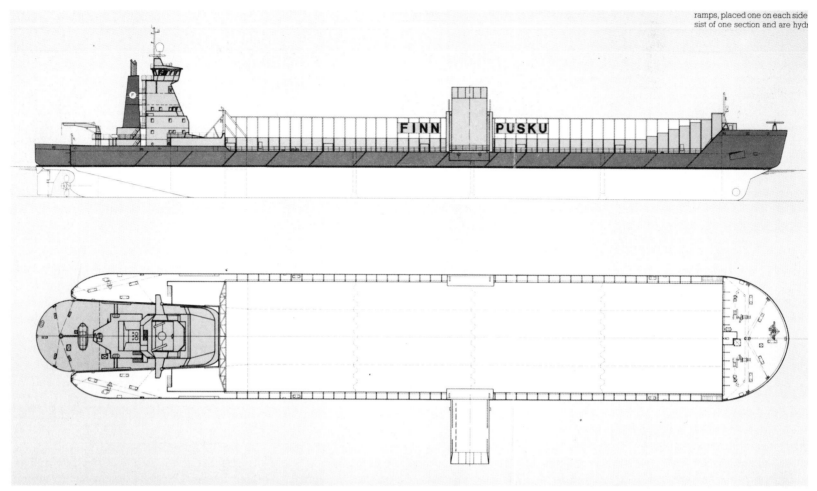

The pusher-tug barge system Rautaruukki *(1562 grt)
and* Kalla *is owned by Rautaruukki Oy (Raahe Iron
Works) and is managed by leading maritime company
Oy Finnlines Ltd, Helsinki. This combination consists of
the 10,400 bhp pusher tug* Kalla *and the 14,000-ton
cargo capacity barge* Rautaruukki. *With its high
coamings, the barge is suitable for bulk cargoes, such as
ore, dressed ore, limestone, coal and coke, and also for the
carriage of logs and forest products.* (Hollming Ltd)

significantly in Japanese trades and growingly
in Europe. The ITB system arrived in Europe
in 1969 when a two-tug, four-barge network
was introduced between Poland and France/
Belgium, mainly for coal but also for grain and
paper pulp. There were occasional trips across
the North Sea to Immingham but return cargoes were hard to find and despite promising
studies of the potential for ITBs the system
stopped operating in the mid-1970s only to be
re-introduced in a different form in the
mid-1980s. In the United States nearly half of
all the coastal trade is now by ITBs and Japan is
using them increasingly for a range of domestic
and also longer deep-sea trades. In both
Japanese and European trades it is important to
note the growing use of what is best termed the
'drop and swap' method of operating.

In the model situation this would involve

one tug and three barges – while one barge is in
transit the others are loading/unloading at the
two end ports and as one barge is delivered
another is ready to be picked up. Effectively,
one manned tug (propulsive unit) replaces
three conventional vessels. Provided that the
number of barges in the system always exceeds
by two the number of propulsion units and the
loading and unloading can be completed by the
time the voyage is completed the ITB is ideally
suited to such drop and swap operations. In
particular, this has advantages in the regular
movement of large volumes of bulk commodities and it is precisely for this type of trade
that the ITB has been introduced in Europe.

In 1986–87 Rautaruukki Oy and Finnlines
Ltd took delivery of two tugs and five barges
based on a Wartsila design and built by Hollming, both of Finland. The coupling system
known as Wartsila Marine Locomotive is a
variation on the Breit-Ingram design and allows unlimited ocean transportation. The
pusher fits into a deep notch in the stern of the
barge and rigid connection is effected by one
fixed wedge on the tug bow and by two
hydraulically operated wedges well aft on the
barge and at different levels to provide for different loading draughts. The pusher is fitted

with heeling and trimming tanks to adjust
draught to that of the barge. The main characteristics of the unit are as follows:

	Pusher	Barge	Linked unit
Length, overall (m)	42.0 (137ft)*	151.9 (498ft)	166.6 (546ft)
Length dwl (m)	40.2 (132ft)	141.6 (464ft)	162.6 (533ft)
Breadth (m)	15.5 (51ft)	27.2 (89ft)	27.2 (89ft)
Depth to upper deck (m)	10.0 (33ft)	10.0 (33ft)	10.0 (33ft)
Draught (loaded) (m)	6.7 (22ft)	6.7 (22ft)	6.7 (22ft)
Speed (kts)			15
Crew	6–9		

*Dimensions in feet given as approximate
conversions.

The unit is designed to the ice class '1A Super'
for year-round Baltic operation and the barge
has sloping sides to prevent sticking in ice
ridges. The barge has a bow thruster to facilitate manoeuvring. Originally the barges were
open with high sides but with ramp access on
each side to take axle loads of 70 tonnes. More
recently the barges have been given lightweight hatch covers comprising a cushion of
air between two blankets and this provides better protection in Baltic winter conditions. The

Rowbotham Tankships Ltd, which owned its first vessels in 1899, and owners of one of Europe's largest fleets of coastal and short-sea tankers, became a wholly-owned subsidiary of Marine Transport Lines Inc, USA, in 1985. Prior to this the company had for a few years been a subsidiary of another US company, Ingram Corp. More recently P&O Group has taken a 50 per cent share in the company, which continually updates its fleet, ranging from 1560 to 10,720 dwt. Here Cableman *(built 1980, 8496 dwt) is pictured in the River Tees. A product of Appledore Shipbuilders Ltd, she has fifteen tanks and a cargo capacity of 10,555cu m. Together with the entire Rowbotham fleet,* Cableman *was transferred from London to the British offshore registry of the Isle of Man in 1988. (Alan Sparrow)*

barges main deck has been strengthened to handle grab loaders.

The system has been designed particularly to transport bulk materials in the Baltic – iron ore from Lulea in Sweden and coal from Poland to the Raahe steelworks in northwest Finland, coke from Ventspils (Latvia) to Raahe, coal from Poland to southern Finland and logs from Finland to Poland. It is estimated that the annual capacity of the two pushers and five barges is three million tonnes with the loading times ranging from five hours for iron ore to forty-eight hours for logs. According to the operating company the system is aiming to replace bulk carriers and force foreign-flag vessels out of this particular market.

In 1972 the Japanese introduced a new connecting system, Articouple, in which the tug sits in a relatively shallow notch in the barge stern and is connected rigidly by deck mounted hydraulic pins which push metal 'shoes' into ratchets on either side of the barge notch. This allows connection with the barge draught at

anything from 2.72m (9ft) to 6.52m (21ft) in steps of 0.38m (1ft 2½in). This system was adopted by the Svitzer Salvage Company of Denmark to supply Danish power stations with coal from Poland, West Germany and the United Kingdom and two other operators are using Articouple units for moving coal to Norwegian power stations, limestone (Slite to Oxelosund) and pulpwood and wood chips (Oslo-fjord to Tofte). In the 1970s, eleven operators introduced Articouple units (altogether some fifteen tugs and twenty-two barges) in Asian trades centred on Japan with barge sizes varying from 1500 dwt to 4800 dwt, and in 1900

state-owned Neste OY, Finland, took delivery of two units with 4000 dwt barges for the movement of bitumen and other high temperature cargoes.

There is certainly the suggestion that the Articouple system has proved successful, certainly with small to medium-size barges and in a great variety of operating environments and further developments appear more than likely to take place.

The barge carrier vessel (BCV)

The underlying logic of the barge carrier vessel (BCV) is quite simple. Barges were coming down the Mississipi to Gulf ports where their cargo was off-loaded into seagoing ships for the journey to Europe. On arrival at the European ports the cargo was often reloaded on to barges for its onward movement – why not leave the cargo on the barge and lift the barge

The stern of the US-flag barge carrier Austral Lightning, *one of the several vessels of this type built in the USA during the 1970s. Originally named* LASH Espana *and operating between the US and Mediterranean, this vessel was purchased by Farrell Lines of New York in 1976. With the decline in barge carrier operations the vessel eventually found itself, with many others, in the US Government Reserve Fleet. A product of the Avondale Shipyard in Louisiana, in 1971,* Austral Lightning *could carry 40 barges or 564 TEUs below deck and 30 barges or 276 TEUs above deck. The gantry crane seen here at the stern, to facilitate barge operations, has a lifting capacity of 446 tons. (D Hilling)*

on to the ship? The first BCV was introduced in 1969 to do precisely this. The Lighter Aboard Ship (LASH) system was not developed as a manning rule beater but as part of a strategy to maximise the benefits of inland waterway transport and also in places to avoid port congestion. As in the ITB system the cargo carrying barge can be separated from the propulsive unit, in this case the mother-ship, so that loading and unloading of cargo does not require the capital intensive, crewed propulsive unit to stay in port for longer than it takes to separate barge and mother ship.

The first ship, *Acadia Forest* (built 1969, 36,862 grt) was designed by Friede & Goldman of New Orleans and built in Japan for operation on a long-term charter by Central Gulf Steamship Corp on a contract to move raw materials for the European paper-making industry from Mississippi exporting mills. The LASH system incorporated elements of deep-sea, coastal and inland shipping.

In the LASH system the barges are lifted on and off the mother-ship by a single gantry crane but in order to reduce dependence on a

Barges on board Bacat I, *the short-lived barge carrier concept introduced in 1974 by Danish operators. This vessel, which could carry thirteen 'Bacat' barges, was intended for service between Hull and Rotterdam. Following operational problems in the UK, the vessel was sold in 1978 to Indian interests where it fared little better and was laid-up at Bombay in 1982. In 1987 it was scrapped.* (D Hilling)

single crane Lykes Bros Steamship Co Inc, of New Orleans, introduced the Seabee system in which two barges could be lifted or lowered at the same time by a multi-motored elevator at the ship's stern. The Russians have adopted both the LASH and Seabee systems and float-on/float-off systems have also been developed which eliminate complex lifting devices and rely instead on partial submersion of the mother-ship by ballasting. Representative types of barge carrier are described in the Table on page 118.

The first BCV designed for short-sea trading was one which acted as a feeder barge carrier for the larger sea-going ships. Initially these were towed, semi-submersible carriers for eight barges and operated in the Arabian Gulf and Bay of Bengal and took the name 'FLASH' (Feeder LASH). In 1972, Van Der Laan, a subsidiary of Holland America Line introduced *Docklift I* (2425 grt), a semi-submersible vessel of 342ft in length which could carry barges, pontoons and other floating cargo in its open well deck. With cargo floated in, an enclosing stern door (which could double as a roll-on/roll-off ramp) was closed and the vessel de-ballasted. A considerable number of such semi-submersibles of different sizes now operate in deep-sea and short-sea trades and are particularly useful in carrying smaller vessels (tugs, harbour launches), oil field equipment and heavy loads.

In 1974 a new BCV design specifically for short-sea operation was developed after close co-operation between the Danish shipowner and broker Gustav Drohse and the Frederikshavn Vaerft shipyard. Once called the dwarf son of LASH and Seabee, the BACAT (barge catamaran) system adopted a small barge module size which allowed penetration of the waterways in the Humber hinterland as well as in Europe. Three LASH barges could be locked in position between the ship's double hull and ten BACAT barges could be lifted on to the deck. In operation this system proved highly efficient and cost effective but proved too successful for the Hull dockers who saw their livelihood floating past to be handled by dockers at small up-river locations. The dockers were able to use union muscle to boycott the system forcing withdrawal in 1975 – the ship was to go on for a number of years linking the Arabian Gulf with Bombay where it proved to be an effective congestion beater.

Towards the end of the 1970s a self-propelled feeder system for LASH barges (SPLASH) was introduced between Britain and the Middle East and later between Britain and European ports and also in the Far East.

Able to carry 18–19 LASH barges with a simple float-on/float-off technology these too proved efficient in operation. In 1979 another BCV design entered service between north-west European ports and West Africa. This was the *Baco-Liner* system of three ships owned by a consortium of West German river and deep-sea operators under the Rhein-Maas und See umbrella. *Baco* refers to the ship's barge and container carrying capacity with twelve 800 barges accommodated in the hold (and floated in and out through bow doors in the mother ship) or a combination of smaller barges together with 500 TEU container capacity on deck. The ship has an on-board gantry crane for handling the containers so can operate independently of shore facilities.

Although different in size, the barges of the BCV systems are alike in being very box-like with low freeboard. This means that they are suitable for towing in sheltered water but not in themselves able to make short-sea voyages. A small number of the barges have in fact been given improved hatch covers and load lines and these are used on coastal services, for example, between the Weser and Elbe rivers. While BCVs are still being introduced in Russia, connecting northern rivers and providing links between the Danube and Black Sea and the Far East, many of the United States vessels have been converted to pure container carriers or are now in military use. As a technology for short-sea and trans-oceanic services, the BCV is not as cheap as a pure bulk carrier for large volumes of bulk cargo or as cheap as a container ship for high value general cargo. However, there are still LASH services from Europe to the Middle and Far East and Felixstowe is connected to Rotterdam and Bremen with the feeder barge carrier *Spruce*.

Developing countries

Small ships are the lifeline of islands throughout the world. The most significant areas are in the island regions of the developing countries within the West Indies, South East Asia, the Pacific and Indian Ocean. Many thousands of islands are linked by inter-island shipping services which are vital for the economic and social life of scattered communities.

The shipping revolution has had impacts on the island trades, and it is still working its way through the system. There is considerable diversity in the shipping involved although there are a number of common problems and trends between the various regions. The penultimate section of this chapter summarises this and provides an account of the types of craft involved.

Like many oil companies, BP Oil Ltd, London, owns a fleet of coastal and short-sea tankers. Here BP Warrior, *built at Aberdeen in 1964, is pictured entering the River Tees. She is of 1592 grt, has twelve cargo tanks, and her length of 75.95m includes a 44.5m trunk deck.* (Alan Sparrow)

West Indies

Because of proximity to the United States, Panama Canal and Central and South America there is a vast amount of small ship activity in the island regions of the West Indies. The short sea trade is dominated by vessels from ports along the southern part of the United States. These comprise short-sea container ships of 1000 to 24 TEUs, many types of roros, and barges varying from quite massive triple-deckers to small sizes.

The trade between the islands is carried out by some of these American vessels and by many other local ships. There are, perhaps, around 400–500 local small craft engaged almost exclusively in inter-island trading, and there is the regional shipping line Wisco which also provides cargo links between small islands on a regular basis.

The vessels dedicated primarily to inter-island services fall into two general categories. There is a range of steel-hulled ships of around 200/300 dwt which are mainly old coasters and river craft purchased from Europe and the US. Many of these are operated by a captain-owner and a crew of around six. The second major category of inter-island vessels are the schooners. They range from about thirty to sixty tons and are wooden-hulled sailing craft with auxiliary engines.

South East Asia

The inter-island shipping in South East Asia serve primarily local archipelagic hinterlands, but some extend beyond their own territories expecially in operations to Singapore. The principal areas of operations are in the archipelagos of Indonesia and the Philippines. In Indonesia the largest cargo and passenger carriers are the regular liner services (RLS). There are about 380 steel-hulled ships of 500–2000 dwt in this sector. There are also 1000–2000 small, wooden motor-driven craft, and several thousand prahu owned and operated by village people. All of these play vital parts in the economy of Indonesia.

In the Philippines the local fleet comprises about 15,000 vessels in the range 800–1500 dwt. In addition there are small sailing craft some with auxiliary engines. These are engaged in passenger and cargo carriage main-

ly in the southern islands. Several are dual purpose and are involved in transport and fishing.

The Pacific Islands

In the Pacific ocean there are many archipelagos and also numerous single remote islands. Populations are small, local products are of low value, yet people now need a great range of consumer goods. There are a number of main ports in the Pacific island region at which overseas ships call. Cargoes from and to these are transported by inter-island vessels directly to the nearer islands. Some cargoes are also trans-shipped to more distant secondary ports by feeder ships, and from there trans-shipped yet again to the outer islands.

Old coastal vessels, wooden cutters and schooners are used. However, barge transport is also now employed, and in the higher density trades roro vessels have been introduced. Feeder services are conducted by self sustaining container vessels, although only under subsidy.

The future

The shipping revolution continues in the short-sea, coastal and inter-island trades. The most recent developments relate to the design of the Techno-Superliner (TSL) in Japan. These types of vessels will use buoyancy and dynamic lift, and buoyancy and air pressure

technology. Hulls are of aluminium alloy and stainless steel and they will carry 1000 tonnes payload at 50kts with a range of 500 miles. Such ships will operate on the short-distance, high-value routes by 1995. For trades such as those in developing country islands it will be the pensioned off craft displaced by such advanced vessels which will be adopted.

Liquid cargoes

Whilst this chapter has been concerned mainly with the dramatic changes that have taken place in dry cargo shipping it would be wrong to ignore the liquid cargo, foremost of which is oil.

After the Second World War consumption of oil products rose spectacularly and one short-sea shipping company, F T Everard & Sons Ltd purchased thirty-six tankers of from 180 to 5000 dwt in the ten years after 1945. At that time most European oil was imported ready refined and many of the smaller tankers were involved in distribution from main importing centres such as Avonmouth and existing refineries such as Llandarcy (Swansea). Some tankers were equipped with heating coils which allowed them to carry heavier oil products and also, with tankers in suitable condition, commodities such as lard, edible oils and molasses.

In the 1960s there was massive expansion of oil refinery capacity in northwest Europe to meet growing demand for products and there was also the emergence of large-scale petrochemical industries in port areas such as Rotterdam, Teesside, Merseyside and Swansea. There was therefore a demand for more sophisticated product carriers for the new range of chemical feed stocks – ethylene, propylene, liquefied gasses. There are stringent international regulations for the carriage of such hazardous cargoes and while some tankers were converted for them many more were built for the new trades. There was a trend towards the sub-division of tank capacity so that vessels could carry different 'parcels' of products and some of these vessels were larger than the normal short-sea distribution tankers. Overall, there was a general increase in the size of vessels employed and 3000 to 5000 dwt is quite common.

In one area much larger vessels are used. The development of the North Sea oil fields, in cases where pipelines were not provided to link production platforms with shore refineries, required the use of tankers for the carriage of crude oil. Despite the very short distances involved, tankers of up to 120,000 dwt are used – vessels which just twenty-five years ago would have been considered very large for the longest trans-oceanic hauls. The North Sea oil industry has also created the demand for a great variety of support vessels that are described in Chapter 8.

A very different type of liquid cargo is wine. Where the demand is considerable as for some cheaper wines such as Lutomer Riesling or Vermouth it is easier to ship the wine in bulk and bottle at the market. Equipped with stainless steel lined tanks, several of these wine tankers are in excess of 3000 dwt.

The future

It seems likely that developments within a European Single Market will in time lead to more centralised and concentrated systems of stockpiling and production in heavy manufacturing industries so creating long-term, high volume and fixed trade routes for some types of bulk cargo. There is the possibility that this could open up further opportunities for the employment of tug-barge systems in short-sea trades. While shipping is generally thought to be slow it is often the case that what is needed is an even, regular flow so that stock-piles can be reduced and with more of the raw material 'in the pipeline' to arrive 'just-in-time'. Such just-in-time deliveries are becoming in-

creasingly important in distribution systems and shipping is able to provide reliable, regular movement that satisfies this type of requirement.

The trend towards concentration of port activity to maximise economies of scale on the trans-oceanic haul will continue in both bulk and general cargo trades and this will lead to a growing demand for coastal and short-sea feeder services to serve the new 'hub and spoke' patterns. Trans-shipment and feeder services are critically dependent on the lowest possible cost on the feeder routes and this could mean using the largest feasible vessels for each route or possibly using tug-barge systems.

Speed of cargo handling in ports will also be vital because many of the feeder services will become something like ferry links in which maximum vessel utilisation will be essential to reduce costs. The introduction in 1990 by Bell Lines of a hatchless container ship on short-sea routes was just to reduce port time and the use

of self-discharging bulkers is for the same reason. The introduction in 1991 by Seacon of a waterjet propelled ship, the *Sea Orade*, which has a high degree of manoeuvrability with very little water under its keel could also herald a trend allowing as it does greater flexibility to meet tidal 'windows' for access to coastal and river ports. This form of propulsion also has immunity to the damage to which the conventional propeller and rudder are prone.

There is already evidence that environmental pressures will mean more serious consideration of water transport (inland, coastal and short-sea) which economises on fuel, reduces noise, air pollution, vibration and visual intrusion and in many situations provides a means of taking heavy goods vehicles off already congested roads. Germany's ban on the weekend use of heavy lorries has greatly stimulated container and roll-on/roll-off services on the Rhine and a 1990 European Community study on transport proposed policies to encourage

Table 6/1: The Changing Style of Short-Sea Vessels

	Steam coaster[1] (1909)	Motor coaster[1] (1953)	Motor coaster[2] (1961)	Motor coaster[3] (1966)	Mini-bulker[4] (1984)	River-sea ship[5] (1983)
Length (m)	56.2	60.4	48.5	41.6	79.0	79.0
Beam (m)	8.4	10.4	8.0	7.6	12.8	11.6
Draught (m)	4.3	6.4	3.0	2.3	4.5	3.3
Air draught (m)	–	–	–	5.6	–	5.7
Grt	600	900	386	199	799	499
Dwt	805	1347	515	358	2415	1562
Speed (kts)	10	11	8	8.5	10	10
Crew	17	15–21	7–8	4	5	5–6
Grt: dwt ratio	1:1.34	1:1.49	1:1.33	1:1.79	1:3.1	1:3.1

Notes: 1. Adapted from HMSO, 1980;   2. *Mary Coast*;   3. *Sheena K*;   4. *Selectivity*;   5. *Sea Ems*

Table 6/2: Typical 'Series' Buildings

Builder	Start year	GRT	DWT	Length	Beam	Draught	Air draught	Other	Example vessel
Ferus Smit (Westerbroek)	1983	998	1522	78.9	10.1	6.8	6.7	BT	BORNRIF
Yorkshire Dry Dock (Hull)	1984	794	1400	58.3	9.4	3.9	7.3		HOO FINCH
Thyssen (Emden)	1985	999	2584	95.9	14.1	4.1	10.3	BT, roro	LINDA BUCK
Damen (Gorinchem)	1985	996	2821	89.3	12.5	4.4	8.8	BT, BB, RW	JADE
Sürken (Papenburg)	1985	1291	1548	74.9	10.6	3.4	5.7	BT, BB, RW	SEA THAMES
Rauma (Uusikaupunki)	1988	1853*	2075	82.5	11.3	4.0	7.0	BT, BB, RW	LADOGA 106
Cochrane (Selby)	1990	2230*	3222	99.9	12.6	4.27	6.35	BT, RW	UNION JUPITER

Notes: BT: bow thruster;   BB: bulbous bow;   RW: retractable wheelhouse;   * grt under Universal Measurement System.

The Crescent Shipping tug Dragette *is pictured here towing eight LASH barges. These barges, 18.7m in length, with a breadth of 9.5m and draught of 2.7m, have a hold measuring 18.3 × 9.1m and hatch size of 13.7 × 7.9m. The maximum deadweight is 270 tonnes.* (FotoFlite)

the environmentally friendly modes. Proposals for a sea-going ship which can be split along its length to give two water-jet propelled barges for the penetration of waterways in the Humber hinterland which cannot take conventional river-sea ships is the first of what could be a line of innovative technologies to provide more efficient short-sea links. The creation of the Single Market and the closer integration of eastern with western Europe especially after the completion of the Rhine-Main-Danube link in 1992 will further encourage the use of shipping technologies able to provide through links – river-sea ships and tug-barge systems provide just such technologies.

The completion of the Channel Tunnel and the bridge links in Scandinavia will undoubtedly in the short term serve to reduce the demand for short-sea shipping. However, this will be most marked in the shortest distance ferry services and possibly some container trades but is unlikely to be of significance in the bulk and general cargo shipping which has been the concern of this chapter. However, it is likely that shipowners will have to react by maximising the efficiency and reducing the cost of their operations if they are to stay in business. The evidence of this chapter is that they will find ways of doing just this.

David Hilling and Andrew Traill

Typical low-profile short-sea vessels since 1965

Ship	Flag	Built	By	GRT DWT	Length (oa) × breadth × draught × air draught Feet–Inches Metres	Cargo handling gear	Engines	Speed	Remarks
ANTON HELD	WG	1967	C Cassens, Emden	299 468	158–5 × 24–8 × 8–4 × 14–1 48.29 × 7.52 × 2.56 × 4.3	Derricks 2 × 2 tons	1 Atlas-MaK diesel, 400bhp; 1 shaft	9.5kts	1 hold, 1 hatch
JUSTINE M	UK	1976	Wroclawska Stocznia Wroclaw	499 768	164–7 × 29–4 × 11–2 × 21–8 50.17 × 8.95 × 3.4 × 6.6	Gearless	1 Mannheim (MWM) diesel, 700bhp; 1 shaft	10kts	1 hold, 1 hatch
SEA ESTE	WG	1982	J J Sietas, Hamburg	999 2890	288–6 × 37–2 × 15–4 × 20–0 87.95 × 11.33 × 4.68 × 6.1	Gearless	1 KHD diesel, 1800bhp; 1 shaft	11.5kts	1 hold, 1 hatch 90 TEUs
ARDENT	UK	1983	Yorkshire DD Co, Hull	498 1180	164–0 × 31–1 × 11–9 × 23–8 49.99 × 9.5 × 3.59 × 7.2	Gearless	2 Cummins diesels, 730bhp; 2 shafts	9kts	1 hold, 1 hatch
HOO LAUREL	UK	1984	Yorkshire DD Co, Hull	794 1394	191–2 × 31–2 × 12–9 × 24–0 58.27 × 9.5 × 3.9 × 7.3	Gearless	2 Cummins diesels, 730bhp; 2 shafts	8kts	1 hold, 1 hatch
PAULA	WG	1985	J J Sietas, Hamburg	999 3053	288–8 × 42–0 × 15–1 × 36–1 87.99 × 12.81 × 4.6 × 11.0	Gearless	1 KHD diesel, 1190bhp; 1 shaft	11.5kts	1 hold, 1 hatch 153 TEUs
LINDA BUCK	WG	1985	Thyssen Nordseewerke, Emden	999 2680	314–8 × 46–8 × 13–4 × 33–10 95.92 × 14.23 × 4.07 × 10.3	Roro; stern door/ramp	1 KHD diesel, 815bhp; 1 shaft	10kts	1 hold, 1 hatch 180 TEUs
JEROME H	WG	1985	Hermann Sürken, Papenburg	1289 1525	245–9 × 34–9 × 11–1 × 18–0 74.91 × 10.6 × 3.39 × 5.5	Gearless	1 MAN-B&W diesel, 600bhp; 1 shaft	10kts	1 hold, 1 hatch
LESLIE JANE C	UK	1990	Cochrane SBs, Selby	2230 3222	327–1 × 41–4 × 14–0 × 21–0 99.73 × 12.6 × 4.27 × 6.4	Gearless	1 MAN-B&W diesel, 1018bhp; 1 shaft	11.2kts	2 hatches, 86 TEUs

Typical mini-bulkers since 1970

Ship	Flag	Built	By	GRT DWT	Length (oa) × breadth × depth × draught Feet–Inches Metres	Cargo handling gear	Engines	Speed	Remarks
BOTNO	Nor	1971	Orens MV, Trondheim	455 1240	245–6 × 32–11 × 18–11 × 12–2 74.83 × 10.04 × 5.77 × 3.72	Derricks 1 × 3.5 tons 1 × 2.5 tons	1 Lister Blackstone Mirrlees diesel, 1000bhp; 1 shaft	11kts	1 hold, 2 hatches
SEA AVON	Pan	1977	Kanrei Zosen, Tokushima	1102 2273	226–5 × 44–5 × 17–9 × 14–9 69.02 × 13.54 × 5.41 × 4.49	Gearless	1 Niigata diesel 1200bhp; 2 shafts	10.5kts	1 hold, 1 hatch
NORBRIT FAITH	UK	1982	Cochrane SBs, Selby	1597 2387	230–0 × 42–11 × 19–8 × 16–3 70.12 × 13.07 × 6.0 × 4.96	Cranes 2 × 10 tons	1 APE-Allen diesel, 1370bhp; 1 shaft	11kts	1 hold, 1 hatch; 70 TEUs
WILLONIA	UK	1984	Cochrane SBs, Selby	799 2415	259–2 × 41–8 × 20–8 × 14–11 79.0 × 12.68 × 6.3 × 4.55	Gearless	1 Krupp MaK diesel, 1285bhp; 1 shaft	10kts	1 hold 1 hatch; 94 TEUs
SENIORITY	UK	1991	Appledore SBs, Appledore	3493 5163	327–11 × 54–2 × 22–3× 17–9 99.95 × 16.52 × 6.8 × 5.42	Gearless	1 Ruston diesel, 2680bhp; 1 shaft	11kts	2 holds, 2 hatches

Typical barge carriers 1969–1979

Ship (Type)	Flag	Built	By	GRT DWT	Length (oa) × breadth × depth × draught Feet–Inches Metres	Cargo handling gear	Engines	Speed	Remarks
ACADIA FOREST	Nor	1969	Sumitomo SB, Yokosuka	36,862 49,835	857–8 × 106–11 × 60–0 × 40–0 261.42 × 32.59 × 18.29 × 12.2	Crane 1 × 510 tons	1 Sumitomo/Sulzer diesel, 26,000bhp; 1 shaft	18kts	80 barges
LASH ITALIA (LASH type)	US	1970	Avondale SYs, Avondale, La	26,406 30,298	820–0 × 100–2 × 60–0 × 40–10 249.94 × 30.54 × 18.29 × 12.45	Cranes 1 × 446 tons, 1 × 30 tons	2 De Laval steam turbines, 32,000shp, 1 shaft	22.5kts	70 barges or 840 TEUs
DOCTOR LYKES (Seabee type)	US	1972	General Dynamics, Quincy, Ma	21,667 39,026	875–11 × 106–3 × 53–8 × 39–1 266.99 × 32.39 × 16.36 × 11.93	Stern lift	2 General Electric steam turbines, 36,000shp; 1 shaft	19.5kts	38 barges or 1800 TEUs
BILDERDYK	Ne	1972	Cockerill Yards, Hoboken, Belgium	36,974 44,799	857–8 × 106–3 × 60–0 × 37–0 261.42 × 32.29 × 18.29 × 11.28	Crane 1 × 455 tons	1 De Schelde/Sulzer diesel, 26,100bhp; 1 shaft	18kts	83 barges
DELTA MAR (LASH type)	US	1973	Avondale SYs, Avondale, La	32,306 41,363	893–4 × 100–4 × 60–0 × 38–1 272.3 × 30.56 × 18.29 × 11.62	Cranes 1 × 510 tons, 1 × 30 tons	2 De Laval steam turbines, 32,000shp; 1 shaft	22.5kts	85 barges or 1728 TEUs
BACAT 1 (Twin hull)	Dmk	1974	Frederikshavn Vaerft, Frederikshavn	1399 2682	339–5 × 61–0 × 34–4 × 18–1 103.51 × 18.8 × 10.52 × 5.42	Crane 1 × 2 tons	2 Alpha diesels, 4320bhp; 2 shafts	13kts	13 barges
JULIUS FUCIK	SU	1978	Valmet OY, Helsinki	35,817 37,850	874–2 × 114–11 × 75–3 × 36–1 266.45 × 35.03 × 22.94 × 11.0	Stern lift	4 Wartsila/Pielstick diesels, 36,000bhp; 2 shafts	19.75kts	26 barges or 1552 TEUs
FLASH IV (Dockship)	Lib	1975[1]	Sumitomo SB, Yokosuka	1380 8172	369–1 × 112–3 × 21–4 × 14–3 112.5 × 34.22 × 6.51 × 4.35	Float in/ float out	2 General Motors diesels, 43,000bhp; 2 shafts	14kts	
MAMMOTH WILLOW (Dockship)	Lib	1978	Sumitomo HI, Yokosuka	1856 13,231	441–4 × 112–3 × 24–8 × 17–0 134.52 × 34.21 × 7.52 × 5.18	Float in/ float out	2 Nippon Kokan/ Pielstick diesels, 5880bhp; 2 shafts	10.25kts	18 barges and 108 TEUs on deck
BACO-LINER 1	WG	1979	Thyssen Nordseewerke, Emden	23,321 21,801	669–8 × 93–6 × 46–7 × 21–10 204.1 × 28.5 × 14.2 × 6.65	Float in/ float out (bow doors) Crane 1 × 40 tons	1 B&W diesel, 10,700bhp; 1 shaft	14.4kts	14 barges and 501 TEUs incl. 78 ref

Notes: [1] Converted from non-propelled barge carrier 1978.

7

Specialised Cargo Ships

THE term specialised ship is not a precise technical category but rather a all-encompassing phrase to include the more significant merchant cargo vessel type developments not covered elsewhere. Basically it is intended to cover types designed and built to fit a specific or dedicated purpose, but not in such large numbers as, for example, tankers and container ships.

Apart from some larger classes of dry and liquid bulk carriers and numerous short-sea carriers, ships are seldom produced in very large series and many still tend to be 'tailor made' or 'customised' to suit the specific requirements of owners. Many are designed and built with a specific trade, purpose or cargo in mind, and it is this aspect, not the size, construction or the equipment which makes them specialised. The authors have selected representative types which have developed into a precise market or function. The vessels included do not therefore form a definitive or exhaustive list but a representative collection.

For the purpose of this study the ships have been categorised as follows:

1. Heavy lift vessels: lift-on/lift-off/semi-submersible/dockship.
2. Waste carriers: nuclear/chemical/sludge/ incineration.
3. Livestock carriers.

Basically these groups contain ships which, if they did not exist, the cargo could not move in the form in which it is carried for either technical or legal reasons.

4. Vehicle carriers.
5. Forest product carriers: logs/wood-chips/ timber/newsprint.
6. Tanker variants for wine and alcohol/ fruit juice/molten sulphur/phosphoric acid/ molasses/bitumen/alkyl-lead compounds.
7. Cement carriers.

These vessels, in most cases, offer an alternative mode of carriage which is more economic, more efficient, safer and more environmentally friendly.

The heavy lift vessel

The lift-on/lift-off (lolo) heavy-lift vessel

In the early 1920s, Captain Christen Smith, a Norwegian shipowner, developed a heavy-lift vessel type, which not only became renowned but was also widely copied. An expert in heavy-lifts, Captain Smith took delivery of the steamers *Belfri* and *Belgot* (about 3400 dwt) in 1920–21. These were rather ordinary vessels of the three-island type but they made news thanks to the British firm of Armstrong Whitworth which had 200 heavy railway locomotives to deliver to the Belgian State Railways which was desperately short of equipment after the First

The 1962-built Peter Rickmers *was equipped with two sets of the popular 'Stülckenmasts', a heavy-lift system which ranges from about 100 to 300 tons swl. These examples on board* Peter Rickmers *are each of 130 tons lifting capacity.* (Skyfotos)

World War. Captain Smith advised Armstrong Whitworth to modify the vessels to transport these locomotives in assembled form. The vessels were not equipped with gear which could load the locomotives, but they did transport them in assembled form, in contrast to previous practice which was to carry such loads dismantled. By dispensing with re-assembly time, the locomotives were in service within 24 hours of delivery.

After this success, Christen Smith was entrusted with the carriage of a large number of locomotives from Britain to India for the Bombay, Baroda & Central Indian Railway, and which led to the construction of three purpose-built motor ships, *Beldis* (3440 dwt), *Belnor* (4075 dwt) and *Belray* (4235 dwt), completed during 1924–26. In 1926 the larger *Beljeanne* and *Belpareil* (About 7150 grt) entered service and these were the true forerunners of heavy-lift vessels of future years. Seeing worldwide service, they were conceived as vessels of then unprecedented capabilities, intended to carry full loads of assembled locomotives and their tenders, railway coaches, and small craft such as ferries, tugs, barges, pilot vessels, etc. These could be carried both in the holds and on deck, and occasionally in more than one tier.

Great stability was necessary, as were strong decks, hatch coamings and covers, and long pillar-free holds. Of great importance also was self-sufficiency for loading and discharge of cargo. Three hatches each 75ft long were each served by a 125-ton capacity derrick, and several smaller.

Beljeanne and *Belpareil* brought the term 'Belships' into the maritime dictionary, and later a small group of standard vessels of similar size built in Britain at the end of the Second World War were given the heavy-lift (*Bel*) ship anotation. Later developments saw the introduction of new types of masts and derricks including the very successful Stülckenmast, designed and produced in West Germany.

One of the modern high capacity heavy lifters is a class developed by the leading Netherlands heavy lift company Mammoet Shipping. Although classified here as a lolo vessel, there

are also the possibilities of roro operations. In this way the vessel to a great extent resembled dockships although there are a few distinct differences.

This type of vessel is not designed particularly for extremely wide or very voluminous cargoes as are dockships or submersibles, but as lolo operations are usually rather speedy, the advantages of this design lay in exactly that field. The philosophy behind the concept is the rapid cargo handling of even the largest and heaviest of lifts. The carriage of containers seemed too good an opportunity to just ignore, so a full load of limited weight containers can also be handled when required.

The main deck is as wide and flush as possible with the main cargo gear on the starboard side. The two 360-degree revolving high-capacity cranes are literally rooted into the starboard hull leaving the centre and port side completely free. On the port side the reach is up to 9m outboard, on the starboard side even up to 30m. The single crane capacity is 550 tonnes, in tandem the load can be doubled to 1100 tonnes.

The hold is covered by very strong and completely closed box type covers which can be

used as floating pontoons if so required. The hold dimensions were adapted to container size, and eight wide can be positioned. The beam of the vessel also gives enough stability when lifting maximum lifts in tandem.

In the hold there is a tween-deck on to which roro operations can take place through the stern door (7.5m × 21m) which acts as a ramp; the roro capacity is 2500 tonnes in one unit. When in place the lower hold and the tweendeck can both accommodate two-high tiers of containers.

The engine-room is aft under in the stern, while bridge and accommodation are at the bow. As with dockships this type is designed to sail with all hatch covers open or any combination of closure.

The dockship

Based on the ideas of how heavy lift transport would shape up in the near future, a Netherlands company designed and ordered three new ships and of very versatile type at the end of 1977. They were to be capable of lift-on/lift-off, roll-on/roll-off and float-on:in/float-off:out operations, making them unique and thus

The stern of the roro/dock ship Dock Express 10, *built 1979, showing the cargo handling capabilities: lift-on/lift-off (up to 1000 tonnes), roro (up to 2000 tonnes) and float-in/float-out (floating objects up to 5m deep).* Dock Express 10, *together with two sister-ships, was built by Verolme, at Heusden, Netherlands, and is 153.78m long. Its hold area, seen in this photograph, is 113.4m long. The gantry cranes each have a lifting capacity of 500 tons.* (Dock Express)

The semi-submersible heavy-lift vessel Dan Lifter *(10,282 grt), was built in 1982 for Frigg Shipping Ltd, Nassau, Bahamas, an associate of J Lauritzen AS, Denmark. The capabilities of vessels such as these are clearly shown here in 1983 when carrying the landing ship* Sir Tristram *(5674 grt), heavily damaged during the Falklands War. The lifting capacity of* Dan Lifter *is rated at 12,000 tonnes and the wide deck space makes it suitable for the carriage of oil platforms, specialist barges, pontoons, and other large loads. (FotoFlite)*

competitive. At that time they were also the largest, self propelled units offering multiple cargo-handling facilities. The three vessels were all in service by 1979 and typical 'cargoes' transported have included dredgers, fully assembled container gantry cranes and drilling rigs.

In particular the energy related industries in gas/oil/petrochemical/nuclear fields have shown the tendency of building large plant using prefabricated modules of ever-increasing dimensions. The sophisticated transport possibilities of dockships are very suitable for the transportation of such items, but as module sizes increased even further the need was felt for a slightly longer version of the ship, which soon after was designed and built.

One variant is the Baco-liner. This is a German version, slightly smaller and less sophisticated, in which barges are floated into the dock hold through bow doors while containers can be carried on the upper deck.

Another variant is the Condock ship in which floflo operations of barges take place into the hold via a stern door opening, but containers can be carried on the hatches covering the dock hold. The basic design consists of a huge hold, with a stern door that can be opened enabling floating-in or rolling-in of cargo, depending on how far down the vessel has been ballasted. The vessel becomes more or less flexible and versatile depending on the amount and type of additional cargo handling gear fitted. The hold can be covered by removable hatch covers or left open allowing for high or voluminous units carried in the dock hold. The hatch covers when not in use can be stacked on the aft outriggers or hung on the sides of the hull. As they are hollow closed steel boxes they offer buoyancy and widening of the waterplane area.

A watertight bulkhead which can be placed in the middle of the hold enables combinations of wet and dry cargo handling into the dock hold and obviously a high capacity ballast system is available. Roro operations can take place into the hold via the aft bulkhead door (in this way 2000 tons capacity is available), or on to

the deck via the stern outriggers along rails on either side of the main deck over which self propelled bogies can be driven. These rails can even be extended on to the quayside enabling a pick up further away from the vessel and loads of up to 1000 tons can be taken on.

Finally, lolo operations can be carried out up to a maximum of 1000 tons by movable gantry cranes, either over the side or over the stern. In order to guarantee high manoeuvrability into remote confined port areas the vessels are fitted with bowthrusters and a spudpole forward.

Self-propelled semi-submersibles

It had been customery for ultra-heavy objects such as jack-up rigs and floating factories to be towed to their destination. This so-called wet tow had certain distinct disadvantages:

- because of non-ship like shape only a very low speed was possible;
- the forces on the structure had to be compensated by stronger construction;
- higher insurance premiums;
- little or no maintenance possible during the voyage.

Because of these factors, eventually many such shipments were placed on barges and transported as a so-called dry tow. By submerging the barge, either by the stern, bow or completely, until it rested on the sea-bottom, cargo was floated over its deck and the barge was then refloated with its cargo. The salvage company Ulrich Harms started using this method in the 1960s with submersible pontoons, and in

the 1970s a Netherlands competitor followed suit.

In 1976 the Netherlands company Wijsmuller brought two *Ocean Servant* type barges into service. They were fitted with air chambers fore and aft which enabled horizontal submerging and refloating. This allowed them to load cargo irrespective of water depth as the barge did not have to rest on the bottom. They were also fitted with two omni-directional Schottel rudder-propellers allowing remote steering of the barge from a tug in confined waters.

During 1979–82 a self-propelled ship version of this design, although rather unusually modelled, was introduced. These were the *Super Servant*s (Netherlands), *Dan Mover* and *Dan Lifter* (Denmark) and *Dyvi Swan* and *Dyvi Tern* (Norway). The speed of loading was increased with this new type and the loss of a tow due to a parting tow-line became history.

At about the same time tankers were converted into semi-submersible heavy-lift vessels, resulting in a 117,000 dwt tanker being converted into *Sibig Venture* and another became *Ferncarrier*.

In view of what was becoming fierce competition, in 1983 a further upgrading of the design was undertaken in the Netherlands and this resulted in the *Mighty Servant* class. The *Super Servant* concept was generally followed with the addition of a heavy-lift derrick creating more versatility. Although not a very large market there are several self-propelled semi-submersible heavy-lift vessels in service.

The vessels can be submerged and refloated horizontally, thus facilitating cargo-handling. Additionally there is a roro capability on the main deck and, in some cases, lower-hold, and lifting derrick or crane. The barge-shaped vessel usually has crew accommodation forward and two buoyancy casings aft, allowing appropriate stability during submerging and rising. The hull contains ballast tanks, engine-room and bunker spaces. The casings consist of exhaust funnels and a ballast tank.

There is a very sophisticated ballast system for submerging and refloating for floflo operations or ballasting down to quay level for roro operations. This can also be used for influencing the ship's centre of gravity and compensation of intolerable hull stresses. The system uses air compressors to fill and empty the tanks. Submerging can be undertaken by flooding the tanks, suction filling by compressor vacuum or a combination of both. The air compressors have a capacity of about 2500 cubic metres/hour enabling submerging or rising to take place in about 4 hours.

The waste carrier

The irradiated (spent) nuclear fuel and radioactive waste carrier

The use of nuclear power plants require the transport of nuclear fuel and radioactive waste. The transport and storage is dealt with in various ways in various countries. The sea transport becomes a primary means if the nuclear plants are located near the waterside. Because of the high risk factor, special purpose built vessels are utilised for this transport.

The safety aspect of course has top priority and the nuclear material is carried in special casks which are securely seafastened on a transport vehicle which is then secured to the hold floor. Depending on the precise nature of the material transported there are special transport containers for spent fuel, reactor core components, reactor waste and low level waste.

Ships carrying this type of cargo are probably not going to grow in size very much as the ports of call often have restricted water depths and manoeuvring space. Furthermore a large ship could carry a large number of containers/flasks but this does not seem necessary as there would be much idle time due to long turnaround periods.

Because of the high risk factor the vessel should give protection to the cargo upon collision or grounding. Therefore a double hull and double bottom become essential. Reliability is increased by twin screw and duplication of generator equipment.

The vessel can be loaded in roro and lolo style. Normally the cargo is driven aboard but the hatches can also be opened up if required to load by shore cranes.

The bulkheads between the cargo hold and engine-room are radiation shielded by a 15cm thick concrete wall. The cargo holds and engine-rooms are equipped with instruments for radiation measurement. Furthermore there is a lab for measuring radioactivity on board. Between crew accommodation and cargo hold there is a water-filled tank for radiation protection.

Vertical fire protection zones safeguard the vessel and its cargo from damage by fire. Extensive communication equipment allows for continuous tracking of the vessel while underway.

The chemical waste carrier

The seas and oceans have been considered the biggest and best dumping bins on earth. In recent years however man has become more environment-conscious and aware of the need to restrict the dumping of all kinds of industrial and human waste in the open waters. For the purpose of dumping chemical waste various types of ships have been designed.

Many chemical waste products tend to have a disastrous effect on flora and fauna if applied in too high a concentration. In order to control the concentration of dumped material, vessels so employed are fitted with mechanisms for accurate quantification. One development has been the introduction of the split bottom barge or ship.

However, this type of vessel, if not becoming redundant altogether, will certainly only be used in future for the dumping of less harmful materials. Applications could then very well be in port construction and underwater engineering for which sand or gravel could be dumped. Further applications could be for various allowable types of sludge or gypsum waste and other such materials.

For controlled quantification of dumping a split bottom hull, which opens up longitudinally, is utilised. This opens by means of an hydraulic mechanism which forces the two hollow buoyant hull sections apart. The hull sections are connected by hinges fore and aft at deck level. The hold is coated for protection of the steel from the chemicals that are carried, and in order to facilitate rapid loading the hatches are not covered.

The sludge discharge vessel

As is the case with other waste discharge vessels environment protection makes most of them questionable to say the least. Depending on the composition the dumping of certain types of sludge is still found acceptable.

The vessels used can either be designated sludge carriers or combinations of, for instance, sludge and chemical disposal ships.

All vessels built for the carriage of nuclear waste have been the subject of controversy and the 1982-built Sigyn was no exception. The 3923 grt roll-on/roll-off vessel was built by At & Ch du Havre to carry irradiated fuel along the coasts of Europe, and the Swedish Government granted her owners, Société Franco-Suedoise d'Armement Maritime, an export licence to allow the vessel to operate between Sweden and France where irradiated fuel is processed. In 1985 she was acquired by Svensk Kavnbranslehantering AB (Swedish Nuclear Fuel & Waste Management). (FotoFlite)

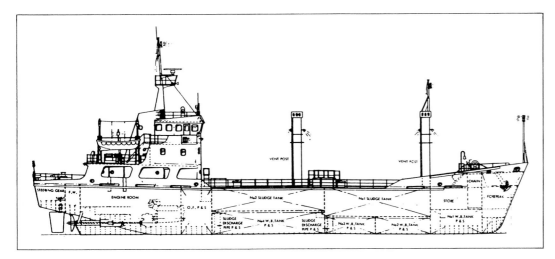

The British-owned sludge vessel Divis II *(820 grt), operated by the Department of Environment for Northern Ireland, was built by James Lamont at Port Glasgow, and completed in 1979. The vessel has two sludge tanks, from which ventilators via the two prominent ventilator posts are linked.* (Ship & Boat International)

Various types of ships and barges are used and as long as the sludge can be pumped a variant using tanks is quite feasible.

For the more solid types split-hull barges can be applied. The size of the vessels tends to be fairly modest as they are usually employed in coastal waters carrying small volumes of cargo.

The sludge can be loaded through the sludge hopper which is situated on the main deck.

There are usually a number of sludge tanks and ample ballast capacity to be used to keep the vessel manoeuvrable when the 'cargo' has been discharged.

The ventpost will obviously have openings well above the level of the accommodation.

Liquid sludge is discharged through a pump/pipe system and the amounts dumped are carefully monitored. Positioning of the dumped material is by means of an accurate position fixing system.

The incinerator vessel

Waste products can generally be dumped, stored, recycled or destroyed. For liquid chemical waste the latter alternative is frequently used, and this can be either total or it can have a non-pollutive by-product, and can be achieved by burning up the liquid chemical waste either on land or at sea. However the pollution restrictions are less tight at sea, while the sea air and water can act as neutralising agents if so required. This is the principle behind sea-going incinerator vessels.

The disposal of almost any kind of waste chemicals ashore presents problems. 'The group of chlorinated hydrocarbons can however be burned resulting in hydrochloric acid, and this still cannot be disposed of freely ashore. But when passed through a scrubber and neutralised by means of lime or sodiumhydroxide, common salts such as sodium-chloride or calcium-chloride are formed, and these can be easily disposed of in the saliferous seas without further polluting the environment.

On ocean burners the stack scrubber can be omitted as the buffering capacity of the marine waters is used to neutralise the acid stack gasses.

Some waste products upon combustion are completely destroyed and a destruction efficiency of up to 99.999995 per cent is said to be reached. Nevertheless the concept of ocean incineration is being questioned and it is thought that there will be land based alternatives that will see the end of the incinerator vessel for burning at sea.

As the cargo is of a chemical nature the vessel design and equipment has to comply with the IMO 'Chemical Carrier' BCH code. This dictates, among other things, that there is side and bottom protection of the cargo area by means of side tanks, double bottoms and void spaces depending on the type of chemical to be carried. The waste product is carried in the cargo tanks, with the superstructure to the front and the incinerator to the rear of the vessel. The incinerator itself consists of a large combustion oven, with a high rising funnel, lined with fireproof material for protection of the vessel's steel structures.

The chemical waste is pumped to the burners where the combustion takes place and from which the exhaust gasses are carefully monitored. There is no cargo discharge system in these vessels other than the incinerator which decreases the chances of leakage, spillage or dumping.

Furthermore the vessels are required to be equipped with an automatic waste feed shut-off system which will stop the flow of waste to the burners and power to the pumps in the event of an overload on the pumps, fan, a loss of flame or reduction of funnel wall temperature.

The livestock carrier

It is known that in ancient times animals were transported by sea. In those days it was mainly horses, especially for war purposes. Around 1519 there was extensive transportation of horses from Europe to Central and South America. These were for military activities and related to the establishment of colonies.

Later on more than 200,000 horses were exported from England and Argentina to South Africa during the Boer War.

Cattle transport has only become of any importance during the last century. In 1870 the British Government had to interfere with sea transport for fear of spreading cattle diseases, and 1898 saw the movement of 95,000 beef cattle from Argentina to Europe.

A major event bringing about an historical change was the arrival of the British vessel *Dunedin* in England from New Zealand with a cargo of frozen meat in 1882. This was one of the first ships with refrigerated cargo capacity and the beginning of the decline of the transport of large quantities of livestock. Animals were still transported live for breeding purposes or for zoos but in these cases sea voyages were usually not very long.

Shortly after the Second World War the development of the short-sea livestock trades started again; for instance from the Netherlands to Ireland slaughter horses were transported.

In 1964 the motor vessel *David* (499 grt), which was a converted coaster, carried 60 cattle and 237 sheep from Sheerness to Ostend. Nineteen seventy saw the advent of *Hereford Express* and *Jersey Express* owned by Vroon & Co. Pedigree cattle transport was their main purpose and made these ships a success, leading to the longer ocean routes being started up again. Many developing countries wanted their own herds of cattle and Muslims require live animals for their religious slaughter, justifying the revival of long haul animal transport, and this presented further opportunities for trade.

The market of this type of transport is dominated by a few operators particularly from the Netherlands, Denmark and Kuwait. The large volumes of stock which are now transported

The livestock carrier Rabunion XIX *was one of a large fleet of coaster-size livestock carriers which operated mainly in the Mediterranean and Black Sea. The first vessel in the fleet,* Rabunion I *was acquired in 1974 and in the meantime the owners, Union Commercial Co, of Beirut, have sustained several losses, involving heavy loss of livestock. Meyer Werft, Papenburg, converted this vessel from the general cargo carrier* Beckumersand *in 1983, to its new role transporting 1276 head of cattle, or 15,574 head of sheep with pens constructed to meet Irish, British and Australian rules for carriage of livestock.* (FotoFlite)

The car carrier

from Australia and New Zealand to Arab countries has seen a corresponding increase in the size of the vessels. Several are over 25,000 tons gross, and the largest afloat in early 1992 was the Kuwaiti-owned *Al Shuwaikh*, built in 1967, of 34,082 grt. Like many others of this larger size, she is a converted tanker.

The further sophistication of this transport has brought about many rules and regulations: the Netherlands, Australia and the United States all have rules for sea transport of animals, and for animal type and weight a certain minimum required floorspace is prescribed. This varies for sheep, cattle, pigs, horses and goats. Other animals are dealt with individually according to general regulations.

The most often used basis for livestock carriers are general cargo vessels, but a few roros,

The pure car/truck carrier Madame Butterfly, *built by Kockums at Malmo, Sweden, has thirteen decks which can be clearly seen in this drawing. The midships section shows truck decks, normal car decks and hoistable decks. Three decks can be used as truck decks, and the car decks above these are hoistable. Truck capacity is about 530 units with 2900 cars, or combinations of these. Total truck area is 12,400 sq m and car area 24,700 sq m. The vessel is equipped with two external ramps, one quarter ramp at the stern with 50 tons load capacity and one amidships of 10 tons capacity.* (Kockums)

tankers, passenger ships, ferries and bulk carriers have been converted for this role. The animal pens are either placed in the holds or mounted on the upper deck. Today we are seeing more purpose-built ships because higher conversion costs brought about by stricter rules on loading and discharging, maximum carrying capacity is better realised within the given dimensions and better fuel optimisation.

The animal pens or stables are either in the hold, on deck, or both. There are various devices on board for animal care during the voyage, such as feeding equipment, drinking water system, water manufacturing system, manure removal and drainage system, fire fighting appliances, ventilation system and veterinarian equipment and humane killing device.

Further consideration is given to access means, pen dimensions and strength, lighting and ship stability in order to assure proper animal handling and transport. The intact stability when carrying livestock should meet certain set criteria taking into account shift of livestock, fodder and the effect of wind on the upper deck pen structure.

Because pigs have to be kept wet in hot climates as they have no means of perspiring, it is mainly cattle and sheep that are carried on the longer routes.

In the earlier days of the motor car it was not unusual for a few vehicles to be carried as hold cargo or after-deck cargo on lines voyaging to the European colonies or, for example, Argentina and Brazil.

When the Second World War ended, the automotive industry rapidly converted to peacetime production again and began to produce motor cars in ever-increasing quantities. Exports from America to Europe were resumed, and by the beginning of the 1950s, Europe had also begun to export cars to the US.

There were problems to be overcome, especially concerning the increase in the volume of vehicles loaded, the frequency of sailings, and the damage sustained by the vehicles. The time had passed when cars were boxed for transport, and existing ships were not suitable for transporting unboxed cars in such growing numbers as trade in the 1950s demanded. Cars are considered as lightweight goods, and ships' ballast tanks were not always large enough to provide sufficient stability to transport cars without damaging them.

One particular shipowner, Wallenius, of Sweden, which had some experience in the transport of vehicles, studied these problems closely and was able to develop a new design of vessel for the car transport trade. The first two, of what became the world's leading fleet in car

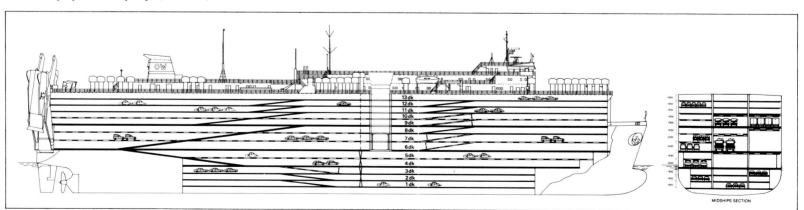

A floating advertisement for the manufacturers was the 16,867 grt car carrier Kyushu Maru, *owned by Nissan Senyosen Unyu KK, before the cars manufactured by this concern changed their popular name from Datsun to Nissan. The box-like build is typical of modern ocean-going car carriers. The stern quarter ramp, port side can be clearly seen in this FotoFlite picture and another port ramp is located between T and S of DATSUN in the hull legend. The majority of car carriers have a relatively fast service speed – that of* Kyushu Maru *is 19.25kts.*

transportation, *Rigoletto* and *Traviata*, were delivered in 1955, with loading through a side door and ramp.

They remained in service with Wallenius for several years and were improved by having two extra decks fitted (above deck). When these vessels were delivered, primarily for the trade to and from the Great Lakes, they could each load 290 cars. A vessel of conventional design on the Great Lakes run could load only 175 cars. With the opening of the St Lawrence Seaway in 1959, limitations on draught were eased and much larger vessels could enter the Great Lakes.

The idea of special car transport proved to be a practical success, manufacturers became interested and the demands for tonnage to meet their needs rose. More ships were ordered by Wallenius, not only for service to the Great Lakes, but also within northwest Europe.

Wallenius has retained its prominent position in the car transport trade for almost 40 years, and today operates a substantial fleet, named after ballets and operas, a long-established style for the company. The latest addition to the fleet, the 1991-built *Aida* (52,288 grt), has capacity for well over 6200 cars.

However, Wallenius now only has a relatively small proportion of the international trade, which is carried in a large world-wide fleet, many owned within Europe and Scandinavia, but the majority, not surprisingly, owned in Japan, with a substantial number from South Korea.

Nissan, Mitsubishi, Mazda, Honda and Hyundai, all ship their products on vessels produced in large numbers in Japanese and Korean shipyards in the 1970s, '80s and '90s. *Nissan Bluebird* and *Nissan Laurel*, both built in

1985, and over 47,000 grt, and a series of *Hyundai*s, leave no doubts as to whose products are carried.

From a single car carried in the hatch of a passenger ship, via the holds of a conventional lift-on/lift-off general cargo vessel to the decks of the roro freighter, we now find cars in large numbers carried in the designated car decks of the pure car carrier (PCC) and pure car truck carrier (PCTC).

The difference between the PCC and the PCTC lies in the height and construction of the decks: on the PCC only suitable for passenger cars; on the PCTC a few higher and stronger decks as well in order to accommodate larger vehicles and other rolling stock.

In the 1960s the full roro principle was introduced so apart from the entry ramp, internal ramps were also fitted connecting the various decks, allowing for a full roro cargo process.

The need for improved hold ventilation became apparent due to the exhaust fumes of all this roro-ing around inside the vessel. The sizes by 1963 had reached 1880 cars in 25,000 dwt vessels, named *Carmen* and *Medea*, and joining a rapidly-expanding fleet of car carriers by then owned by Wallenius. They were both built by AG Weser, Bremen. It was in 1965 that the first purpose built PCC entered service for a Norwegian operator.

An intermediate development, although not really successful, but worth mentioning was the car-bulk carrier and the roro-car-bulk carrier. The 1970s saw a few of these vessels mainly on the Japan trades, where maximisation of vessel use was sought after. Unlike round the world traders the Japan car trade was very much one way, due to Japanese import restrictions. Bulk material however was in high demand (to produce cars!) so it seemed logical that this particular combination would develop.

However, the rapid increase in the volume of vehicle exports from Japan and Korea has seen an increase in those countries' own car carrier fleets.

Usually 10–14 decks are fitted in the latest generation PCTCs, and of these 4–8 are full-strength construction decks and the others intermediate car decks only.

The sensitivity to transverse winds will be obvious due to the high superstructure. Therefore there is a need for bow and/or stern thrusters. The car deck heights vary from passenger car height 1.65m to light truck height 2.45m and the truck deck heights vary from 3.60 to 6.20m. An intensive ventilation system is required to avoid explosive or toxic atmospheres to develop.

Because of the roro concept transverse watertight bulkheads are omitted. Sometimes a longitudinal watertight bulkhead is fitted amidships reaching from inner-bottom to access deck. The advantages and disadvantages of this type of vessel are:

– less damage; no hatch cleaning; fast turn-around in ports; independent of shore cranes and facilities;
– restrictions due to standard, fixed, deck heights.

The forest products carrier

Forest products are shipped in many forms, including logs, sawn timber, pulp, wood-chips, and rolls of paper or board. The first transport of forest products was in the form of logs and this was on board traditional tween-decker general cargo vessels.

There has developed an increasing use of bulk carriers and latterly more specialised purpose-built roro and container vessels.

The first transport of processed timber was in packages on bulk carriers of up to about 15,000 grt, but because of the efficiency of bulk carriers, variations have been developed for more product-orientated carriage, including open-hatch bulkers, log carriers and wood-chip carriers.

The main trades are basically from large forestry regions to principal user regions, for example, British Columbia to world-wide destinations (sawn timber); logs from Malaysia and Indonesia to Japan; wood-chips from Australia, New Zealand, North and South America, to Japan; logs, sawn timber, pulp and paper from Russia and Scandinavia to the rest of Europe on short-sea trades.

The first so-called open-hatch bulk carriers, with large square flush holds without tween-decks, appeared in about 1963 and were suitable for most medium and long runs, whereas the roro was more appropriate for short-sea trading.

The log carrier

In 1974 MacMillan Bloedel Industries Ltd, Canada's largest forest owner and producer, took delivery of the 13,971 dwt log carrier *Haida Monarch*, to carry large quantities of logs from the company's own logging camps on the north end of Vancouver Island to sawmills at Port Alberni.

The vessel is a far cry from methods of a hundred years ago when logs were transported in the form of flat booms. In making up a flat boom, four logs are chained together to form a square. The square is then filled with loose logs and towed away by tugs to its destination.

In the summer of 1900, scores of spectators gathered near Brockton Point to watch the steam tug *Active* tow a record 20 sections of logs through First Narrows. Over the years, the sizes of booms have increased until tugs hauled up to 100 sections. These booms have two main disadvantages: some of the logs within a boom will become waterlogged during the long run down the coast and will drop out; and, if the tug and boom is caught in a storm, some logs may jump the boom, or a boom chain may break and scatter much of the 'cargo'.

Haida Monarch, owned by Kingcome Navigation Co, Vancouver, was the world's first self-discharging, or dumping, log carrier, and is a self-propelled version of its predecessor, the self-dumping barge. A bow thruster propeller enables the vessel to navigate in small sheltered bays and 'log ponds' where the log cargoes are kept. With the similar Haida Brave, this vessel is used primarily to transport logs from the Queen Charlotte Islands to the lower mainland of British Columbia, undertaking the round voyage in 5 days compared with the previous 7+ days of the towed barges. (John Hammond)

At the first sign of a storm, boom-towing tugs steered for shelter. It was not uncommon even three decades ago to see five tugs with their booms, sheltered behind an island for five days or more, riding out a storm. So flat rafts were not the most-efficient ways of transporting logs to sawmills.

Around 1916, the Davis raft was developed. Logs were chained together in huge bundles, resembling a huge floating cigar. Their disadvantage was that because they were four-fifths under water they were hard and slow to tow; and when they were unbundled some of the waterlogged logs dropped out and were lost.

Nevertheless, scores of Davis rafts were towed from the Queen Charlotte Islands to Vancouver, the spruce being loaded aboard ship during the First World War years to be sent to England to build fighter planes.

Shortly after the Second World War logs began to be towed down the coast in hulls of old sailing vessels, and in 1947, four laid-up tankers were towed to Vancouver from Venezuela for conversion to log barges.

In 1954, the first self-dumping barge was built, but it was not until 1961 that a self-loading, self-unloading barge was launched. In 1965, Island Tug & Barge Ltd built the world's largest self-loading, self-unloading barge – a vessel costing $1.75m, and measuring 111m in length and with a breadth of 24m. It could carry 2.75 million board feet of logs and it was towed by the 2400 bhp tug *Island Sovereign* at 8 knots. In 1974 the new MacMillan Bloedel vessel *Haida Monarch* appeared and was the world's first self-propelled, self-loading and self-unloading log barge. The engines had to have special mounts, and all equipment in the

living quarters for the thirteen-man crew had to be specially designed. The vessel has proved to be more manoeuvrable and faster than similar barges towed by tugs, and when the company was required to augment its fleet it opted to build another self-propelled vessel, appearing in 1978 with the name *Haida Brave*.

The trend, today, is away from flat booms and logs are sorted on dry land, instead of being dumped into the water to be sorted – with land sorting it is easier and quicker to load barges than to make up log booms.

Haida Monarch and her near-sister have the appearance of self-propelled carriers with bridge forward, machinery aft, and two deck cranes each with a capacity of 40 tonnes, whereas earlier non-propelled types were of barge construction and looked nothing more than that.

The method of operation commences with the loading of logs athwartships on deck and discharge, into water, is by listing the vessel. At first the vessel is ballasted down to a draught which will prevent too fierce a jumping-back after off-loading the cargo. The ballast is transferred within the hull by pumping and creates the required sliding list of about 35 degrees.

The employment of the type, particularly useful in British Columbia, has not been generally developed.

The wood-chip carrier

Many industries using wood as a basic raw material do not require this to be in the form of logs or planks. Small chips of wood produced by special cutting machines can be used in fibre-board, chipboard and hardboard manu-

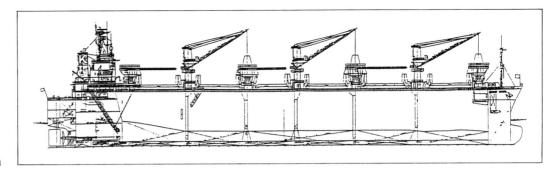

Side elevation of the Liberian-flag wood-chip carrier Sweet Brier, *built by Koyo Dockyard, Japan, in 1989, and with a cargo carrying capacity of 90,614cu m. The depth of the six holds (extreme 15.563m) can be clearly seen in this drawing. The three electric cranes each have a capacity of 14.5 tons. Length is 192.94m, breadth 32.22m, and depth to main deck 21.60m and draught 10.019m.* (Koyo Dockyard)

facturing, achieving considerable savings in transport costs and in the use of otherwise wasted material.

Europe and Japan are the biggest importers of wood-chips and the main routes are to these areas from the major timber producing areas – northwest coast of North America, southeast Asia and South America.

It was the Japanese who pioneered the type of vessel required for this trade in the 1960s, and at the end of that decade several vessels were in service. Amongst these were *Daiki Maru* (built 1968, 24,928 dwt), *Tonami Maru* (1969, 42,124 dwt) and *Nansho Maru* (1969, 26,531 dwt). The new vessels gradually replaced conventional bulk carriers which had been used in the trade, but as the cargo has a low specific gravity it was found feasible to build vessels of a lighter construction.

In the first vessels discharge was undertaken by grab cranes, but these were eventually replaced in some cases by conveyor belts, which are on board, as well as conveyors which feed the chips ashore.

A recent variant is a screw movement mechanism in the lower hold moving the cargo on to conveyor belts in the lower sidetanks, and from there up to the deck and overboard. As the whole process can take place inside the covered ship the cargo operations then become weather independent. A possible disadvantage of this development could be the space required by this equipment – roughly 15 per cent on a 35,000 grt vessel. The prospects of shipping chip-slurry is now being considered.

The Japanese have maintained their dominance in this trade, and in 1992, of the world fleet of 101 such vessels, no less than 84 were beneficially owned by Japanese interests. Of the remainder Taiwan owned four, Hong Kong interests four, and others were in groups controlled by European and eastern interests.

The majority of the vessels are between 40,000 and 47,000 tonnes deadweight. Some of the early vessels have already been scrapped, but in early 1992, two were still in existence, one in Japanese and one in Greek hands. The most prolific flag involved is that of Panama accounting for 55 of the vessels, followed by Liberia with 22, the majority of which were controlled by Japanese interests.

The largest of the vessels in service is *Forestal Esmerelda* (built 1988, 65,517 dwt), which has been employed in trade between Tasmania and Japan. The vessels employed on the British Columbia trade are restricted by their size and those of up to 45,000 dwt are usually found here. Many of the vessel's names, although generally unattractive, do give an indication of the geographical areas or trade in which they were intended, for example *Brazilian Sky*, *Forest Prince*, *Madang* and *Pacific Taio*. However, one which did emerge in 1992 does not follow this pattern – *Donald Duckling* – maybe reflecting the shipowner's taste in entertainment.

The lumber carrier

The lumber carried has developed in sophistication since the 1960s, and these developments have been made by a combination of the interests of shipowners and cargo shippers.

Lumber or sawn timber is usually shipped in rectangular bundles, and in order to avoid broken stowage and seafastening the shape of the hatch should match the shape of the cargo.

As the cargo is relatively light there is usually enough weight available to carry a considerable amount of deck cargo, calling for a well planned layout of deck and cargo handling equipment. As lumber only might not always be available combination shipments with newsprint or woodpulp do occur.

Scandinavian and British interests, Japanese, and northwest European shipowners have developed the rather ordinary bulk carrier type of

The newsprint and lumber carrier Thorseggen *(18,567 dwt), operates on the west coast of North America carrying its cargoes mainly between British Columbia and San Francisco/Los Angeles. Many of the ports at which the vessel calls do not have shore cargo handling gear and it is here that* Thorseggen's *two gantry cranes of 25 tons capacity are put into use. Built by Swan Hunter Shipbuilders, Wallsend, it is owned by British investment house 3i plc, and managed by Norsk Pacific Steamship Co, of Walnut Creek, California.* (FotoFlite)

the 1960s into the self-loading and discharging carrier of the present day.

The newer breed of carrier has large rectangular holds and hatch openings and a common feature is a double skin creating straight rectangular holds and flush inner hatches, allowing exact fitting of cargo, almost the timber trades' equivalent of the fully-cellular containership.

Deck cranes are an important feature and these are usually on elevated mounts enabling lowering of jibs even when deck cargo reaches a considerable height.

Although there are many minor variations in Japanese vessels in the trades, in Europe two which have proved to be both popular and successful are 'standard' types produced in Norway and Germany.

In the 1960s and '70s the Fredriksstad shipyard of Norway produced a series of vessels, for a number of owners, of about 22,500 grt and 38,400 dwt. They each had six hatches and could carry over 45,000 cubic metres of timber. The majority had six deck cranes each with a capacity of 15 tons and this allowed rapid simultaneous loading and discharge from each hold.

Later in the 1970s the Flensburg shipyard in Germany launched a series of vessels for European owners including *Thamesfield* for Hunting & Son Ltd of Newcastle-upon-Tyne. This 50,300 dwt bulk carrier, designed for the carriage of lumber, pulp and newsprint, emerged from the Flensburg yard in November 1977.

Six larger hatches and holds gave a capacity of 64,060cu m, and six cranes of 20 tons capacity each were installed.

The newsprint carrier

A number of Baltic countries have forest products as a major export item, and in particular reels of paper for newspaper production. Although not a very spectacular design, specialised ships have been constructed for this type of cargo.

Initially general cargo vessels were used but there are some specific requirements which made it logical to aim for specialised vessels.

Arthur Guinness Son & Co Ltd of Dublin owned its first vessels in the 1870s, but it was in much later years that it carried its well-known product in 'tankers'. At Dublin the 1345 grt The Lady Patricia *(built 1962) loads Guinness from a road tanker into the sixteen independent stainless steel tanks on board. Since the Second World War the Guinness company has employed several vessels trading across the Irish Sea, the latest being the 1976-built* Miranda Guinness. *(Arthur Guinness)*

Furthermore much of the trade is short-sea so the use of the roro concept became common and, in order to assure maximum versatility general roro cargo can very well also be transported along with paper products.

Apart from roro facilities and a high degree of cleanliness, dewpoint control is an important aspect of these vessels. Therefore a sophisticated cargo ventilation system may be required, especially when carrying reeled paper.

In addition to the dehumidifier system, another dewpoint control system has been introduced which is said to be more flexible and economic. It is the so-called Inductherm system, where by means of hot water radiators and fans, the hold air is heated until above dewpoint, thus omitting the risk of sweating cargo as the warmer air is able to contain more moisture than cold air. In some designs the holds are lined with plyboard material in order to protect the sensitive cargo from mechanical damage as well, all light fixtures are in recessed alcoves in the holds and no water or discharge pipes are lead through the hold above the cargo. Pallet handling can either be via a roro ramp or through a side loader/pallet lift combination with short conveyor belts. Ships' own electrical forklift trucks complement the equipment.

However, newsprint carriage is by no means restricted to roro vessels and many ocean-going bulk carriers are able to accommodate this type of cargo, either as a full load or as part cargo.

Tanker variants

The wine and alcohol tanker

Wine and alcohol has been shipped in casks for centuries. After the Second World War, it was carried in special deep tanks from South Africa to Europe, and today the international trade from South Africa and Australia has been containerised.

The European wine trade is dominated by France and Italy, which together with Spain have extensive vineyards and annually export large quantities of wine in bulk to be bottled by the importer. Argentina, Portugal, the United States, Russia, Algeria, and Morocco also produce large volumes of wine and alcohol for shipment by sea.

French and Italian vessels are dominant in the carriage of wine by sea, and Russia is also involved to a much lesser degree. The largest fleet of wine tankers is operated by Vinalmar SA, of Geneva, Switzerland, which also uses its vessels in the chemical trades.

The practice of carrying wine in bulk in tankers seems to have been introduced first after the Second World War when in 1946 the 1899 dwt tanker *Sloughs* was built.

In addition to wine and alcohol tankers some specialised carriers have been developed for the distribution of popular brands of beer, amongst these being the well-known Irish Sea vessels owned by Guinness of Dublin.

Because of high value and demand factors

wine and alcohol tankers tend to be small, ranging from 1200 dwt to about 6000 dwt. There are about forty suitable vessels available for this trade as many smaller chemical carriers can be used.

Basically a suitable tanker would be in the size range indicated and have stainless steel tanks and be able to ensure that the temperature on the voyage does not exceed 27 °C.

The wine tanks should also be fitted with an air fan and a suitable 'gas' warning system is necessary. Many of the ships are owned and operated by shipping companies engaged in the chemical trades whereas the beer carriers are usually owned by the producers.

The fruit juice carrier

Demand for fruit juices, particularly orange and more recently apple juice, has been growing steadily during the last two decades.

Traditionally the juice has been carried in drums and tank containers or containers (standard 20ft) fitted internally with flexible bags. Standard containers so fitted can carry up to 20,000 litres.

However on certain routes from the main orange growers to the United States and Europe the demand is sufficient to make special fruit juice tankers viable.

The first such ship appropriately named *Orange Blossom* (9984 grt) was built in Norway and delivered to Atlantic Reefer Corp of Liberia in 1985. The beneficial owners are a Swiss

concern. The second, *Bebedouro* was built in South Korea and delivered in August 1986.

The tanks are lined with smooth stainless steel to meet World Health Organization requirements. All welds inside the tanks are polished and all surfaces which come into contact with the cargo are passivated and sterilised. Because of the need for smooth surfaces, all stiffening members are fitted outside the tanks. They are fixed to the main structure of the ship by transverse, rather than longitudinal, members since this should minimise the effects of hull flexing on tanks. There are also adequate tank cleaning facilities.

Because of the high density of concentrated orange juice (about 1.32 tonne/m³) substantial volume is needed to maintain buoyancy. There are design spaces between the cargo tanks, used to circulate cooled air for refrigerating the cargo. A sophisticated computer-based monitoring system is also fitted allowing the cargo to be monitored at several key places throughout the ship.

The ships are fitted with a cooling plant designed to maintain a temperature of −7 °C, the same temperature at which the juice is loaded. Nitrogen is used to prevent the cargo from oxidising, and the tanks are kept inerted even when they are empty. This helps reduce any risk of bacterial development and mould growth.

No other cargo can be carried in these specialist vessels and return voyages are in ballast.

Other vessels have been converted for this

The world's first purpose-built orange juice carrier is Orange Blossom, *built in 1985 by Trosvik Verksted, Brevik, Norway, for Atlantic Reefer Corp Inc, Liberia, an associate of Atlanship SA, Switzerland. The vessel carries 12,200 tonnes of frozen orange juice concentrate in bulk at −12 °C, plus about 300 tonnes of orange peel oil. The pioneering vessel in a new concept, this vessel was evolved by Atlanship in conjunction with Danish naval architects Dwinger Marine.* Orange Blossom *is now one of a small and modern fleet of specialised carriers for the transportation of orange juice, a trade which has expanded considerably since the mid-1980s, particularly from Brazil to the US and northwest Europe.* (Atlanship)

specialist role, one being the former Blue Star Line refrigerated cargo ship *Andalucia Star*, which was altered in 1987 by Bremer-Vulkan at Vegesack.

The conversion of the vessel, which was built in 1975, consisted mainly of the installation of twenty independent stainless steel tanks, welded to the hull's steel plating.

The molten sulphur tanker

Sulphur and its derivative sulphuric acid is used in large quantities as an artificial fertiliser and also in many industrial processes.

It is exported in large quantities from the United States, Mexico, Canada, Poland, France and Iran, and although it can be and is carried in conventional bulk carriers it does present difficulties because of dust, and is liable to ignite and explode and interact in various ways with the vessel structure.

Following the Second World War experiments were made in carrying sulphur in molten form and by the 1960s a regular trade from the United States in specialised tankers was established. Many of the carriers then in service were converted tankers built during the Second World War, but some new tonnage did enter the market on charter to US operators.

In 1991 there were about thirty vessels capable of carrying molten sulphur with sizes varying from 1000 to 30,000 dwt.

Sulphur solidifies at about 114 °C and becomes very viscous above 160 °C. Therefore to be transported in molten form it needs to be carried at a temperature between 138 °C and 155 °C. This temperature is maintained on board ship by circulating steam through acid resistant stainless steel coils on the tank bottom.

The tanks are usually rectangular and independent and insulated from the main body of the ship and must also have a good ventilation system to ensure that gases generated can escape at predetermined positions and at sufficiently safe distances from the working areas.

Each tank is filled with deepwell pumps which operate automatically during loading and discharge. The pumps and their lines are double skinned so that steam can be circulated to maintain the 140 °C during cargo transfer. Some of the ships are fitted with 'slurry tanks' so they can carry liquid chemical slurry on the return voyage.

A typical ship of the type is the Polish *Tarnobrzeg*, built in 1973 and she was one of four ships built in Sweden for the Polish Steamship Co of Gdynia. Designed for use on the Poland/Rotterdam/United Kingdom trade, this ship incorporates four insulated centre tanks for the carriage of molten sulphur and 16 tanks for the carriage of oil and oil products. It can also carry sulphuric acid in its centre tanks.

The Ship Research Institute at Szczecin has presented the idea of a sulphur-propelled floating sulphuric acid plant. The ship would load sulphur and deliver sulphuric acid using the heat generated by the process to propel the ship.

The phosphoric acid tanker

Phosphoric acid is an intermediate stage in the chain from phosphate rock to finished fertiliser.

The development of the world phosphoric acid movement has provided considerable employment since the late 1960s. Before that there were some coastal tankers and tank barges operating around the United States coast. Since 1969 world trade in phosphoric acid has grown considerably, standing at some 38 billion tonne miles in 1990. Major producers are North America, Russia and a number of others, including Morocco.

Clarkson's Tanker Register 1990 listed twelve vessels specified as phosphoric acid tankers.

Eleven have deadweights between 10,000 and 23,000 tonnes and one is of 59,800 dwt. There are many other smaller coastal vessels and standard chemical carriers can be used. There are some forty major terminals throughout the world specialising in the handling of phosphoric acid.

Basically it is a dedicated chemical carrier where the cargo tanks are either high grade stainless steel or rubber-line coated. Heating coils in the tank are corrosion resistant (cargo, liquifies at 40 °C and is carried around 50 °C).

Because of the tendency of the phosphoric acid to form sludge, means must be provided, in the form of, for example, an agitator, to keep the sediment permanently in suspension so that only a very small quantity remains in the tank after discharge.

In each centre tank and slop tank the cargo is pumped on to the tank bottom and returned through a diffusor on the tank bottom. By forcing the cargo through the diffuser a flow is created in selected directions and angles, strong enough to erode the layer of sediments which have settled on the tank bottom.

Additional features usually also include independent ventilation lines, vapour return connection and provision for nitrogen blanketing.

Many of the vessels involved in this trade are operated or owned by Marphocean, the Moroccan agency concerned with export of this commodity.

The molasses tanker

The molasses tanker in this specialised carrier section is different in two major respects. Firstly it is a relatively low value cargo and secondly it is probably the oldest specialised carrier mentioned in this section. Athel Line, a well-known British molasses tanker fleet, was formed in 1939 to take over the fleet of the United Molasses Co but the first recorded bulk movement of molasses by tanker seems to have been in 1912 when *Sunlight* discharged 1800 tons in Hull after a transatlantic crossing from Santa Domingo in the West Indies.

Molasses is a product of cane sugar and sugar beet with a long sea transport pedigree, being

The small, but modern, merchant fleet of Morocco includes a number of specialist carriers, particularly in the oil-related and chemical fields. Amongst these is the chemical carrier Azzahraoui, *owned by Société Maroc Phosphor Ocean (Marphocean), a shipping company formed by the national line and Office Cherifien des Phosphates. The vessel has a cargo capacity of 7250cu m in seven tanks and was built by the France-Dunkerque shipyard, Dunkirk, in 1982. (FotoFlite)*

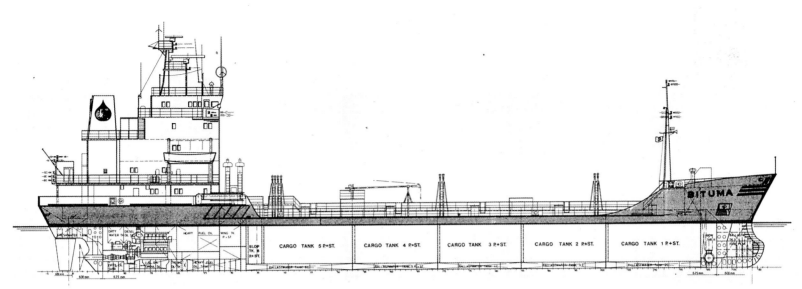

The 2750 dwt bitumen carrier Bituma, *is managed by a firm in Kungsbacka, Sweden, and operates mainly in northwest Europe and Scandinavian waters. Typical of bitumen carriers, many of which operate in Europe, she can also load oils and certain chemicals up to 2837m². The cargo heating installation can maintain a temperature of 200 °C.* (Partrederiet for ms Bituma)

shipped back from the West Indies in casks by returning 'slavers'. By 1980 Brazil was the largest exporter, shipping out over one million tonnes in that year.

Up to the 1950s, however, a molasses tanker was virtually interchangeable with the standard all-purpose tanker of that period that was fitted with steam reciprocating pumps. Athel tankers were frequently used for carrying oil, and it was not unusual for oil tankers to carry molasses.

However when in the 1960s oil tankers become bigger, more specialised and fitted with centrifugal pumps the molasses tanker became more identifiable as a specialised carrier.

The specialised tanker section of *Clarkson's Tanker Register* 1990 identifies about 125 ships between 5000 and 30,000 dwt as molasses/chemical tankers or molasses/oil tankers.

Compared to oil, molasses is a heavy cargo having a specific gravity of 1:34. A molasses tanker therefore needs to be of stronger construction.

At normal temperatures molasses is very viscous and to facilitate discharge it needs to be heated to around 40 °C. It is also more difficult to pump than the oil which is why even modern molasses tankers keep to the older steam reciprocating pumps or perhaps have electrically driven screw pumps.

Molasses also has a high degree of expansion so there must be adequate ullage space and obviously a reasonable degree of cleanliness is required.

The asphalt/bitumen carrier

Of all petroleum products, asphalt or bitumen is the oldest in the service of mankind and the earliest recorded use was by the pre-

Babylonian inhabitants of the Euphrates valley in Iraq about 3800 to 2500BC. The term 'asphalt' has different meanings in different countries. There are in fact many different grades and types of asphalt/bitumen.

Native asphalt is a material resin formed by the natural drying up of rock oil or petroleum in its bed, deposits of which are found in Trinidad, Cuba, Venezuela, Peru, France, Russia, Greece, the United States, and other countries. The best known and largest are those of Venezuela and Trinidad.

Asphalt or asphaltum (bitumen) is also obtained from petroleum by distillation and is exported in large quantities from the Caribbean and certain other oil producing and refining countries. About 80 per cent of the world production in bitumen is used in road construction which has been an area of tremendous growth since the Second World War. During the 1970s world production of bitumen increased by over 40 per cent but since then there has been a decline in bitumen tanker tonnage.

Bitumen has a specific gravity of about '1' and a viscosity (Redwood) of 500,000 secs and has a high flash point.

Traditionally much of the bitumen/asphalt trade had been carried in drums but since the late 1920s converted tankers (tar boats) began to appear for the carriage of bitumen, eg *Arthur W Sewell*, built 1926, 6030 grt was the first such conversion.

Clarkson's Tanker Register 1990 lists less than twenty such vessels between 5000 and 30,000 dwt although there are many other smaller vessels in this trade. There are about seventy-five bitumen carriers the majority of which are less than 5000 dwt.

An interesting development reported in 1989 is the carriage of emulsified asphalt in

conventional tankers. This emulsion is made by emulsifying 50–70 per cent by weight of asphalt in presence of 0–5 to 0–1 per cent by weight of emulsifying agent, usually soap.

The basic problems of carriage are *heating* the cargo adequately so it can load/discharge in a liquid state, rugged efficient pumps and the problems of *cleaning*. The tanker must therefore have adequate heating arrangements as the carrying temperature should be about 180 °C (oxidised bitumen is carried at temperatures of 220 °C). Modern bitumen carriers have a complete double skin to act as insulation. Without this insulation some carriers allow the bottom layers to cool to a semi plastic condition which acts as an excellent insulator. Because of the high loading and carrying temperatures the tanks need to be preheated for at least 12 hours to reduce hull stress. This preheating also evaporates any water and reduces the risk of valves sticking. Heat monitoring equipment for each tank and level is also obviously required and wooden clogs are usually provided for the crew walking on the hot decks.

The double skin also enables the tanks to be kept free of stiffening construction which greatly assists in cleaning.

The alkyl lead compounds carrier

Alkyl lead compounds cover the range of lead additives used in the manufacture of gasoline as anti-knock agents. The more commonly used of these are the tetraethyl and tetramethyl leads. These chemicals are classified by IMO as dangerous cargoes and marine pollutants (volatile and emits toxic vapours).

Lead compounds may be carried in bulk or packaged form, the latter is governed by the IMDG code for the carriage of dangerous goods in packaged form. Where alkyl lead compounds are carried in bulk the problem of last cargo compatibility requires that dedicated tankers be used.

Specialised ships for the carriage of lead compounds can be traced back as early as the 1950s (*Essi Kari* and *Eid*), when the market was dominated by two companies (Gatx Corp and Ruud-Pedersen) with a combined fleet of nine vessels ranging in deadweight from 2430 to 18,112 tons, and chartering out ships to chemical companies. *Clarkson's Tanker Register* (1992) shows only three specialised carriers over 5000 dwt and these are about 16,000 dwt.

In keeping with the wide distribution of oil refineries today and the reduction in the use of lead compounds in gasoline manufacture (especially in United States) the tankers have largely retained their small sizes and one would assume that with the modern drive for lead-free petrol that this must be a declining trade.

In accordance with the IBC and damage stability requirements of SOLAS the ship should be 'IMO class type 2' with the following technical features:

Tanks – independent self-supporting tanks to minimise damage to tank in event of hull damage.

Gauging system – must be closed-type, thus while penetrating the tanks it must be completely sealed off from the atmosphere.

Tank vent system – tank ventilation system to be at a minimum B/3 or 6m above main weather deck (B = ship's moulded breadth).

Ventilation system – for closed space containing cargo handling equipment or where work is performed on cargo the system should be such as to allow for air changes at 45 per hour with exhaust outlets 12m from ventilation inlets.

The cement carrier

Cement can be carried in bulk on conventional bulk carriers and a large proportion of the trade is transported in this way. However, loading and discharge does create the environmental problem of dust and delays can be incurred by rain. During the voyage, there is also the possibility that the cargo will compact, and this will cause problems upon discharge.

For these reasons, specialist cement carriers have been developed, and these have a self-loading/discharging capability allowing a fast rate of loading (averaging 1200 tonnes/hour) and discharge of up to 1000 tonnes per hour. There are several types of cargo system and these vary, either with mechanical (earlier vessels) or pneumatic (later vessels) or a combination of these depending on the type of hull or the size of vessel or even trade requirements.

The first self-unloading cement carrier seems to have been the Swedish-owned motor vessel *Vika*. However, carriage of cement by sea was nothing new then. In the UK the Blue Circle Group when trading as Associated Portland Cement Manufacturers Ltd had its first cement carrier in service in 1900, and amongst other early examples Wilsons of New Zealand apparently had a cement carrier in service in 1915, and Cementa AB of Sweden entered the market in 1924.

There are now hundreds of vessels afloat which have been purpose-built or converted for the carriage of cement in bulk. Conversions allowed alternative employment for redundant or potentially redundant non-purpose built tonnage. An example of this was the conversion in 1956 of the former 'Liberty' ship *Janet Lord Roper* (built 1943) which became *Florida State*. She had already been *shortened* and converted to a self-discharging collier in 1948, so the amount of conversion work required was minimal.

Elsewhere in the United Sates, Cement Transit Co, of Cleveland, have in service the 1906-built self-unloader *Medusa Challenger* (6967 grt), probably the oldest cement carrier afloat. Several Great Lakers have been involved in the carriage of cement, often being conversions from ore or coal carriers.

Today's large fleet of carriers are to be found world-wide, with proliferations in the America's, Europe and the Far East, particularly Japan and Taiwan. Aalborg Portland Cement of Denmark has one of the most modern and largest carriers, the 1984-built *Dania Portland*, which has a capacity of 29,750 cubic metres.

At the very top end of the scale, although not strictly carriers, but nevertheless having the capability, are vessels owned and operated by Red Sea Cement Jeddah Co Ltd, of Saudi Arabia. Purchased and converted from tankers, these vessels have been utilised to satisfy the enormous consumption of cement in Saudi Arabia. Based in Jeddah, the largest, described variously as a floating factory/store/self-discharger, is the 111,788 dwt *Red Sea Cement*, converted in 1981 from the Japanese tanker *Kikuwa Maru*. Although an extreme example,

The 25,400 dwt cement carrier Helvetia, *built in 1980, was converted from a conventional bulk carrier in 1982, at the J J Sietas shipyard in Hamburg. Helvetia was built at the G Dimitrov Shipyard, Varna, Bulgaria, for Cement Suppliers SA, Panama, an associate of Deutsche Afrika-Linien GmbH, Hamburg. Her six holds have a total cement capacity of 32,478cu m and her self-unloading gantry can be seen clearly in this FotoFlite picture.*

the same group has other such vessels ranging from 54,000 to 95,000 tonnes.

For domestic and short and short-sea routes bulk cement carriers are usually in the 3000–7000 dwt range, and on deep-sea voyages the most common are up to 30,000 dwt.

Conclusion

From such a differing collection of ship types it is difficult to draw many firm conclusions, but it does seem possible to discern certain patterns, ie that there does seem to have been a considerable emergence of specialised ships following the Second World War and in the 1960s and '70s but relatively little since then.

One could perhaps make the obvious deduction that for specialised ships to emerge successfully from concept to reality (and many 'good' ideas such as submarine tankers never seem to bridge that gap) there must be – (a) high demand but relatively low freight rates which means only efficient sea transport can be economically successful and (b) a relatively stable period of trade to make the long term 'risk' involved in a non-flexible capital investment justifiable. Both the above conditions existed in the 1950s, '60s and early '70s.

Furthermore the risk takers for these developments will usually be either shipping companies, 'vertically integrated' into multinational enterprises, or ship operators with long-term contracts of affreightment to such enterprises or with operations on specific well established routes which have dedicated terminals to serve their needs.

With regard to the future, we have in some cases indicated directions in which the particular specialised ship might develop. Generally their growth and further refinement will depend on demand, profitability, and market stability and changes in safety and liability legislation.

However a possible development could be the change in philosophy in some trades from 'fitting the ship to the cargo' to 'fitting the cargo to the ship', which certainly does seem to hold considerable potential for the future.

Is the carriage of emulsified asphalt in conventional tankers an example of this?

**Professor P M Alderton
and Captain S Cross**

Typical heavy-lift vessels in service since 1945

Ship	Flag	Built	By	GRT DWT	Length (oa) × breadth × depth × draught Feet–Inches Metres	Cargo handling gear	Engines	Speed	Remarks
General cargo vessels with heavy-lift derricks									
BELPAREIL	Nor	1926	Vickers-Armstrong, Newcastle	7203 10,282	427–10 × 68–8 × 33–6 × 24–6 *130.39 × 20.92 × 10.21 × 7.47*	Derricks 3 × 125 tons (200 tons in tandem), 12 × 5 tons	2 Armstrong-Whitworth/Sulzer diesels, 1700ihp; 2 shafts	12kts	Crew 40
BENALBANACH	UK	1946	Vickers-Armstrong, Newcastle	7795 10,450	469–10 × 66–8 × 33–6 × 26–7 *143.19 × 20.32 × 10.21 × 8.09*	Derricks 3 × 120 tons, 6 × 10 tons, 6 × 5 tons	2 Metro-Vickers steam turbines, 6800shp; 1 shaft	15kts	
PETER RICKMERS	WG	1962	Rickmers, Bremerhaven	9643 13,670	496–7 × 67–2 × 40–4 × 31–5 *159.7 × 20.48 × 12.3 × 9.58*	Derricks 2 × 130 tons, (Stülcken), 12 × 5–10 tons, 6 × 5 tons	1 MAN diesel, 7800bhp; 1 shaft	17.5kts	7 holds 5 hatches
STRATHEDEN	UK	1977	Stocznia Gdanska, Gdansk	12,598 16,641	557–4 × 76–2 × 43–8 × 32–0 *169.88 × 23.22 × 13.31 × 9.77*	Derricks 1 × 300 tons, 4 × 5 tons; cranes 5 × 12.5 tons, 2 × 5 tons	1 Cegielski/Sulzer diesel, 13,200bhp; 1 shaft	18kts	4 holds, 5 hatches, 368 TEUs
Dockships									
DOCKLIFT 1	Pan	1972	Verolme, Heusden	2425 4099	346–9 × 67–4 × 34–5 × 16–4 *105.7 × 20.53 × 10.49 × 4.98*	Cranes 2 × 320 tons; stern door	6 Caterpillar diesels, 5100bhp; 2 shafts	12.75kts	1 hold 1 hatch
DOCK EXPRESS 10	Ne	1979	Verolme, Heusden	5495 7071 (open) 13,000 (closed)	504–6 × 88–0 × 49–3 (upper deck) 504–6 × 88–0 × 21–4 (closed) *153.78 × 26.83 × 15.02 (upper deck) × 6.5 (closed)*	Cranes 2 × 500 tons	2 Stork-Werkspoor diesels, 8500bhp; 2 shafts	16kts	1 hold 1 hatch
Semi-submersible heavy lift vessels									
DAN LIFTER	Bhs	1982	Mitsubishi HI, Nagasaki	10,281 13,282	456–0 × 105–7 × 27–11 × 19–9 *138.99 × 32.19 × 8.51 × 6.02*	Submerges to max draught 14.5m	2 Mitsubishi/MAN diesels, 9000bhp; 2 shafts	13kts	
MIGHTY SERVANT 1	Ne	1983	Oshima Zosen, Nagasaki	19,954 23,760	525–7 × 132–5 × 39–5 × 31–2 *160.2 × 40.37 × 12.02 × 9.51*	Submerges; derrick 1 × 250 tons	2 Stork-Werkspoor diesels 18,370bhp driving 2 generators each 6500kW connected to 4 electric motors each 4215shp; 2 shafts	14.25kts	

Typical waste carriers since 1974

Ship	Flag	Built	By	GRT DWT (Cargo capacity m³)	Length (oa) × breadth × depth × draught Feet–Inches Metres	Cargo handling gear	Engines	Speed	Remarks
Irradiated nuclear fuel									
SIGYN	Fra	1982	At & Ch du Havre, Le Havre	4166 1249 (—)	296–4 × 59–2 × 21–10 × 13–1 *90.33 × 18.04 × 6.66 × 4.01*	Ramp	1 B&W Alpha diesel, 3180bhp; 1 shaft	11kts	
					Carries irradiated nuclear fuel in 10 special flasks (1200m³); or 64 TEUs				
Chemical waste									
L'ARTHA	Fra	1974	Fr Krupp, Druisburg	1483 2700 (1800)	262–6 × 37–5 × 18–5 × 14–9 *80.02 × 11.41 × 5.62 × 4.49*	—	2 Baudouin diesels, 1280bhp; 2 shafts	8kts	
Sludge discharge									
DIVIS II	UK	1979	Jas Lamont, Port Glasgow	820 892 (800 tonnes)	183–9 × 36–8 × 16–5 × 10–10 *56.01 × 11.18 × 5.01 × 3.31*	—	2 Mirrlees Blackstone diesels, 1370bhp; 2 shafts	10.5kts	
Incinerator									
VESTA	WG	1979	Gutenhoff Sterkrade, Walsum	999 1716 (1116)	235–7 × 36–5 × 17–3 × 14–1 *71.8 × 11.1 × 5.26 × 4.3*	—	1 Mannheim diesel, 1200bhp; 1 shaft	11.25kts	

Typical vehicle carriers since 1955

Ship	Flag	Built	By	GRT DWT	Length (oa) × breadth × depth × draught Feet–Inches Metres	Cargo handling gear	Engines	Speed	Remarks
RIGOLETTO TRAVIATA	Swe	1955	Kieler Howaldtswerke, Kiel	1905 2776	258–0 × 43–0 × 32–0 × 18–7 *78.63 × 13.11 × 9.75 × 5.66*	Cranes 4; derricks 2 × 3 tons	1 Kieler/MAN diesel, 2000bhp; 1 shaft	12.5kts	290/350 cars
DON JUAN DON CARLOS	Swe	1975 1976	Wartsila, Turku	14,480 15,000	664–9 × 92–4 × 69–10 × 28–0 *202.62 × 28.15 × 21.29 × 8.53*	Side loading ramps	1 Wartsila/Sulzer diesel, 17,400bhp; 1 shaft	19kts	5000 cars
HUAL LISITA	Nor	1980	Tsuneishi Zosen, Numakuma	14,155 12,003	590–7 × 96–0 × 41–1 × 27–11 *180.02 × 29.27 × 12.53 × 8.50*	Quarter stern door, side door	1 Mitsui/B&W diesel, 11,200bhp; 1 shaft	17.5kts	3500 cars
MADAME BUTTERFLY	Swe	1981	Kockums, Malmo	18,728 28,223	655–2 × 105–11 × 102–4 × 38–1 *199.7 × 32.29 × 31.2 × 11.61*	Quarter stern door, side door	1 Gotaverken/Sulzer diesel, 13,500bhp; 1 shaft	19.6kts	6150 cars or 2900 cars/ 530 trucks
NOPAL BARBRO	Nor	1983	Mitsui E & SB, Tamano	20,299 17,863	638–1 × 105–8 × 65–2 × 31–11 *194.49 × 32.21 × 19.87 × 9.72*	Quarter stern door, side door	1 Mitsubishi-MAN/ B&W diesel, 18,400bhp; 1 shaft	19.7kts	5630 cars/ 356 TEUs
FALSTAFF	Swe	1985	Hitachi Zosen, Innoshima	51,858 28,070	664–0 × 105–11 × 70–0 × 38–3 *202.39 × 32.29 × 21.34 × 11.66*	Quarter stern door, side door	1 Hitachi/B&W diesel, 16,980bhp; 1 shaft	19.5kts	6180 cars or 3100 cars/ 500 trucks
HYUNDAI NO 106	Pan	1987	Hyundai HI, Ulsan	41,721 12,939	604–4 × 100–6 × 90–7 × 27–0 *184.21 × 30.64 × 27.61 × 8.22*	Quarter stern door, side door	1 Hyundai/B&W diesel, 14,408bhp; 1 shaft	19.5kts	4800 cars

Typical modern livestock carriers

Ship	Flag	Built	By	GRT DWT	Length (oa) × breadth × depth × draught Feet–Inches Metres	Capacity	Engines	Speed	Remarks
RABUNION XIX	Leb	1970	C Lühring, Brake	1599 3326	302–6 × 44–7 × 23–7 × 20–0 92.21 × 13.59 × 7.19 × 6.09	Cattle 1276, Sheep 15,574	1 KHD diesel, 3000bhp; 1 shaft	15kts	Converted from general cargo 1983
BENWALID	Tur	1973	Appledore SBs, Appledore	5395 4184	375–8 × 44–5 × 35–0 × 22–6 114.5 × 13.55 × 10.65 × 6.85	Cattle 2115, Sheep 21,400	1 Crossley Premier/ Pielstick diesel, 6000bhp; 1 shaft	15.5kts	Converted from container vessel 1986; 13 decks

Typical forest products carriers since 1965

Ship	Flag	Built	By	GRT DWT (Cargo capacity m³)	Length (oa) × breadth × depth × draught Feet–Inches Metres	Cargo handling gear	Engines	Speed	Remarks
Log-carrier HAIDA MONARCH	Can	1974	Yarrows, Victoria, BC	9519 13,971 (7075)	423–3 × 88–0 × 29–0 × 20–7 129.01 × 26.98 × 8.84 × 6.27	Cranes 2 × —	2 General Motors diesels 7200bhp; 2 shafts	12kts	Discharge list up to 40°
Wood-chip carriers DAIKI MARU	Jap	1968	Uraga HI, Yokosuka	18,799 24,928 (45,669)	551–4 × 82–2 × 35–6 × 56–2 168.03 × 25.05 × 17.12 × 10.82	Cranes 2 × 10.5 tons	1 Uraga/Sulzer diesel 8000bhp; 1 shaft	14kts	6 holds, 6 hatches
SCANSPRUCE	Lib	1977	Imabara Zsn, Muragame	32,715 38,408 (81,504)	639–10 × 98–7 × 68–11 × 34–0 195.03 × 30.05 × 21.01 × 10.36	Derricks 3 × 11 tons	1 Mitsubishi/Sulzer diesel 12,000bhp; 1 shaft	14.75kts	6 holds, 6 hatches
FORESTAL ESMERALDA	Pan	1988	Koyo DY Co, Mihara	48,717 65,517 (127,452)	751–3 × 114–11 × 61–8 × 39–5 228.97 × 35.04 × 22.5 × 12.02	Cranes 3 × 14.5 tons	1 Mitsubishi diesel 10,600bhp; 1 shaft	14kts	6 holds, 6 hatches
OJI UNIVERSE	Pan	1991	Shin Kurushima, Onishi	38,679 46,899 (99,839)	631–8 × 106–2 × 73–4 × 36–2 192.54 × 32.25 × 22.35 × 11.03	Cranes 3 × 14.5 tons	1 Kobe/Mitsubishi diesel 10,000bhp; 1 shaft	14.5kts	6 holds 6 hatches
Timber/lumber carriers ROALD JARL	Nor	1965	Fredriksstad MV, Fredrikstad	21,937 35,562 (41,201)	634–4 × 86–2 × 50–3 × 36–6 193.35 × 26.27 × 15.32 × 11.14	Cranes 6 × 8 tons	1 Fredriksstad/ Gotaverken diesel, 10,700bhp; 1 shaft	14.5kts	7 holds, 7 hatches
STOVE CAMPBELL	Nor	1973	Fredriksstad MV, Fredrikstad	22,495 38,406 (45,332)	634–7 × 86–1 × 52–9 × 38–7 193.43 × 26.24 × 16.08 × 11.77	Cranes 6 × 15 tons	1 Fredriksstad/ Gotaverken diesel, 10,700bhp; 1 shaft	15kts	6 holds, 6 hatches
THAMESFIELD	UK	1977	Flensburger Schiffsb, Flensburg	30,428 50,300 (64,060)	700–0 × 100–0 × 56–9 × 39–11 213.37 × 30.48 × 17.3 × 12.16	Cranes 6 × 20 tons	1 MAN diesel, 16,000bhp; 1 shaft	16kts	6 holds, 6 hatches
BELTIMBER	Sgp	1985	Tsuneishi Zosen, Numakuma	27,470 39,240 (46,793)	654–2 × 97–10 × 48–1 × 33–11 199.4 × 29.82 × 14.66 × 10.35	Cranes 2 × 40 tons, 1 × 10 tons	1 Mitsubishi/B&W diesel, 10,970bhp; 1 shaft	15kts	7 holds, 7 hatches, 1780 TEUs
Newsprint carriers THORSEGGEN	UK	1983	Swan Hunter SBs, Wallsend	14,578 18,567 (24,650)	544–0 × 82–2 × 40–11 × 26–11 165.82 × 25.05 × 12.48 × 8.2	Cranes 2 × 25 tons	1 Kincaid/B&W diesel, 6730bhp; 1 shaft	15kts	6 holds, 6 hatches
TRANS DANIA	Nor	1989	Hermann Sürken, Papenburg	5167 5353 (9048)	372–1 × 57–5 × 36–1 × 22–0 113.42 × 17.5 × 11.0 × 6.7	Roro/pallets	1 Bergen/Normo diesel, 4000bhp; 1 shaft	15kts	

Typical specialist tankers since 1969

Ship (Class)	Flag	Built	By	GRT DWT (Cargo capacity m³)	Length (oa) × breadth × depth × draught Feet–Inches Metres	Tanks	Engines	Speed	Remarks
Wine and alcohol VINDEMIA	Swe	1969	Vaagen Verft, Kyrksaeterora	1421 1687 (1500)	280–3 × 34–10 × 19–5 × 15–3 *85.43 × 10.62 × 5.92 × 4.66*	68	1 KHD diesel, 1600bhp; 1 shaft	12.75kts	wine/ alcohol
Fruit juice BEBEDOURO	Lib	1986	Hyundai HI, Ulsan	10,195 13,609 (8846)	487–10 × 75–1 × 40–1 × 28–9 *148.7 × 22.89 × 12.22 × 8.75*	14	1 Hyundai/Sulzer diesel, 8640bhp; 1 shaft	17.5kts	
Molten sulphur TARNOBRZEG	Pol	1973	Lodose Varv, Lodose; lengthened and completed Oskarshamns Varv, Oskarshamn	6967 9813 (5607)	479–8 × 52–6 × 36–2 × 25–0 *146.21 × 16.01 × 11.03 × 7.61*	14	1 Ruston Paxman diesel, 4670bhp; 1 shaft	14kts	oil cargo capacity 5543m³
Phosphoric acid AZZAHRAOUI	Mor	1982	Ch France-Dunkerque, Dunkirk	4752 6585 (7250)	363–4 × 58–6 × 29–3 × 23–3 *110.75 × 17.84 × 8.92 × 7.1*	7	1 CCM Sulzer diesel, 6325bhp; 1 shaft	14.5kts	
Molasses TORM HERDIS	Lib	1989	Hyundai HI, Ulsan	22,838 39,777 (47,371)	609–11 × 90–1 × 55–9 × 40–1 *185.9 × 27.46 × 17.0 × 12.22*	7	1 Hyundai/B&W diesel, 10,670bhp, 1 shaft	14kts	oil/ chemical/ molasses
Asphalt and bitumen BITUMA	Swe	1981	Nobiskrug, Rendsburg	1599 2770 (2837)	285–4 × 41–0 × 19–9 × 16–6 *86.98 × 12.5 × 6.02 × 5.04*	10	1 Krupp MaK diesel, 2445bhp; 1 shaft	12.5kts	asphalt/ bitumen/ oil
Alkyl-lead compounds GENNARO IEVOLI	Ita	1989	Soc Esercizio Cantieri, Viareggio	4200 7180 (7200)	379–5 × 57–5 × 26–3 × 20–6 *115.65 × 17.5 × 8.0 × 6.25*	—	1 Wartsila diesel, 4080bhp; 1 shaft	14.25kts	

Typical bulk cement carriers since 1964

Ship	Flag	Built	By	GRT DWT (Cargo capacity m³)	Length (oa) × breadth × depth × draught Feet–Inches Metres	Cargo handling gear	Engines	Speed	Remarks
KIYOSUMI MARU	Jap	1964	Nippon Kokan, Tsurumi	3146 5553 (4429)	341–2 × 49–5 × 25–7 × 20–8 *103.99 × 15.07 × 7.8 × 6.3*	Self-unloader	1 Ito Tekkosho diesel, 2800bhp; 1 shaft	13kts	3 cargo tanks
VENCEMOS III	Ven	1970	E N Bazan, San Fernando	3458 3887 (4522)	335–0 × 52–1 × 25–6 × 20–1 *102.11 × 15.88 × 7.78 × 6.12*	Self-unloader Crane 1 × 8 tons; derrick 1 × 3 tons	2 MAN diesels total 4600bhp driving 2 generators connected to 4 electric motors each 986shp; 2 shafts	14kts	2 holds, 2 hatches
INVICTA	Pan	1983	J J Sietas, Hamburg	9948 16,430 (15,212)	475–9 × 71–4 × 40–4 × 30–4 *145.01 × 21.75 × 12.3 × 9.23*	Self-unloader Cranes 2 × 9 tonnes	2 MAN diesels, 9000bhp; 1 shaft	15kts	8 holds
DANIA PORTLAND	Dmk	1984	Dalian SY, Dalian (Dairen)	18,102 28,251 (39,750)	639–9 × 75–10 × 46–11 × 33–7 *195.0 × 23.12 × 14.3 × 10.24*	Self-unloader	1 Hitachi/B&W diesel, 10,700bhp; 1 shaft	14.5kts	5 holds, 5 hatches; converted from bulk carrier 1986

8

Service, Support and Industry Vessels

Seamen have always studied the sea; their survival and profit have depended upon it. Throughout history they have taken soundings, observed tides and currents, compiled their sailing directions and, more often than not, they have also taken pains to keep their knowledge to themselves. Fishermen and admirals and oil companies still do. But nowadays, thanks to the work of marine scientists, much is also generally known about the seas and oceans.

Research and survey vessels

Marine science is the systematic observation and measurement of the marine environment. Its origins date from the mid-nineteenth century and coincide roughly with the publication in 1855 of Matthew Fontaine Maury's seminal work *The Physical Geography of the Sea* in which he attempted to establish the relationship between seasonal wind patterns and ocean currents. Before that time explorers and navigators were primarily interested in discovering and mapping the disposition of the land.

Their achievements were considerable. A profound debt is owed to navigators like James Cook and Matthew Flinders who laid the foundations of modern hydrography in the mid-eighteenth century. Yet despite their endeavours and those of others less celebrated, practically nothing was known about the world's oceans, their depths and circulations, even at the end of the eighteenth century. In fact it was not until the beginning of the twentieth century that a fairly accurate picture of the Earth's ocean basins began to emerge.

A significant point in the history of marine scientific observation was marked by the *Challenger* expedition of 1872–76 under the leadership of Sir Charles Wyville Thomson. During its four year circumnavigation of the globe this pioneering effort led to the discovery of nearly five thousand species of marine life. Hundreds of deep ocean soundings were made and enough data were collected to fill fifty volumes of reports. These were published over subsequent decades, under the supervision of Sir John Murray.

Challenger, an auxiliary spar-decked corvette of 2360 tons, was not the first vessel to be used for marine research. She was preceded in this by several other naval vessels including, from the United States, *Blake* and *Arctic* and from Britain, *Lightning* and *Porcupine*; significant expeditions were also conducted around the 1870s in the USS *Tuscorora* and in the German vessel *Gazelle*. Nevertheless *Challenger* is still perhaps the most famous name in marine scientific research and today lives on in Britain as one of the vessels of the present Natural Environment Research Council fleet.

The development of marine science in the first half of the twentieth century continued to be associated with the names of vessels in which major expeditions were mounted: *Discovery*, *Meteor*, *Albatross*, *Vitiaz* spring to mind in this respect. Today, however, the world's fleet includes more than one thousand marine research and survey vessels and the scale and scope of scientific operations at sea have grown to an extent barely imaginable even twenty-five years ago. Increasing general awareness of the importance of the marine environment for the future of mankind accounts for much of this growth.

Moreover, the organisation of marine science has gained an international dimension through the activities of institutions such as the International Commission for the Exploration of the Seas, Intergovernmental Oceanographic Commission, International Hydrographic Bureau and the United Nations Food and Agriculture Organisation.

There has also been the establishment of collaborative programmes such as Joint Oceanographic Institutions Deep Earth Sampling (JOIDES); Ocean Drilling Programme (ODP); World Ocean Circulation Experiment (WOCE) and General Bathymetric Chart of the Oceans (GEBLO), which brings together marine scientists of many nations.

One of the most advanced research ships built in Germany, the Arctic research and supply vessel Polarstern *was delivered to the Bremerhaven-based Alfred-Wegener Institute for Polar Research, in 1982. The vessel, which acts as a floating research station in the northern Polar Sea and the Antarctic, is officially described as a research, and oceanographic and weather survey vessel.* Polarstern *was built by Howaldtswerke-Deutsche Werft, Kiel, and is 10,878 grt.* (FotoFlite)

The Netherlands-flag research and oceanographic survey vessel Mitra *was delivered by Scheepsw Damen, at Bergum, to the Netherlands Rijkswaterstaat in 1982. She is employed in the northern continental shelf off the Netherlands and apart from survey work is also capable of combating oil pollution.* (FotoFlite)

The scope of marine science

The sea has always been important as a source of food and minerals and as a medium which facilitates transport and communications. But its significance extends far beyond these; by storing and distributing solar energy it acts as a global heat engine, driving the earth's hydrological cycle and maintaining its surface temperature within limits favourable to life. It is chemically stable, yet it contains practically all known chemical elements, and is the probable source of all life-forming molecules. Moreover, it is capable of sustaining life forms ranging from the smallest to the largest on earth.

As a consequence of advances in technology the sea now offers great opportunities for socio-economic development. It has, therefore, gained in political significance. Moreover, it is becoming increasingly evident that many of the conflicts and problems associated with the division and use of the land also occur at sea. Thus collecting and analysing marine environmental data have never been more important than they are today.

Marine science embraces several disciplines including physics, chemistry, biology, geology, meteorology and hydrography:

1. *Physical oceanography* is concerned with the behaviour of the sea as reflected in currents, waves and tides and also the physical properties of the water column – especially conductivity, temperature and density.
2. *Chemical oceanography* is concerned with the composition of seawater which is a complex solution having both organic and inorganic constituents. Environmental pollution is now a major area of study within chemical oceanography.
3. *Biological oceanography* is concerned with the study of the marine biosphere – the complex ecology of the seas and oceans. Fisheries science and fishing are usually included within this branch of marine science.
4. *Geology*, including geophysics and geomorphology are branches of science concerned with the composition, structure and surface shape of the earth. Marine geology is important because so much of the earth's surface lies beneath the sea. Many important geological processes take place within the ocean floor, and continental shelves have become important as sources of hydrocarbons and other minerals.
5. *Meteorology*, atmospheric science, is closely related to marine science, especially physical oceanography. The physical processes which take place within the atmosphere have their counterparts in the hydrosphere.
6. *Hydrography* is concerned with measuring the disposition of land and the sea floor for such purposes as the production of nautical charts and the erection of offshore structures. It is the oldest branch of marine science and underpins the others since every observation at sea must be accompanied by position data. The term hydrography is sometimes used synonymously with physical oceanography.

Like all branches of science, marine science has its own special instruments for measurement and analysis. However, the marine scientists' most important tool is, perhaps, the research vessel which is his laboratory, instrument platform and transport.

General characteristics of research and survey vessels

A wide variety of ships owned or operated by international organisations, government departments, private firms or scientific institutions support marine science.

The world's marine research and survey fleet currently includes fishing and naval vessels, offshore supply ships and converted cargo ships, as well as many purpose-built to facilitate scientific work at sea. They range in size from small launches and inshore fishing vessels of less than twenty metres in length to ocean-going ships of more than seventy-five metres. While most are conventional mono-hulls, catamaran and swath (small waterplane area twin hulls) hull forms also meet the requirements of research vessel operations.

Some research vessels are multi-purpose, intended to support scientific work in several disciplines such as physical oceanography, chemical oceanography or geophysics, although not necessarily at the same time. Others are designed to support just one type of work such as fisheries research or hydrography.

General purpose research vessels can be employed in support of investigations in any major area of marine science and, depending upon their size and purpose, they may operate in coastal and near-shore waters, in exclusive economic zones or world-wide in the service of academic, industrial or government scientists.

Fisheries research vessels can be employed to find new fishing grounds or to monitor fish stocks and they may engage in a variety of activities including exploratory fishing, fish population surveying and gear testing.

Unlike vessels engaged in trade whose main purpose is to go from port to port safely and economically, marine research and survey vessels perform their main function at sea, often in remote and inhospitable regions. A research vessel must therefore be capable of making long passages and also remaining on station for the duration of its mission. It must provide accommodation for scientists and laboratory space for their instruments. It must have the means to navigate accurately and to manoeuvre precisely and quietly at low speed. And, depending upon the nature of its mission, it must be able to deploy scientific apparatus on the seabed and tow instruments, often at great depth.

Seismic survey vessels, which are employed more or less exclusively in offshore prospecting usually for hydrocarbons, share many of the features of research and survey vessels engaged in the pursuit of science. Geophysical investigations may involve the discharge of explosives or the use of air guns to provide bursts of energy underwater.

General arrangement of research and survey vessels

Hull and superstructure

Most research vessels have conventional hull-forms which are designed, so far as is practicable, to take account of a number of operational requirements, including: economical passage-making at a cruising speed of eleven to fifteen knots; good manoeuvrability at low speeds to facilitate station-keeping and overside handling of scientific apparatus; good initial stability; good sea-keeping characteristics which minimise deck wetness; low freeboard at the working deck – to the extent that this is consistent with the last mentioned aspect; low hydromechanical noise (turbulence and cavitation), especially in the vicinity of instrument transducers. Some vessels may have specially strengthened hulls to permit operation in ice.

The superstructure contains accommodation, laboratories and other spaces. In modern research vessels the superstructure often has a roughly triangular profile with the wheelhouse or navigational control room at its apex near or just forward of amidships. This arrangement gives the officer of the watch a good view ahead when navigating on passage, and also enables him to see the working deck areas when scientific equipment is being deployed or recovered. Engine uptakes are sometimes located outboard of the main superstructure rather than on the centreline so as to avoid obstructing arcs of visibility from the wheelhouse.

Deck layout

Much of the apparatus now commonly used by research vessels is bulky and heavy; clear working areas on deck are therefore essential.

The principal working deck is usually aft. Many modern research vessels have a broad transom stern which allows the full breadth of the working deck to be maintained as far aft as possible, thereby maximising the usable area available. Some vessels also have additional working deck space along one side, and in a few the foredeck can also be used in good weather conditions.

The layout of the working deck spaces is governed by a number of operational considerations, including:

1. Provision of lifting equipment – many research vessels which deploy scientific apparatus over the stern have a transom-mounted A-frame; hydraulic slewing and luffing cranes are also common in larger vessels.

2. Provision of oceanographic winches – scientific apparatus that is towed or lowered to the seabed is attached to the ship by means of special, faired cables with signal and control conductors built into them; such cables are often very long and fragile, and require powerful high capacity winches.

3. Provision of container anchorage points – the configuration of general purpose research vessels is often changed by the addition or removal of special scientific equipment to suit the requirements of particular scientific programmes; in order to facilitate such changes, equipment items and sometimes even complete laboratories may be containerised.

4. Provision of stern ramp – especially in fisheries research vessels to facilitate the handling of trawls.

5. Provision of fishing equipment – fisheries research vessels carry a variety of equipment such as trawls, trawl winches and net haulers, to facilitate the testing of fishing gear or to make sample catches.

6. Provision of survey launches – hydrographic survey vessels are usually equipped with small boats for working inshore; stowage, launching and recovery facilities are required for them; some research vessels have facilities for handling small submersibles or remotely operated vehicles (ROVs).

Propulsion and auxiliary machinery

The main propulsion machinery of a research vessel must be capable of economical operation while on passage, good slow speed manoeuvring, quiet operation and vibration-free operation. These requirements usually dictate a different propulsion system from the large slow speed marine diesel engine and fixed pitch propeller found in most cargo-carrying merchant ships.

Diesel-electric drive is quite a common arrangement for research vessels. This consists of one or more medium or high speed diesel engines driving generators (or alternators in newer vessels) which in turn provide current for an electric motor that turns the propeller. The advantages of this system are that the propeller speed can be accurately and easily adjusted electrically, the diesel engine(s) run at a constant speed which gives good vibration characteristics – especially when the engines are flexibly mounted, and at slow speeds the required power output is low and can be achieved by running only one engine.

Another common arrangement consists of medium or high speed diesel engine(s) coupled through a gear box to a single controllable pitch propeller. In this case the engine(s) and propeller run at constant speed while the speed and direction of the vessel through the water is adjusted by varying the pitch of the propeller blades. Most research vessels are single screw.

Many larger research vessels have bow thrusters to assist slow speed manoeuvring. Vessels engaging in operations such as drilling or coring that involve maintaining a fixed station relative to the seabed may be equipped additionally with a dynamic positioning system. This automatically adjusts the main propulsion and thrusters so as to maintain the vessel above a fixed point on the seabed.

The endurance of research vessels varies from a few days to two months or more depending upon their size and operational requirement.

Scientific spaces

The range of scientific facilities found on board research vessels depends upon the work being undertaken. In general, however, all research vessels have laboratory spaces of some sort, including wet spaces located adjacent to the working deck area for the reception and preliminary treatment of samples; clean spaces for the recording and analysis of data; scientific storage spaces, including refrigerated space.

Like laboratories ashore, those on board research vessels have to be supplied with services such as compressed gases and water supplies to suit the type of scientific work that is being conducted on board. Additionally they should have stable electric power supplies, electronic data highways for linking scientific instruments, and satellite data communications links to laboratories ashore.

Other scientific spaces which may be

Hollming OY, of Rauma, Finland, in 1989 delivered to the USSR Academy of Sciences the 6231 grt Akademik Ioffe. *This oceanographic research vessel is wind-assisted and its two windsails can be clearly seen high on the superstructure. Fitted with two Russkiy-Diesel/Pielstick diesel engines, with a total 9520bhp, the vessel has a cruising speed of 15kts. (Hollming-Finnyards)*

A profile of the Natural Environment Research Council's Discovery, *built in 1962, and which underwent an extensive conversion in Portugal during 1990–92. This included lengthening by about 10m, fitting of a completely new superstructure, fitting a new power plant for both propulsion and scientific needs, and many detailed improvements dictated by changing scientific demands. The profile is as how the vessel appears following the conversion.* (NERC)

found on board research vessels include: scientific navigational plot, computer room, photographic dark room, library and conference room, special storage for scientific equipment, magazine for explosives, including ready use lockers on deck, and scientific workshop.

As a consequence of operational experience gained in the offshore industry an increasing number of research vessels now have a moonpool. This is a vertical trunk, located on the centreline near amidships, which passes right through the hull, from upper deck to keel. Its purpose is to facilitate the deployment of scientific apparatus through the hull, into the water and down to the seabed.

Scientific equipment

Equipment employed in marine science has become larger, heavier, more complex and more expensive during the last thirty years; research vessels have evolved correspondingly during that time. Common types of marine science equipment include: CTDs (conductivity, temperature, density measuring arrays); current meters; gravimeters and magnetometers; seabed corers; seismic arrays; sidescan sonar and echo-sounders; towed bodies; submersibles and ROVs.

Trends for the future in marine science

During the last two decades the equipment used for marine science has become larger, heavier more complex and without doubt much more expensive. This has placed considerable demands on scientists in respect of the quantities of data which can be generated by modern instruments and which therefore has to be analysed. For example, GLORIA (Geological LOng Range Inclined Asdic – towed body) is capable of surveying an area of seabed the size of Wales in one day. It has also placed considerable demands on research vessels in respect of their ability to support such powerful instruments. For example a typical instrument package which has to be handled overside might weigh fifteen tonnes today.

There seems little doubt that development along the lines of recent years will continue.

Some new developments which will have an impact on research vessels are also taking place:

1. *Earth observation satellites* have been used in atmospheric and environmental science, resource assessment studies, and for many other purposes for more than twenty years. They are being used to obtain oceanographic data and there is no doubt that they will become increasingly valuable for this purpose. Some marine scientists are of the opinion that satellites will eventually do away with the need for research vessels. This is an extreme view which is unlikely to be borne out by events in the foreseeable future because of the need for *ground truth observations* to complement those made remotely from space.

2. *Autonomous submarines (AUTOSUB)* are approaching an advanced stage of development in the United Kingdom and elsewhere. Unlike the manned submersibles that have been used in oceanography for many years, autonomous submarines are unmanned vehicles capable of navigating independently for lengthy periods while carrying sensors which can transmit or store data for later recovery. Such vehicles are potentially capable of assuming many of the functions of instruments that are now towed and even some of the functions of research vessels themselves.

Example of a research vessel

Discovery is a large general purpose vessel capable of undertaking work in most areas of marine science and of handling most of the latest scientific instruments. She was lengthened, re-engined and completely rebuilt in 1990–92 to give her a further twenty years of life and making her currently the most advanced vessel of her type in the world. She is employed in world-wide operations. Built by Hall, Russell & Co Ltd, Aberdeen, and completed in December 1962 for the Natural Environment Research Council, the following are her principal data following rebuilding:

Length overall	90.25m
Breadth	14.02m
Draught	5.30m
Speed	11.00 knots
Normal endurance	45 days
Total power	3.75 MW AC
Propulsion	1.50 MW DC
Officers	9
Crew	13
Scientists	28

Scientific handling systems
  main traction winch and reels
  CTD traction winch and reels
  A-frame aft
  A-frame amidships starboard
  A-frame forward starboard
  Four cranes
Scientific spaces
  Twenty-seven laboratories, workshops, storerooms and other dedicated scientific spaces located throughout the vessel.

J King

Support to the offshore industry

The supply vessel as a ship type is unique in that it did not develop from any other sort of craft, except that in common with all other ships it has a hull, engines and a bridge. The first supply ship, *Ebb Tide*, was built in Louisiana in 1955 to a design initiated by Alden J 'Doc' LaBorde, then president of ODECO (Ocean Drilling & Exploration Company).

LaBorde had recently invented the submersible drilling barge which took to the water a year previously, and was developed to enable ODECO to drill in deeper water than had previously been possible. Up to that time drilling barges had been floated into position and then sunk to the seabed, which naturally limited their operating depth to the freeboard of the barge. The new vessel, *Mr Charlie*, was in effect two barges separated by ten columns, which allowed the lower part to lie on the sea-bed while the upper part, on which was mounted the drilling rig and accommodation, remained above the water atop the columns.

Supply of the primitive offshore drilling units had up to the arrival of *Ebb Tide* been undertaken by a variety of craft including shrimp boats, tugs and former landing craft, none of which was particularly suitable for the task. Hence, somewhat typically, Laborde decided to start with a clean piece of paper and design a ship which would be ideal for the job, and it may only be the fact that he was not a seafarer or naval architect that such a design, which must have looked wildly impractical at the time, came to fruition.

Ebb Tide was 119ft in length with a clear deck of 90ft and a beam of 31ft, and she drew 8ft 6in fully loaded. The wheelhouse, uniquely placed on the forecastle was scavenged from an old tug as were the two 600bhp engines. As soon as she entered service her advantages could be seen by other oil companies and before long a further three vessels had been ordered, all operated by the company set up by LaBorde, Tidewater Marine Service Inc. These four vessels were the beginning of a whole new industry which initially proliferated in the Gulf of Mexico. All the early supply vessels were slightly enlarged versions of *Ebb Tide*, carrying as deck cargo drill pipes and chemicals, hardware and food, and below fuel and fresh water in tanks.

The Gulf of Mexico supply vessel has changed little since those days, the concept being to have ships capable of operating out of any creek or backwater close to where offshore exploration is taking place. They must therefore be as simple as possible with low horsepower engines, shallow draught, and a form of construction which will allow repairs to the hull to be carried out by anyone with a welding torch and a big hammer.

However, just as the first supply vessel design was initiated by changes in offshore drilling techniques, so was the next, which was the arrival of the jack-up, with its widely spaced legs, often equipped with protruding teeth capable of biting into a ship's hull. Up to then supply vessels had been able to lie alongside offshore structures in an entirely conventional manner, but with nothing to lie alongside they were now required to drop an anchor and back up to the structure, and then be secured astern by two ropes. This was a sort of Mediterranean mooring, and the early supply ship masters took the manoeuvre in their stride. One can imagine them, stern on to the structure, shouting out of the front window of the wheelhouse to the mate, to drop the anchor, and then backing up looking over their shoulders, engines churning astern, and sweating as they got close. Probably the crane would manage to drop a rope on the deck as the stern swung past, the deck-crew would leap to it and turn it down, and the vessel would be drawn up sharply to hang between the single rope and the anchor cable. They would then go through a process of shortening up the first rope, and then taking a second one, and finally tightening up on the anchor cable until the ship was secured and cargo could be worked over the stern.

Over the ten years following the arrival of *Ebb Tide* more similar supply vessels made their presence felt in the Gulf of Mexico, Lake Maracaibo in Venezuela, to which *Ebb Tide* was soon dispatched, and then in the Arabian Gulf. It was a decade of steady development, all operations taking place in calm conditions and shallow water. However two further important events in the oil industry shaped the supply vessel for the next few years.

The first was the development of the semi-submersible drilling rig. This form of rig did not rest on the sea-bed at all, but in fact operated at two draughts. The light draught allowing it to be towed from one point to another and the deep draught, allowing it to remain stable as a drilling platform. In its drilling configuration it was necessarily kept in position by anchors which had to be positioned by the support vessels.

The second important event, and probably the one with the greatest influence on the development of the supply vessel, was the arrival of the exploration rig in the North Sea. In 1966, only twelve years after *Ebb Tide*, *Mr Capp*, an ODECO jack-up started work in the shallow waters off the coast of East Anglia, and it was soon followed by other jack-ups, which began to strike gas both in the United Kingdom sector and the Netherlands sector.

These rigs were supported initially by Gulf of Mexico supply vessels with American crews, but the opportunity for profit was soon seen by a number of eminent British shipping companies. P&O Lines plunged in with International Offshore Services (IOS), and Cunard started up Offshore Marine. In addition a number of European shipping companies waded in with their own fleets. Leading German companies banded together to form OSA, the Offshore Supply Association, and the Rotterdam tug and salvage company Smit started, together with a Netherlands liner company, an offshore subsidiary under the title Smit-Lloyd.

The North Sea supply vessels of the late 1960s were only a marginal improvement on the American imports. They were a little larger, and had a little more freeboard, but the difference would hardly be noticed by the uninitiated. However, by 1967 Offshore Marine was incorporating a number of features, necessitated by the environment, and the requirements of the semi-submersible rig.

Typical of the vessels of the period was *Essex Shore* (499 grt), built at Rotterdam in 1967. Although the general shape was still that of the

The very first purpose-built offshore supply vessel was Ebb Tide *completed in 1955 by Alexander Shipyards Inc, New Orleans. Although devoid of the sleek lines of its successors, the overall shape has stayed with this vessel type – notably the raised forecastle, bridge forward and long open deck cargo space. At 119ft in length and powered with two 8-cylinder General Motors diesels totalling 1000bhp,* Ebb Tide *lasted until the late 1970s. A slightly younger sistership,* Rip Tide, *is still in service in the New Orleans area. Owners of* Ebb Tide *were Tidewater Marine Service Inc of New Orleans which within a few years were destined to become operators of the world's largest fleet of offshore industry support vessels. (Tidewater Marine Service)*

Built for operations in the North Sea, regarded as the most testing for offshore service vessels, was Essex Shore, *completed in 1967 for Offshore Marine Ltd, London.*

Described as an anchor handling tug/supply vessel, Essex Shore *carried a substantial deck cargo and had a total deadweight of 807 tonnes. Later in her career she was renamed* Essex Service *when Offshore Marine became part of the US-controlled Zapata Offshore Group.* (FotoFlite)

traditional Gulf of Mexico supply ship, it had a stern roller, to allow rig anchors to be lifted to the surface, and a winch to carry out the task. It was also capable of towing, having a bollard pull of 22.5 tons. While this figure seems ludicrous today, a mere 25 years ago *Essex Shore* was a powerful vessel, its two Blackstone engines producing 2000bhp. She had further innovative features to help her tie up stern-on to the rigs. Forward she was fitted with a gill jet, a diesel driven 500bhp omni-directional thruster, and on the bridge she had a set of controls facing aft, so that the stern could be seen from the control position. The master could then drop the anchor and steer the vessel astern using the bow thruster until he was within range of the crane, and then manoeuvre while the ropes were attached.

This additional equipment naturally involved some rethinking on the part of the seafarers, and to actually drive the ship while facing aft needed considerable retraining, all of which was done, 'on the job'. In aft conning position, if the master pushed the engine control 'ahead' he would actually be going astern and if he moved the rudder control to port he would actually be applying starboard rudder. Additionally since reversed rudder indicators were not then available the aft rudder indicator would show the rudder moving in the opposite direction to the direction of the control. The after controls and the bow thruster also promoted the development of a technique known as snatching. As the name implies this activity allowed the rig crane to pick up single urgent lifts without the supply vessel tying up, and in its earliest form consisted of the supply vessel

drifting slowly past the structure while the deck crew quickly hooked on the lift before the crane was out of range.

The bow thruster allowed the master to apply forces with it, and the engines and rudders which would keep the ship within range of the crane for longer periods, sometimes allowing complete deck cargoes to be discharged and loaded. It did however require a great deal of concentration on the part of the driver, since the crane booms were short, and the ship had to remain a few feet off the legs of the rig, even to allow cargo to be taken from and landed on the stern.

The stern-to method of loading and discharge meant that all the cargo had to be presented to the crane a few feet from the after end so that the supply vessels had to be fitted with small winches on the deck known as tuggers, a name derived from the winches used on board the rigs to pull items of drilling hardware around the drill floor.

From the late 1960s the development of supply vessels world-wide had stemmed from developments within the North Sea, and particularly in Norway. The Norwegians saw the potential for both their seafarers and their shipyards in the newly booming industry and quickly took up a position far in advance of their own oil development. Norway is a seafaring nation and as such has continued to take advantage of its inherent involvement with the sea.

Although this volume is strictly concerned with the sea and the ships which sail thereon, and not concerned with the politics of the marine industry world-wide, the Norwegians have over the years been considerably helped by a tax regime which allows investors to reap returns, which would not be possible in other economic environments, and has allowed them to build ships of great sophistication which might not provide returns elsewhere. Hence, over the years Norwegian shipbuilders have been able to provide their industry with more and more powerful and technically advanced vessels which have been the envy of the seafarers of other nations, and as a result of this long term technical input they have become the most experienced designers and builders of supply vessels in the world. Even during recent years when it may have been more economic to have the hull constructed in Far Eastern yards, most of the equipment, particularly for anchor handling and towing, has been supplied from the home country.

Therefore, if most of what is written here seems to concentrate on the developments on the European continental shelf, it is not that

the rest of the world is being neglected. In fact what happens to the supply vessel in Europe tends to be reflected elsewhere in later years. In the United States the designers and builders have been mindful of their original creed, that of simplicity, and have been able to hold on to it, making the minimum concession to new developments. Elsewhere in the world there is a tendency for ships which have been superseded in Europe to be employed, either doing the same task in calmer waters, or in less arduous activities.

By the early 1970s the search for oil was moving further north into deeper water, and hence the exploration was being carried out by semi-submersibles. As a result almost all the supply vessels being built were anchor-handlers. Anchor-handling operations at that time were fraught with difficulty and disaster. Many early anchor-handlers were equipped only to pull the anchor up to the stern, which would allow them to deliver it to the rig. Should the anchor need to be brought on to the deck this would be done using a large A-frame mounted at the stern, and it was due to the extreme difficulty of this operation that stern rollers were made large enough and wide enough for the anchor to be pulled from the sea straight on to the deck.

Laying piggy-back, or back-up anchors in soft ground was even worse. The vessel with the main anchor at the stern would attach a pennant to the crown and then pass this to another vessel which would have the back-up on the deck. They would both then lower their respective anchors to the sea-bed at the same time. This sounds easy. However it takes great courage and skill to manoeuvre one vessel within heaving line distance of another, even in what passes for calm weather in the North Sea, and doing this as a matter of routine filled the log books of the early anchor-handlers with long reports on contact damage.

In 1972 yet another British shipping company, Ocean Fleets, became involved in the industry. This well known Liverpool liner company formed an alliance with Lord Inchcape's Inchcape Group under the name Ocean Inchcape Ltd, or OIL and in the same year their first vessel, *Oil Producer*, was brought into service. This ship built at Ysselwerf in Rotterdam was then, with 4000bhp available, briefly the most powerful supply vessel in the world. Like its contemporaries of that period the funnels had been moved from either side of the after deck to a position just aft of the bridge. Rough weather in the northern North Sea had resulted in waves going down the exhausts of the low-funnelled Gulf vessels and

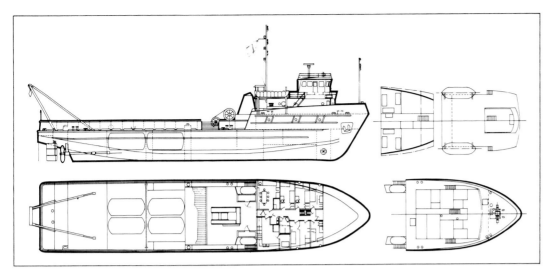

The twin-screw supply vessel and anchor-handler Star Orion *was typical of such vessels appearing in the 1970s.* Star Orion *was built by Mangone Shipbuilding Co, of Houston, Texas, one of the leading offshore vessel builders in the US, and her owners, Star Offshore Services, of London, employed the vessel mainly in the North Sea. With a gross tonnage of 498, this vessel could carry varied cargoes for offshore exploration purposes, for example 551 tonnes of drill water, 160 tonnes fresh water, 410 tonnes fuel oil, and 4000cu ft of bulk chemicals. Total deck cargo capacity was 450 tonnes.* (Star Offshore Services)

putting out the engines. *Oil Producer* and a sister-ship, *Oil Supplier*, went to work for BP during the exploration and development of the Forties Field, and she achieved some fame at the time as the control vessel during the positioning of the Forties Alpha jacket, *Graythorpe 1*, the first fixed oil production platform in the North Sea.

By 1974 British anchor-handlers had increased to about 6000bhp, and the Norwegians, now beginning to make an impression, were building ships of about 7000bhp. The Norwegians were also introducing craft fitted with controllable pitch (CP) propellers, thereby increasing the manoeuvrability of the ships. The CP propeller was introduced to obviate the delay time incurred by fixed pitch propellers in going from ahead to astern. To get over this problem ship masters would place their ships roughly where they needed to be and then put one engine ahead and one astern, countering the tendency of the vessel to turn by putting the rudders over in the opposite direction and using the bow thruster to hold the bow in position, in the same way as helicopter pilots neutralise the tendency of their aircraft to spin in the opposite direction to the main rotor blades by using the tail rotor. The CP propellers also allowed the engines to maintain a constant speed which made them more reliable, since none of the engines used at the time were intended to be prime movers, being derived from marine generator engines.

In 1975 Ulstein of Norway, possibly the world's best known supply vessel builders, designed and built the UT704, the first of the supply ship standard types. This design was a milestone in the development of the type. It was for its time extremely large with over 100ft of clear deck space and powerful with 7200bhp available. From being the most advanced ship available in those years it turned

into the basic workhorse of the industry being built under licence in the Far East, India, Yugoslavia and Spain, and was only superseded by more advanced designs ten years later as the industry was beginning to move into recession.

During the first ten years in the North Sea the ships were also becoming better cargo carriers. Supply ships must be able to carry all the requirements for drilling and in addition everything necessary to keep a marine unit functioning for months, and sometimes years, offshore. They must therefore have deck capacity for drill pipes, drilling tools, scaffolding, helicopter fuel tanks, chemicals, food and maintenance equipment. Under deck they must be able to carry cement in bulk, barytes, bentonite, gas-oil, fresh water, brine and oil-based mud. The builders of early North Sea supply vessels were hampered in their efforts to provide under deck capacity because it was necessary to have large ballast tanks available to ensure that the ships remained stable at all stages of loading and discharge.

During the early 1970s it became obvious that another type of supply vessel would be required when oil companies began to contract for the laying of pipelines from the fields being constructed in the Shetland basin to the mainland and to Orkney and Shetland. The pipe was manufactured and delivered in forty-foot lengths, loaded on to the pipe barges and welded together on the deck, then as the barge moved forward by means of its anchors it was led over the stern and towards the seabed by means of the stinger.

The pipe carriers therefore needed to have decks either capable of carrying two lengths, or three lengths of pipe, and both types of craft were constructed in Norway, Denmark, Germany and the United Kingdom. This phase also saw the emergence of a couple of standard types from Norway, the UT705 and the

ME202. The Maersk Company characteristically went out on their own and built a pipe carrier unique to themselves, as did OSA who constructed large numbers of small vessels capable of carrying two lengths of pipe. The newly-formed British company Star Offshore initiated construction of three pipe carriers, two of which were eventually to become diving ships, since typically in the supply vessel market, the pipe carrier requirement was quickly overtonnaged.

OIL also built a single pipe carrier, *Oil Challenger*, which was unique in being the only supply vessel ever built with aft accommodation. This vessel was specifically constructed to supply the pipe barge *Viking Piper*, but when it started work it was found that when *Oil Challenger* was lying alongside the pipe barge it was doing so much damage that it was quickly taken out of service and spent the duration of its contract lying at anchor in the River Tay.

Towards the end of the decade all supply vessels were being constructed with CP propellers, which meant that the omni-directional bow thruster was no longer a prime requirement, so that many supply vessels appeared with tunnel thrusters. Control systems were becoming more sophisticated and the supply vessel designers borrowed some technology from the diving ships which were now appearing in numbers. The diving ships used computers to maintain station which operated by means of any one of a number of position fixing systems, the most prominent being Artemis, a radar type system involving stations positioned on the offshore installations, and taut wire, which as the name implies consisted of a wire with a weight on the end which was lowered to the seabed.

To allow these vessels to move easily and still to take advantage of the computer installations they were fitted with a joystick, an omni-directional control which provided a facility for the ship to be moved by means of a single stick. It was the joystick and its associated computer which was taken up by the supply vessel oper-

Built in 1984 for operations in the North Sea as a multi-purpose offshore support vessel is Troms Tjeld, *owned by TFDS Offshore of Norway. This 1591 grt vessel has a cargo capacity of 2024 tonnes, including 1200 tonnes on deck, is certified for standby and rescue with facilities for 150 survivors, is an anchor-handler, and is an able towing vessel with a total 12,320bhp and bollard pull rating of 160 tons.* (TFDS Offshore)

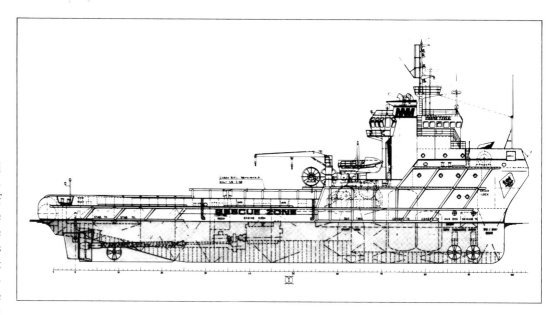

ators, and the installation of this device allowed the supply vessel masters to snatch for extremely long periods in the close proximity of offshore installations. Once confidence in the joystick grew, ship masters began to operate beam on to the installations giving the cranes access to much larger areas of the deck, and it was this development which allowed the pipe-carriers with their long decks and therefore higher carrying capacity to become platform supply vessels.

Meanwhile, as oil exploration began to move into more hostile waters the requirements for anchor-handling and towing were becoming more onerous, and bollard pull was beginning to become the measure of efficiency in this sector of the market. In response to this requirement The Maersk Company initiated the construction of six very powerful anchor handlers, the Maersk R class. The first of these vessels, *Maersk Retriever* (1593 grt), entered service in 1979. This vessel was powered by four MaK engines developing a total of 13,000bhp, giving a bollard pull of 146 tons continuously and a maximum of 160 tons. She was also fitted with two bow thrusters and a stern thruster for maximum manoeuvrability, and winch capable of lifting 260 tons and twin tow drums each capable of holding 1200m of 72mm wire. In common with later Maersk anchor-handlers they were also fitted with effective remotely operated fire monitors capable of spraying a burning offshore structure with over 2000cu m per hour.

This very advanced class initiated yet further advances in specification. The Norwegian designers, not to be outdone, developed the UT712, and the ME303. The ME303 was if possible even more audacious than the Maersk R class. At 68m it was only 1m longer than the Maersk vessels, but the accommodation towered over the working deck like a block of flats. The bridge area was vast, and was fitted with such luxuries as a sink, a settee and coffee-making facilities.

When considering traditional vessels these fittings might seem a little incongruous, but the bridge of a supply vessel already incorporates the radio room and the chart room, and when on location its whole atmosphere as a

working area changes. During anchor-handling operations the after control positions are manned by the master who drives the ship and the chief engineer who drives the winch. Each are seated side by side at their own consoles, facing aft overlooking the working deck, which during the hours of darkness is brightly lit by sodium lighting. It is common for off-duty crew members from the cook upwards to visit the area to see how the work is progressing, and any odd bodies may be pressed into service to provide hot drinks. The master is in constant communication with the offshore installation, the working deck and the engine-room, and so the space is filled with voices. The area therefore ceases to be little more than a passive look-out position and becomes an active operations room.

The first three ME303s were built for Edda Supply Ships of Haugesund, Norway, and for Seaforth Maritime of Aberdeen. In the event Edda never took delivery of their vessel due to contractual difficulties, but *Seaforth Centurion* and *Seaforth Crusader* (both 1590 grt) arrived in Aberdeen in 1983 once more amazing the seafaring community. It did not seem possible that the supply vessel could get any bigger. They had been built in Korea, and their four diesel engines generated 14,040bhp.

In the first years of the 1980s oil exploration was taking place in many seas in all parts of the world. Moderate development was taking place in the Mediterranean, extensive offshore exploration was taking place off the coast of Brazil and Argentina and in various parts of the Far East. Australia was also emerging as a promising area. The Canadians were continuing to explore off the coast of Newfoundland, where in addition to rough seas, the ships were having to deal with the enveloping Grand

Banks fogs, and also looking towards the Beaufort Sea where ice rather than water was the predominant element. The China Sea was looking like a possible source of hydrocarbons and in the Gulf of Mexico and the Arabian Gulf continuous exploration and development was taking place.

There were by now two genuine sources of design, the Gulf of Mexico and the North Sea. American designs continued to be conservative, simple and moderate in size, and these vessels had applications in areas of the world where shallow waters and calm seas provided a reasonable working environment. North Sea designs could be found anywhere where conditions made life difficult, and the penalty for using these ships was the greater technical back-up required to ensure that their complex operating systems and technically advanced hardware remained operational.

However, despite this limitation, European designs continued to advance, and soon after the development of the ME303, Norwegian naval architects Vik & Sandvik unveiled the VS469 and a very similar design, the VS476. The VS469 appeared as *Viking Queen*, owned by Viking Supply Ships. She is 76m long, 18m wide and has a total deadweight of over 5000 tons. Four VS476s were also built, originally for Scandinavian owners but quickly acquired by OIL. These ships, with 14,000bhp on hand and a bollard pull of 170 tons, provided the oil companies with the ultimate support vessels. Their deck area was equal to all but the largest platform supply vessels, giving them a massive cargo capacity, and their large size made them capable of carrying out rig shifting duties in all but the worst weather conditions in the North Sea.

Occasional efforts to construct simpler ves-

The 1984-built Viking Queen *is a typical anchor-handling vessel of this period. Equipped with 5 Wichmann diesels, providing 12,560bhp, a bollard pull rating of 150 tons and speed of 17.25kts, this vessel is owned by Eidesvik & Co, of Norway.* (V Gibson)

sels resulted in disaster. Stirling Shipping of Glasgow produced a design which really ought to have been a winner. Designated the Clyde 252, these vessels were small and extremely manoeuvrable, being powered by a single engine driving an azimuthing propeller and a single omni-directional bow thruster. This made them extremely economical and ideal for operating in the strong tides of the southern North Sea, but despite these advantages they were never popular. They were eventually sold to become standby vessels. A few other simple small ships were constructed in the early 1980s by Smit-Lloyd, Wimpey and Seaforth in the United Kingdom, and although these craft

continue to trade, not all with their original owners, their high crewing costs in relation to size have made them difficult to market.

American designs on the other hand continued to be successful, virtually the only concession to North Sea developments being the placing of the funnels in the area immediately aft of the wheelhouse. Otherwise they were mostly still fitted with fixed pitch propellers and were seldom more than 5000bhp. They were, and are, much cheaper to construct, and are therefore able to trade at lower rates. So, in terms of supply vessel evolution the North Sea remained in the forefront, and where vessels were built outside Europe for service in hostile

waters they were almost always Ulstein or Maritime Engineering designs.

One exception may be the vessels constructed for operation in the Beaufort Sea. In 1983 BeauDril of Calgary built four supply vessels to support their drilling rigs working in the ice. The two smaller vessels, *Ikaluk* and *Miscaroo* were designed by Robert Allen of Vancouver and the two larger, *Kalvik* and *Terry Fox* designed by German & Milne Inc. The statistics for these ships are staggering. *Ikaluk* and *Miscaroo* (3255 grt) are 78m long, and are fitted with four Wartsila diesels producing a combined power of 14,900bhp. They are capable of breaking 4ft of solid ice and penetrating ice ridges fifteen feet high. *Kalvik* and *Terry Fox* (4233 grt) are the largest supply vessels in the world at 88m long, and with 23,000bhp available they have a bollard pull of over 200 tons. However, due to the specialist nature of their operation they are by no means the largest cargo carriers.

The headlong pace of supply ship development was slowed and then stopped by the oil price slump of 1985, and though a number of new ships were delivered during that year, the charter rates available to them only just enabled them to keep running. The oil companies trimmed their activities to a minimum, and kept their reduced operations supplied with the least possible number of ships. Some operated with no long term vessels at all, picking up one of the many modern ships available on the spot market whenever they needed one.

Many older British and Norwegian ships were laid up, and within a couple of years most had been sold off into other industries where they became anti-pollution craft, survey vessels, port control ships and standby ships. Despite the trauma experienced throughout the industry, this weeding-out process was con-

An unusual cargo for the US-flag supply vessel Young America *(built 1971), was the carriage of the much smaller* Jubal Early *to a new assignment in the Gulf of Mexico.* Jubal Early, *described as being of 'under 100 grt', is of a size often seen in its home waters of the Gulf of Mexico but rarely elsewhere, whereas* Young America, *although only 281 grt is suitable for service in most areas. Owned by Offshore Logistics Services Inc, of Morgan City, Louisiana,* Young America *is an anchor handling tug/supply vessel, and has a substantial deck cargo area. Her total deadweight is 1626.* (Offshore Logistics)

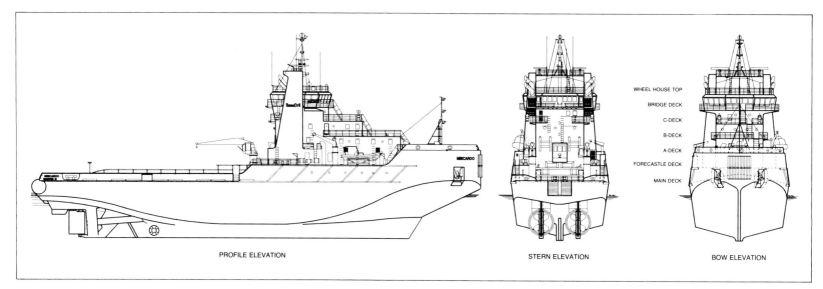

PROFILE ELEVATION   STERN ELEVATION   BOW ELEVATION

WHEEL HOUSE TOP
BRIDGE DECK
C-DECK
B-DECK
A-DECK
FORECASTLE DECK
MAIN DECK

A giant amongst offshore service vessels is the Canadian flag Miscaroo, *built in 1983 for BeauDril, a subsidiary of Gulf Canada Resources. Operating mainly in Arctic waters, the vessel is strengthened for ice-breaking, and has anchor-handling and towing capability in addition to the supply function. Her 14,900bhp engines give a bollard pull rating of 150 tonnes.* (BeauDril)

sidered by many to be long overdue, since supply vessels are solidly constructed, and so well maintained that they will seldom cease to be operational due to age alone. The same process took place in the Gulf of Mexico where many ships were converted into fishing vessels.

Amongst the few newbuildings after 1985 were those commissioned by The Maersk Company, some said because they had to find something for their in-house shipyard to do, and in 1986 they took delivery of what might be considered the ultimate supply ships, *Maersk Master* and *Maersk Mariner* (3949 grt). These craft are over 80m in length, with a large open working deck aft and a cover hatch on the foredeck. They have 14,900bhp available, the thrust being provided by a single large screw flanked by two azimuthing thrusters, thereby providing what would appear to be the best of all worlds. Their technical specification is endless, and includes a dynamic positioning system, fire monitors and multiple working and towing winches.

These two ships were followed by four more conventional anchor-handlers, which nevertheless incorporated many features which make them unique. They are powered by two 6500bhp MaK engines positioned well forward in the ship, allowing the main part of the hull to be used for dry and liquid bulk tanks. They have two tow drums and two work winches to give them towing and anchor handling flexibility, and to make them suitable for working in the deep waters at the edge of the continental

shelf, and in common with a few platform ships their exhaust emerges from the top of the wheelhouse to give the master more than 180 degrees of vision when seated at the after controls. The last of this class was delivered in 1989, coinciding with a steady improvement in the oil price and a resurgence in oil exploration world-wide. Charter rates once more began to rise, and the industry began to look to the new decade, and to define oil company requirements into the twenty-first century.

The first defined necessity was seen to be a number of pipe carriers to service the pipe barges for several new lines to be laid in 1991 and 1992, particularly since all the existing pipe carriers had become platform ships, and so numbers of UT705s were ordered in Norway. It could also be seen that there might be a demand for large anchor-handlers, and the Norwegian companies Sverre Farstad and Viking Supply Ships placed orders for a number of large anchor-handlers to be built in Norway and Singapore. These were all of ME303 MkII design.

Elsewhere Zapata Gulf Marine ordered a number of vessels for service in the Gulf of Mexico, to be built in Singapore, and the best known United States' supply ship builder, Halter Marine, also received orders for new tonnage.

All these designs follow existing formats, so it is possible that the supply vessel has finally arrived. It still shows an almost alarming similarity to *Ebb Tide*, and it is evident that any drastic movement away from the original concept will be dealt with ruthlessly by the customer. That being said, the progress from that simple little, low powered ship into today's hulking high-tech vessels has taken place at breathtaking speed over a mere thirty years. It has been a process fuelled by a curious com-

bination of financial necessity and frontier exploration, and it has been pushed forward by the prime motivation of the oil industry – to find oil, and to extract it from the earth no matter what the obstacles.

The supply vessel is probably the only example of what can be done with a ship, both technically and operationally, if the natural conservatism and caution of the shipowner, the shipbuilder and the mariner are removed. No-one could call it beautiful, but in its own way it has an elegance which comes from fitness for the task. The blunt bows, big winches and vast areas of glass create a feeling of power and efficiency, and evoke that spirit of adventure which is, after all, what ships are really about.

Captain V Gibson

Amongst the numerous types of vessel which service the offshore oil production and exploration industry are those with fire-fighting capability. Here, the 1301 grt Safaniya 6, *built in 1982 for Arabian American Oil Co (ARAMCO), of Dammam, Saudi Arabia, is pictured on her delivery voyage. Described also as a maintenance vessel, she has on board a workshop, sandblasting and painting equipment and undertakes multi-purpose servicing of offshore installations.* (FotoFlite)

Dredgers

The art of dredging refers to the submarine excavation of soils (sediments) and bedrock, and a dredger can be regarded as a vessel incorporating specialised machinery for such an operation. Although the basic principles of dredging methodology have changed little over the post-Second World War years, the technology has done so, and this is reflected in the design and distribution of the various dredger types.

Dredgers are employed in many tasks, including (a) the creation and maintenance of defined water depths in ports, canals, and marinas, (b) provision of landfill materials to create new or improve existing ground, for foundation purposes, and for coastal protection through beach replenishment, breakwaters, and dykes, (c) the mining of certain grades of sediment for use as aggregate, (d) the mining of economically-valuable minerals such as gold and tin, (e) submarine trenching for pipelines, tunnels, cables, and caissons, (f) flood control in rivers and lakes, and (g) environmental improvements, such as the removal of old mine tailings or spoil heaps, and the disposal of pollutants. To accommodate these widely differing tasks, some types of dredger are more suited to one purpose than another.

Dredgers are classified usually according to their operating methods: mechanical, hydraulic, and combined mechanical/hydraulic. Although some dredgers might incorporate a combination of operating methods, the following general types are common:

Mechanical
Bucket dredger
Grab and grab hopper dredgers
Dragline
Backhoe dredger
Dipper dredger

Hydraulic
Stationary suction dredger
Trailer suction hopper dredger
Trailer suction sidecast dredger
Dustpan dredger

Mechanical/hydraulic
Cutter suction dredger
Bucket wheel dredger.

In addition to the above standard dredgers, there is a variety of specialised types, usually small in size, built to tackle specific problems, for which a standard dredger would be un-

suited. These incorporate the utilisation of ploughs, jetting equipment, and variations of one of the standard designs.

Because of the possible multiplicity of function, sometimes it can be difficult to define what vessel is a dredger and what is not. However, there are probably well over 2000 of the standard types in operation world-wide, some types being more common than others. The following percentages of design are probable values: cutter suction dredgers fifty per cent, other suction dredgers thirty per cent, grab and backhoe dredgers ten per cent, and other standard designs ten per cent.

Apart from the possible exception of the bucket wheel concept, the basic principles of operation for the different designs have been used in dredgers for well over a century. Yet, in the years since the Second World War, there has been a major redistribution amongst the dredger types in use, particularly the declining percentage of mechanically-operated vessels and the increasing percentage of cutter suction and trailer suction craft. This trend is due largely to economic factors, such as the bigger production rates of the suction dredgers, and operational factors, such as dredging sites being in more exposed locations or in deeper waters.

Types of dredger

The cutter suction dredger

As the name implies, this craft uses a combination of mechanical cutting tool and suction pump for the excavation process. There are two basic hull forms for this type: stationary and self-propelled. The former is the more common, comprising a pontoon hull, inside which the inboard dredge pump and motor room are located, with the suction pipe being supported in a ladder which is lowered and

raised in an indented section of the pontoon. Because of the effect of dredging depth upon pump efficiency, vessels with the capability of dredging in excess of about 9m often have an additional underwater pump embodied in the suction pipe. The largest dredgers of this type are capable of dredging in depths of between 25m and 30m.

A cutterhead is located at the open end of the suction pipe, being driven by either an electric motor sealed for underwater use and located behind the cutterhead, or by an inboard motor. Several designs of cutterhead exist, most being a variation of an array of spiral blades formed into a basket. The purpose of the cutterhead is to fragment the dredged material prior to suction, and therefore this type of dredger has the capability of excavating a wide variety of materials: clay, silt, sand, gravel, cobbles, soft bedrock *in situ* and fragmented hard rock. Cutterheads with replaceable teeth are used for dredging rock.

In order to operate and move over the dredging area, the hull is equipped with spuds – vertical jacks which are lowered down and into the seabed – and side anchors. The arrangement of the spuds allow the dredger to *walk* towards the dredging face; in many recently-constructed vessels, spuds are installed in sliding carriages, which allow the vessel to advance up to six metres without repositioning the spuds, and hence the saving on downtime; the use of side anchors facilitate a side-to-side swinging movement. Some vessels require the assistance of ancillary vessels to shift anchors, whereas others have anchor booms alongside the ladder gantry for this purpose.

Disposal of the dredged material can be by either a floating pipeline or by discharging into barges alongside. In some cases booster pumps are located at intervals along the floating pipeline, and high production rates can be attained with this method of discharge.

A cutter suction dredger.

Since the mid 1970s, quite a few dredgers of this type have been constructed as self-propelled vessels. From the operator's viewpoint, there are many advantages to this design over the conventional type: these vessels can work in more severe sea conditions, mobilisation to dredging contracts throughout the world is more rapid, there is no dependence upon ancillary vessels for positioning and towage, and more maintenance work can be undertaken at sea.

Traditionally, the performance capability of cutter suction dredgers is gauged according to the diameter of the delivery pipe, which can vary from about 200mm to over 1000mm, although most vessels have pipes in the lower-middle part of this range. Another performance indicator for this type is the total machinery output, expressed in kilowatts, or in horsepower. The largest vessel of this class has an output in excess of 20,000 kilowatts.

The trailer suction hopper dredger

This design of dredger is the only class which exhibits any similarity with a conventional ship hull. It is not only more flexible and more versatile than the cutter suction dredger but also it can be a more complex design. Simply, the type is a self-propelled ship which has a dredging pipe attached to the side of the hull and de-

ployed such that the draghead, attached to the end of the pipe, is *trailed* over the seabed; the dredged material is pumped inboard to a storage tank, or hopper; and, dredging usually takes place in an operating cycle of dredging, sail to spoil disposal site, dump the dredged spoil, and return to dredging site.

Trailers dredge underway, usually at speeds of between two and five knots, and this operating practice means that these vessels have a requirement for high manoeuvrability. Therefore, many such craft are twin-screw with bow, and sometimes stern, thrusters. There are many variants of the basic type, the main elements of variability being the draghead design, pumping arrangements, location of accommodation, and method of spoil disposal.

The purpose of the draghead is to disperse the suction force over a greater surface area and the design used at any one time depends largely on the material being excavated. Standard dragheads can vary from a simple steel grid across the mouth of the pipe to complex structures, such as a flexible visor with a relatively large surface area (California-type), visors equipped with cutting teeth or cutting blades, and visors with ancillary water jets. Various specialised designs have been developed: for example a Netherlands company, IHC, has developed a draghead to deal with fluidised silt/

clay: this design does not have conventional water inlet flaps on the upper surface but instead uses a roller located in the draghead mouth, the *in situ* material being sufficiently fluidised to be transported up the suction pipe as a slurry.

Depending upon the length of the suction pipe, two or three hoist gantries support the pipe and draghead. The aft gantry is usually linked into a swell compensator, the purpose of which is to prevent ship's motions damaging the draghead/pipe on the seabed. In contrast, the forward, or trunnion, gantry merely moves the trunnion, at the pipe end, into a guide on the side of the hull, where at the bottom there is a valve into which the pipe slots for dredging operations. Long suction pipes have articulated joints with replaceable sleeves. Some trailer dredgers are built with two suction pipes, either side of the hull.

In conventional trailer dredgers, the suction pump is housed inboard, but during the past ten years or so, vessels with a deep dredging capability, that is in excess of forty metres, have had the dredge pump built into the suction pipe. Such underwater pumps have been used also in dredgers operating in shallower waters. In addition to facilitating deeper dredging depths, such pumps can produce a higher mixture density.

After passing through the pump, the material is transported into the hopper, via a discharge chute or pipe. In some designs a diffusor has been attached to the chute, to give a more even loading of the hopper. In the hopper, the separation of the liquid phase from the 'solids' depends upon the particle size and the amount of agitation within the hopper. Some vessels have split hoppers, the function of which is to allow greater time for mixture separation. Near the hopper coaming, overflow weirs allow the liquid phase to pass back into the sea.

Hopper capacity is the main descriptor of a trailer dredger's size. A few vessels have been constructed with hoppers exceeding 10,000cu m, but most trailer dredgers vary between 500cu m and 4000cu m capacity.

The sophisticated dredger Gamma Bay *was built in 1981 by IHC Smit BV, Kinderdijk, for Costain-Blankevoort (UK) Dredging Co, London. Of the trailing suction hopper type,* Gamma Bay *has a hinged centreline and split hull to facilitate discharge of dredged material. It has a single side arm (here shipped on the starboard) and is able to dredge to a depth of 20m. The hopper capacity is 2500 cu m. On 2877 grt, length (oa) is 88.02m, breadth 16.62m, draught 5.05m and depth 7m. The port side crane has a lifting capacity of 8 tonnes. (FotoFlite)*

One example of these large capacity dredgers is the Belgian-owned *Vasco da Gama*, which was built at Schiedam, near Rotterdam, in 1971, as *Humber River*. With a gross tonnage of 10,530, this vessel has a hopper capacity of over 10,000cu m, and can dredge to a depth of 30m.

Of all dredger types, the trailer is the most versatile in respect of methods of spoil disposal; options include:

– dumping through doors in the hopper bottom (the doors are actually valves arranged in rows in the bottom, operated by hydraulic rams);
– direct overside dumping by using the vessel's pumps (in this case, the spoil is not transported any large distance from the dredger);
– connection to a pipeline for pumping ashore; and
– jetting the spoil some distance from the dredger through the use of booster pumps (this is mainly used in land reclamation or beach nourishment).

Some trailer dredgers have been built in a split-hull configuration – the two halves of the hull separate through the use of hydraulic rams, which allow a very rapid discharge of the spoil.

The bucket wheel dredger

This type of dredger first appeared in commercial form round about 1980 and is slowly forming an increasing percentage of the total number of dredgers. The dredging wheel concept was borrowed from large, opencast coal mining machines developed in Germany in the 1960s.

The unique feature of this design is the dredging wheel, which comprises a circular array of small buckets rotating about a horizontal axis, cutting the soil and then moving the material towards the mouth of a suction pipe through which it is lifted to the surface.

Basically the remainder of the vessel is similar to a conventional mono-pontoon type of

A bucket wheel dredger. Vessels of this type are usually non-propelled, relying on tugs to place them on station.

cutter suction dredger, particularly in respect of spud carriages and methods of discharge. Originally the bucket wheel type was developed to cope with stiff clay soils, but the concept proved highly efficient in giving high mixture densities with minimum spillage, and it is now more widely used for other materials. The close spacing of the individual buckets means that large stones and debris cannot enter the suction area and are moved aside.

Slow speed, high torque hydraulic motors are used to drive the wheel via a gearbox and suction is provided from an inboard pump, with the option of underwater pumps mounted in the ladder for deep dredging vessels. Small wheel dredgers are often built in a demountable form, for transport by road, rail, or sea to remote sites; such vessels have a capability of usually 6m dredging depth, though there are standard small craft, eg some in the IHC Beaver series, capable of 16m dredging depth. Some wheel dredgers can dredge in depths of 20m to 30m.

The grab and grab hopper dredger

Of those dredgers which utilise purely mechanical methods of excavation, the grab dredger is the most common world-wide. The design has been long valued for its ability to dredge alongside quay walls and other localities of difficult access.

Mechanical types of dredger are derived from onshore excavation methodology. This design has one or more large, slewing, drum cranes which deploy various types of grab bucket, the clamshell type probably being the most favoured. Grab capacity is normally less than 5cu m. The cranes are mounted either on a mono-pontoon, which might have one or two cranes, or on a self-propelled craft of conventional ship-hull form. Up to four cranes might be included in the latter type, which also will have an onboard hopper. Grab dredgers are gauged according to grab capacity, number of cranes, and, if relevant, size of the hopper.

With the ability to interchange grab types, these dredgers can excavate most materials; however, they are not well-suited to dredging soft silts and clays because of a flushing action within the grab as it is being raised. Unlike other mechanical designs, this type is not constrained by water depth, but its productivity is only in the low to moderate category. A grab hopper dredger has a lower production rate than a pontoon-mounted grab because as part of its operating cycle, the vessel has to up-anchor from the dredging site to sail and dump at the disposal site. Pontoon-mounted grab dredgers work in conjunction with barges, or

A typical grab hopper dredger is the 666 grt Hedwin *owned by Port of Tyne Authority and built by Robb Caledon at Leith in 1969. The operating crane has a capacity of 7.5 tons and dumps dredged spoil into a hopper of 590cu m capacity. The hopper has bottom doors and dredging depth on this vessel is 16.7m. (Alan Sparrow)*

scows, so they spend comparatively less time not dredging.

The backhoe dredger

This design evolved as a dedicated dredger in the early 1970s, but despite this, it is difficult to state when the principle of operation was used first for dredging because the technology is simply a marine version of a dry land, back-acting excavator, modern forms utilising an articulated arm driven by hydraulic rams. Moreover, it is not unknown for land-based plant of this type to be temporarily mounted on a pontoon, used for small dredging requirements, and then revert to their normal usage.

Integral backhoe dredgers are generally non-self-propelled pontoons, which normally use spuds for fixing to the bed, for example a stern spud, sometimes in a sliding carriage, and one or two forward spuds. Anchor winches have been used in some craft. The bucket capacity of existing craft varies from 1cu m to over 10cu m, and the largest types have dredging depths in excess of 20m, but up to 12m working depth is more common.

The bucket dredger

At the beginning of the twentieth century, the bucket dredger was the most common type of dredger in Europe, and many other places, and it is still widely used, but in declining numbers.

The basic mechanism of operation involves the rotation of an array of small buckets, spaced in a continuous loop, the bucket chain, and supported by a fixed structure, the ladder, one end of which is lowered to the bed. In modern bucket dredgers, the bucket chain rotation is powered by electric motors through current supplied by diesel generators. Similar motors are used to drive the anchor winches.

A typical bucket dredger is the 450 grt Bottenopp, *owned by Göteborgs Stad (Ports Directorate), of Sweden. This dredger type relies on barges or hoppers to pull alongside to take on dredged spoil, loading through chutes located near amidships.* Bottenopp *was completed in 1966 by specialist dredger builder Orenstein & Koppel, Lübeck, and is 49.92m in length and 10.0m in breadth* (O & K Orenstein & Koppel)

At the bottom of the ladder, the buckets scoop up the material and with the buckets in an upright position, the material is brought up to the surface, to the top of the ladder, where on the return stroke the buckets are inverted and tip their contents into side chutes, for disposal into alongside barges, or scows.

Most bucket dredgers are of static, mono-pontoon design, although in recent years, a number of self-propelled craft have been built. The number of buckets in a chain depends upon the size of bucket and the length of ladder, typical values being about sixty to eighty. Bucket capacities are usually less than 1cu m and ladder lengths on a medium-sized craft would normally facilitate a 12m dredging depth, but some vessels are capable of up to 30m depths. Static dredgers employ winches to move about the dredging site, commonly bow winch, stern winch, and four side winches; consequently, ancillary craft are required to deploy the winch anchors. Movement is effected through pulling forward on the head anchor and alternatively hauling in and paying out the side winches to swing the craft; the stern anchor would be used to keep dredging to the requisite track.

Although bucket dredgers can work nearly all materials, their decline in service can be attributed to low production rates compared to hydraulic and hydraulic/mechanical designs, high noise levels in operation, and the interference of the anchor wires with commercial shipping traffic.

Other types of dredger

Four types of dredger are included in this miscellaneous category, selected on the basis of numbers operating world-wide. These include the dipper, stationary suction, dustpan, and sidecaster dredgers. Specialised vessels, such as the 'Amphidredger', mini-dredgers, and alternative systems to dredging, such as water-jet systems, ploughs, etc are not considered here.

Dipper dredgers were more popular in North America than elsewhere, but gradually they are being replaced by the backhoe type. Even so, some large dipper dredgers still remain in operation. The operating cycle and mechanism of excavation are similar in principle to the backhoe type, except that in the dipper dredger the cut is made by a forward-acting bucket attached to a supporting arm, which in turn is supported from a crane jib. A spud is required at the opposite end of the dredger from the bucket to provide a resistance to the large horizontal forces exerted by the bucket in the digging action. Bucket capacities tend to be large, up to 11cu m, and this type is best-suited to excavating relatively hard bed materials. However, limited dredging depths (up to 12m) have been the main constraint upon future developments of this type, as well as competition from more efficient designs.

Stationary suction dredgers are similar in design to cutter suction dredgers except for the lack of a cutterhead. Although relatively deep dredging depths are possible, the utilisation of this type is restricted to easily-excavated materials such as sands and gravels. Using water jetting to fluidise soils, the dustpan dredger is a variant of the plain suction design. Also, the bottom end of the suction pipe is shaped into a flattened chamber resembling a dustpan. This design is not common and these craft are mainly used in fluvial environments, excavating unconsolidated materials, which, via a short discharge pipe, are returned into higher energy parts of the flow, for the currents to transport away; sometimes the spoil is discharged to onshore lagoons.

The excavation and direct return of the spoil into higher energy regimes is a practice known as agitation dredging, and another exponent of this practice is the sidecasting dredger. A sidecaster is basically a modified trailer suction dredger, except that the dredger spoil is not deposited in the hopper but pumped directly

back into surface currents. Some craft are fitted with long discharge pipes supported in swinging, cantilever supports, and they are capable of jetting the spoil many decametres from the dredger. This technique is effective and economic particularly in open sea, coastal environments where channel bars form across inlets.

Developments in dredgers

A key feature in the technological development of various types of dredger since the 1960s has been versatility, arising from three primary causes: a requirement for increased efficiency in navigational applications, the increasing use of dredgers in non-navigational applications, such as land reclamation, beach replenishment, aggregates dredging, mineral mining, and trench excavation, and increasing awareness (and constraints) of the environmental impact of dredging operations.

Whether it is the initial creation of new bed configurations in port developments (capital dredging) or the preservation of existing water depths in ports and access channels (maintenance dredging), such excavations for navigational purposes form the major employment of dredgers. Irrespective of whether port dredging is being undertaken by a port authority, a separate state organisation, or a dredging contractor, financial considerations are paramount.

Relatively poor rates of production has been one of the major reasons for the decline of many mechanical types of dredger and the increased use of hydraulic and mechanical/hydraulic types in port operations, but even in these types, close attention is paid to efficiency and productivity. After the boom years of port construction and port expansion projects of the late 1960s and early 1970s, the global recession of the mid- to late 1980s has meant that many owners have tended to extend the operational life of a large number of dredgers. A major feature of dredger newbuildings in the past ten to fifteen years has been the incorporation of instrumentation and control system automation to provide more information to assist the dredge master during dredging operations; this applies particularly to trailer suction, cutter suction, and bucket wheel dredgers.

Instrumentation aids two functions: positional control and quantity control. The former is accomplished through electronic position fixing systems, to ensure that dredging is taking place at the correct site. Originally, these were stand-alone systems, but nowadays, they are integrated into onboard computers, which facilitate an immediate display to illustrate how the dredging operation is progressing *vis-à-vis* 2D or 3D displays of bed configuration derived from hydrographic surveys. Quantity control instruments include devices such as load indicators and recorders, production calculators, suction pipe position indicators, and 'speed over bed' meters. Such instruments can be interfaced with control systems, such as automatic control of suction pipe winches and devices like ALMO (automatic light mixture overboard) – a system of valves which directs low density mixtures back over board instead of direction to the hopper. In the case of the trailer suction hopper dredger, the determination of the optimum time to spend loading, as part of the dredging-sailing-dumping cycle, is very important.

With respect to dredging methods and types of dredgers, there are broad similarities in the applications to land reclamation and beach replenishment. The main vessels used are cutter suction, trailer suction, or stationary suction dredgers and the optimum type to use is governed primarily by local circumstances. For these applications, there are no major special requirements made of dredging machinery, and therefore, dredgers used normally in navigational applications can be utilised for such operations.

There is also a broad similarity in the types of dredgers used to mine sand and gravel for aggregate purposes from river beds and offshore deposits, and in mineral mining in like environments. Aggregates dredging, particularly in Japan and the United Kingdom, has been a growth industry since the 1960s. In relatively tranquil environments such as in rivers and lakes, vessels such as stationary suction, bucket wheel, grab, and bucket dredgers are employed, but in the more exposed offshore dredging sites, trailer suction hopper dredgers are used. Usually, these trailer suction dredgers are different to their navigational counterparts: hoppers are normally dry-well and the discharge systems often use drag-scraper buckets or wheel excavators inside the hopper to transport the aggregate on to conveyor belt systems for discharge on to quaysides. Recent newbuildings operating offshore of the United Kingdom have been designed for dredging in deeper waters, and these

vessels have the dredge pump mounted into the suction pipe. Another differing feature of aggregates dredgers is that prior to deposition of the cargo into the hopper, the material passes through static screens, which provides a moderate amount of grade separation.

Typical of the new generation of aggregates dredgers is *Arco Arun* (3476 grt), one of a series of four such vessels built by Appledore Ferguson Shipbuilders Ltd, Appledore, for leading operator ARC Marine Ltd. Completed in 1987, she operates in the Thames estuary, dredging aggregates for transit to up-river locations. She is of the trailing suction hopper type (hopper capacity 5027 tonnes), and can dredge up to a depth of forty-three metres. Her principal dimensions are length (oa) 93.3m, breadth 17.6m and draught 6.26m.

Dredgers used for mineral mining use similar excavation methods to their navigational counterparts, but often their appearance is vastly different. Methods in use include the bucket ladder, bucket wheel, grab, backhoe, and stationary suction techniques. Invariably, these dredgers are not self-propelled and resemble a small building mounted on a pontoon. Such shapes arise from the inclusion of onboard treatment plants on the pontoon, to

Marine dredged sand and gravel is making an ever increasing contribution to British and northern European demand for aggregates as land based resources continue to decline, most noticeably in southeast England. Since its inception in 1961 Southampton based ARC Marine Ltd has progressively expanded and modernised its fleet to meet consumer demand and in the late 1980s took delivery of four large aggregate dredgers from Appledore Shipbuilders Ltd, of which the Arco Axe *completed in 1989, was the last in the series. Seen here during loading trials,* Arco Axe *has a cargo capacity of 4500 tonnes and can discharge this at the rate of about 1800 tonnes per hour through on-board self-discharge equipment, enabling fast turn-round at wharves without such facilities and labour. (ARC Marine)*

separate the target mineral from unwanted material (tailings); treatment plants include machinery such as static and vibrating screens, hydrocyclones, and washing equipment.

During the past fifteen to twenty years, environmental considerations have had an increasing influence on all types of dredging operations. Moreover, international standing conventions, such as the London Dumping Convention, Oslo Convention, and Paris Convention, as well as national legislation, now exert controls on dredging. Irrespective of the dredging application, be it navigational, land reclamation, aggregates winning, or mineral mining, such operations often receive adverse criticism, usually of their environmentally unfriendly nature. These include aspects such as redistribution of contaminated soils, increased turbidity in waters, and the hydrodynamic and biological impacts of reconfiguring the bed morphology through excavation.

In the early 1990s, environmental impact is an important consideration in the planning of dredging operations of all types; however, environmental considerations usually have more bearing on a dredging practice adopted rather than the design of machinery on any given type of dredger being more environmentally-sensitive. In projects or developments where environmental issues are extremely sensitive, selection of the type of dredger is the main consideration; for example, in a situation where a major increase in turbidity would be unacceptable, a trailer suction dredger might not be used because of the overflow, hence, a vessel such as a bucket dredger, grab or backhoe dredger might be used: these will create some turbidity, but not to the same extent as the trailer suction dredger.

Dr C M Davies

Cableships

Early development

Since the submarine telegraph cable was developed in the mid-nineteenth century the necessity to lay and repair submarine cables has produced an evolution in the design of specialist vessels. Initially, conventional vessels of suitable size and manoeuvrability for the task and with sufficient space to carry the cable and equipment were utilised, the most notable and famous ones being the paddle tug *Goliath* which laid the first telegraph cable between Dover and Calais in 1850, and *Great Eastern*

Cable & Wireless plc and its predecessor Imperial & International Communications Ltd have owned and operated cableships since 1929. An addition to the fleet in the early 1960s was Cable Venture *(9019 grt) which operates world-wide. She is fitted with diesel-electric machinery and has a speed of 12.5kts. Together with some other vessels in the C&W fleet she is registered in Bermuda.* (Cable & Wireless [Marine] Ltd)

which laid the first successful transatlantic telegraph cable in 1866.

The first dedicated cableships, *Oersted* and *Faraday*, appeared in 1874, followed in the years up to the Second World War by a long line of vessels built for both the cable manufacturers and the cable owners. The cable manufacturers built laying vessels to enable them to provide a complete cable system provision service to cable owners who did not wish to own vessels. The main cable owners, such as the British Post Office and Cable & Wireless, preferred to lay and maintain their cables and therefore built vessels to fulfil those functions. The main outwardly distinguishing feature of all the cableships was the large bow sheave for laying and picking up the cable. In addition many of the cable-layers also had a stern sheave or chute. Internally large cable engines to lay and pick up the cable, and circular plated or lattice cable tanks instead of cargo holds set them aside from conventional commercial vessels.

However it was only after 1945 when long distance repeatered telephone cables were developed that the sophisticated cableships of today began to appear. The new requirements were for accurate laying to minimise cable wastage, together with the need for rapid and accurate repair capability as fishing equipment became larger and caused more frequent damage. The laying vessels tended to become bigger to give large cable carrying capacity for long ocean lays and sufficient lifting capacity for the increasingly larger and heavier armoured shallow water co-axial cable. These culminated in size in the purpose-built AT&T *Long Lines* (built 1963, 11,326 grt) and the Cable & Wireless (Marine) Ltd *Cable Venture* (9019 grt) which was converted from a bulk carrier. The repair ships tended to divide between larger vessels who could operate in any depth of water, such as BT (Marine) Ltd's *CS Iris* (3874 grt), and smaller vessels to operate in shallow water and estuaries as was seen with Netherlands PTT's *Directeur-Generaal Bast* (built 1969, 629 grt). All vessels were fitted with distinctive gantries or davits over the bow sheaves to handle the delicate but heavy repeaters. However, the distinction between laying

and repair vessels is not finite as all the laying ships also undertake repairs, whilst the repair vessels may undertake short lays over the bow, particularly where the cables come ashore.

As with any other type of vessel, the design and capabilities of the cableships varied with the geographical and technical interests of their owners. The laying vessels owned by the manufacturers needed to operate world-wide. The cable owners required a variety of layers, deep water and shallow water repair ships suitable for their particular areas of operations. With the gradual withdrawal of the manufacturers from shipowning in the 1960s and '70s the cable owners had a greater need for laying vessels, but their size and characteristics still varied considerably. Companies such as AT&T and Cable & Wireless required large vessels to lay long cables across the oceans whilst the companies involved in areas like the North Sea required smaller shallower draught vessels. In the 1980s these shallower draught vessels also needed to operate burial submersibles to protect the cables from fishing activity.

The advent of cables with optical fibre transmission, which are more fragile, and the need to operate cable burial submersibles have made further demands on the design of these vessels. The complexity and investment required caused the cable manufacturers to cease cableship ownership, leaving this to the cable owners. In the 1980s these formed subsidiary operating companies as both the ships and associated submersibles and ancillary equipment became more sophisticated and specialised. In addition the majority of the present commercial cableship owners, originally government administrations, have been or are being privatised. This removes the restraint of governmental specification and funding from the design of new vessels whilst at the same time allowing the individual shipowners to introduce their own competitive considerations into the designs of new vessels.

In addition to the requirements of commercial telecommunication administrations, submarine cables have been, and are still, required

for a variety of military purposes. The need for laying and maintaining these specialist systems, coupled with the security requirement, generated uniquely specialised cableship ownership by a number of military authorities, notably in the United States, Soviet Union and United Kingdom. The design of these vessels has paralleled but, because of the uniquely military functions required, not entirely duplicated normal commercial cableships.

Basic requirements for the modern cableship

The requirements for the cableship of the 1990s are:

1. Large cable storage capacity, with space to carry various types of stock cable simultaneously for cable maintenance operations.
2. Ability to pay out and pick up cable under full control at all water depths, with three-metre diameter sheaves at the bow, and either a sheave or chute at the stern on laying vessels, to ensure that the minimum bending radius of the cable is not exceeded. Cable engines require a safe working load in excess of thirty tonnes to deal with all cables and depths.
3. Highly accurate manouevrability and control at low speed.
4. Sophisticated cable testing and jointing equipment, with a high standard of cleanliness for optical fibre jointing.
5. Highly accurate integrated navigation equipment, capable of interfacing numerous navigation systems both permanently carried and temporarily embarked for a specific project.

In addition, for owners wishing to operate mainly on the continental shelves and carry out work for the offshore industry as well as in their traditional telecommunications field:

6. Ability to operate a variety of submersibles, including high bollard pull ploughs.
7. Large clear deck space and large lifting capacity crane(s) and A-frames, for adaptability to carry and use the variety of cable handling

equipment and submersibles, both existing and that which will be developed during the 1990s and beyond.

The cableships of the 1970s and '80s had some of these qualities. Cableships were amongst the first vessels in the world to have satellite navigation systems and integrated navigation computers. Their slow speed manoevrability and station keeping abilities in manual control were above average. These qualities were adequate for the laying and repair of conventional co-axial cables, but proved to be less so for handling optical fibre cable and operating numerous submersibles. They were also inadequate for operating close to oil and gas platforms and pipelines in order to satisfy the increasing demands from the offshore industry for laying control umbilical and small power cables.

Evolution of the modern cableship

From 1985 onwards the requirement for accurate manoeuvrability, station keeping, submersible operation, and clear deck space led to the chartering and conversion of dynamic positioning oil industry vessels. These were used for specific projects, particularly work associated with oil and gas fields, or when laying telecommunications cables across pipelines. Much as these vessels fulfilled the immediate needs of those particular tasks, they also highlighted their inadequacies as full cableships, particularly in the area of sufficient cable storage facilities for long cable lays. Because of their low afterdecks they also lacked the necessary height of the working deck above the waterline for deeper water work with its requirement to avoid the decks being awash in large swell conditions. What was needed was a ship that had all the necessary qualities and could be adaptable enough to be modified for the changes occurring in the next thirty to forty years.

The vessels now being designed and built will therefore be generally larger with a high beam to length ratio and passive stabilisation systems to provide a steady working platform and the stability to deploy submersibles suspended from A-frames and cranes. Diesel elec-

tric machinery will provide high generating power and fine control to drive large propulsion thrusters and operate powerful equipment. Integrated navigation systems and DP will enable station keeping to a plus or minus three metre accuracy in heavy weather and strong tidal conditions. Large cable storage tanks and cable handling machinery situated inside the hull will give added stability, whilst leaving the open deck clear to deploy specialist equipment and submersibles. Extensive use of closed circuit television cameras and internal communications equipment will allow the bridge staff to monitor and control cable operations, whilst computer controlled cable engines will automatically adjust the cable tension, speed and slack. The first vessels to have this level of sophistication are AT&T's *Global Link* and *Global Sentinal* (United States), KDD's *KDD Ocean Link* (Japan), and Cable & Wireless (Marine) Ltd's *Sir Eric Sharp* (United Kingdom). These vessels have a relatively conventional appearance and are intended primarily for long distance deep water operations.

For more specialist shallow water laying and cable burial work there is an additional need to load large weights on deck and a large internal working area into which can be slotted containers for whatever new technology is required. These vessels tend to have the appearance normally associated with the offshore industry, and where it is intended to operate in those areas helipads are also a feature. This type of cableship is illustrated by *Northern Installer* operated by Cable & Wireless (Mar-

ine) Ltd, a conversion from an offshore industry vessel, and the purpose built Belgian-owned *Discovery* which is also a fully equipped dive support vessel. The latest development in this area is the BT (Marine) Ltd *CS Sovereign* which combines the shallow water lay and burial requirements with the size and cable capacity for long deep water operations.

Summary

The role and appearance of the cableship did not alter significantly from 1945 to 1980 as the traditional requirements remained reasonably unchanged. The development of fibre optic cable with its associated advances in telecommunications technology and the need to protect the cables from fishing and similar activities gave the impetus to develop cable burial techniques. Coupled with the diversification of the commercial aspirations of the cableship operators the changes to the functions and design of the cableship inevitably followed. New technology and specification will ensure that many of the next generation of vessels will have a totally different appearance from the conventional cableship hitherto known.

B Peck

Acknowledgements

The author acknowledges assistance rendered by BT (Marine) Ltd, AT&T, and the article by Captain G W T Holmes, 'Cableships into the 1990s', *Seaways* (July 1991) and a presentation to the Nautical Institute Solent Branch, April 1991.

The bow pay-out/pick-up (repair) equipment can be clearly seen in this photograph of the BT (Marine) cable vessel CS Sovereign. *Built at Krimpen, Netherlands, in 1991,* CS Sovereign *is of 11,242 grt, and carries up to 3320cu m of cable. BT (Marine) Ltd, based at Southampton, is a subsidiary of British Telecom. Older ships in the fleet were acquired in 1981 when BT took over the telecommunications interests of The Post Office.* (BT [Marine] Ltd)

One of the prime functions of modern dedicated icebreakers: Russian icebreakers escorting cargo ships along the Northern Sea Route, a 'short cut' to the Siberian region from European Russia. (Murmansk Shipping Company).

Modern icebreaking ships

The last three decades have witnessed a broad application of advanced marine technologies to a variety of specialised, icebreaking ships. Distinctive icebreakers and icebreaking cargo carriers have been designed and built with features for operating in the Arctic Ocean, Antarctic, Baltic Sea and other sub-Arctic waters that are seasonally ice-covered. Technological solutions to icebreaking in unique environments have been quite innovative and successful, and particularly significant are those ships adapted for operation on the Northern Sea Route (along the northern Russian coast) and on the Siberian rivers.

Most polar and Baltic icebreakers introduced since 1960 have been built for escort duty in support of a marine transportation system. Their primary task is to lead convoys of one or more commercial ships through an ice channel or track they create. Ice strengthened merchant ships, many constructed to specific ice rules or classifications, follow in the ice-breaker's tracks to make a more efficient and safer passage. However, in recent years a number of more advanced Arctic cargo carriers, such as the Canadian bulk/oil vessel *Arctic* (20,118 grt) and the Russian roros of the SA-15 *Norilsk* class (18,627 grt), have been designed to proceed through ice fields under their own power, thereby minimising the requirement for icebreaker escort except for the most difficult of ice conditions. Highly specialised ice-

breakers have also been built for sub-Arctic operations in the Baltic Sea, Great Lakes, Lake Vänern (Sweden) and the shallow Siberian rivers. In response to oil and gas development in the Canadian Beaufort Sea in the late 1970s, a small fleet of privately-owned icebreakers was built for ice management operations in support of offshore drilling rigs operated by Gulf Canada and Dome Petroleum. In contrast, modern Atlantic icebreaking ships are usually deep draught and are of multi-purpose design. Two of their primary functions are logistics to Antarctic research stations and the support of multi-disciplinary science around the continent. An excellent example of such a ship is the German polar research vessel *Polarstern* which has conducted extensive scientific voyages in the Arctic and Antarctic since 1982. Finally, many of the world's most powerful and largest icebreakers in service during 1992 were conceived with a multi-mission capability in mind, whether the tasks be escort, logistics, research, defence or to provide a credible national maritime presence in the polar regions.

Modern ship design, machinery reliability and improved ice information for navigation have allowed marine access by surface ship to nearly all high latitude and remote polar regions of the globe. The extraordinary capabilities of modern icebreaking ships are illustrated in the selection of historic polar voyages found in Table 8/1. Many of these polar operations were once thought to be difficult, if not impossible, to achieve by surface ships: icebreaker transits to the North Pole, winter transits around Alaska, year-round navigation between

Murmansk and the Yenisey River, winter scientific operations in Antarctic waters, and independent transits (without icebreaker escort) of icebreaking cargo ships in the Canadian Arctic and along the Northern Sea Route. The fact that several of these operations can be considered almost routine, is testament to the rapid advancement of polar ship technology since the 1960s.

The polar icebreaker

No mention of modern icebreakers can be presented without first reviewing the extraordinary polar fleet of the former Soviet Union. More than one hundred specialised icebreaking ships have been designed and built for operations along the Northern Sea Route and on the Siberian rivers. Since the late 1950s Soviet designers and shipbuilders concentrated on the development of nuclear-powered icebreakers. *Lenin* (13,366 grt, 44,000shp), now out of service, was the first nuclear surface ship and began escorting convoys in 1960. *Lenin*'s successors, the *Arktika* class with 75,000shp, are the world's most powerful icebreakers. Their steam turbo-electric plants are driven by two pressurised water reactors. While they represent the backbone of the Northern Sea Route convoy operations, the *Arktika* class icebreakers have also made a number of celebrated voyages to the North Pole.

While the Soviets were concentrating on nuclear power for Arctic ships, the Finnish shipbuilder Wartsila developed a fleet of polar and subarctic icebreakers for the USSR from the mid-1950s through to 1990. Three polar ice-

Russian nuclear polar icebreaker Arktika, *first surface ship to reach the North Pole on 17 August 1977.* (Murmansk Shipping Company)

Table 8/1. Significant polar voyages and selected icebreaker operations since 1960

Polar ships	Flag	Time of year	Route or location	Significance
LENIN	SU	Summer 1960	Northern Sea Route	World's first nuclear surface ship commences icebreaking escort duties.
MANHATTAN	US	Autumn 1969	Northwest Passage	Experimental voyages to test the feasibility of commercial tankers in the Arctic.
LOUIS S ST LAURENT and CANMAR EXPLORER II	CAN	Aug 1976	Northwest Passage	Successful escort of a drill ship from Atlantic to the Canadian Beaufort Sea.
ARKTIKA	SU	Aug 1977	Murmansk to the North Pole and return	First surface ship to reach the Geographic North Pole (17 August 1977).
SIBIR and KAPITAN MYSHEVSKIY	SU	May–June 1978	Northern Sea Route (north of the Siberian islands)	First high latitude, experimental 'trans-Arctic' ice escort.
Polar icebreakers and icebreaking carriers	SU	Navigation season 1978–79	Barent and Kara Seas	First successful year-round navigation from Murmansk to Dudinka on the Yenisey River.
POLAR STAR and POLAR SEA	US	1979–86	Bering, Chukchi and Beaufort Seas	Arctic marine transportation ('trafficability') studies around Alaska.
POLAR SEA	US	Jan–Mar 1981	Bering Sea to Beaufort Sea	First winter transit to Point Barrow, Alaska.
POLAR STAR	US	Dec 1982–Mar 1983	Antarctica	First complete high latitude circumnavigation of Antarctica in modern times (above 60°S).
LEONID BREZHNEV (now ARKTIKA) and 12 other icebreakers	SU	Oct–Nov 1983	North coast of Chukotka, Siberia	Rescue of a 51-ship convoy trapped in severe ice conditions.
ARCTIC	Can	Aug 1985	Bent Horn, Cameron Island	First cargo of crude oil from the Canadian Arctic.
VLADIVOSTOK and SOMOV	SU	June–Sep 1985	Near Russkaya Station, Hobbs Coast, Antarctica	Rescue of the Soviet Antarctic Expedition flagship drifting in heavy ice.
Three SA–15 icebreaking carriers	SU	Nov–Dec 1985	Northern Sea Route	Experimental navigation season extension with sailings from Vancouver to Archangel.
POLARSTERN	WG	July–Aug 1986	Weddell Sea, Antarctica	Winter oceanographic operations.
SIBIR	SU	May–June 1987	Central Arctic Basin	Evacuate drift station 27 and establish drift station 29; second surface ship to reach the North Pole (25 May 1987).
SA–15 icebreaking carriers	SU	Summer 1989	Europe to Japan via the Northern Sea Route	Soviet Arctic carriers under charter to Western shippers for commercial voyages across the top of the Soviet Union.
ROSSIYA	SU	Aug 1990	Central Arctic Basin	Transit to the North Pole (8 Aug 1990) with Western tourists aboard.
ARCTIC	Can	June 1991	Northwest Passage to the Polaris Mine, Little Cornwallis Island	Earliest seasonal surface ship transit in eastern reaches of the Northwest Passage; mine reached 23 June 1991.
SOVETSKIY SOYUZ	SU	July–Sep 1991	Central Arctic Basin and Northern Sea Route	Transit to the North Pole and along the Northern Sea Route with Western tourists.
ODEN and POLARSTERN	SWE WG	Aug–Oct 1991	Central Arctic Basin	International Arctic Ocean Expedition; reached the North Pole (7 Sep 1991).

breaker classes, the *Moskfa*, *Ermak* and *Kapitan Sorokin* types, were all designed with diesel-electric power plants. The *Ermak* class (12,230 grt) are the highest-rated diesel-electric icebreakers today at 36,000shp. The *Kapitan Sorokin* class (10,610 grt) of four ships was specially designed for shallow-water operations. These large vessels with 22,000shp, a 27ft draught and an installed hull air lubrication system for reducing the friction of ice,

have pioneered the escort of convoys into the shallow river mouths of Siberia.

Two polar icebreakers, *Taymyr* and *Vaygach* (both 20,790 grt), in many ways represent the most technically-advanced Arctic ships at the end of the century. Added to the Murmansk Shipping Co in 1989 and 1990, they employ a unique combination of systems to conduct icebreaking in the shallow Yenisey and Ob rivers and along the entire Northern Sea Route.

Nearly 500ft (150m) in length, they are nuclear-powered (using a single reactor generator, 44,000shp) and thus have virtually unlimited endurance. Their key advantage is a 26ft (8m) draught in contrast to the 36ft draught of the *Arktika* and other Russian classes. Designing and building *Taymyr* and *Vaygach* involved a decade-long collaboration between Finland's Wartsila shipyard and a host of Soviet ministries.

US Coast Guard polar icebreaker Polar Sea *in the Amundsen Sea, Antarctica, during March 1992 with her sister* Polar Star. *These are the US Coast Guard's largest vessels and were their first new icebreakers built for twenty years.* (Author)

During the mid-1970s the US Coast Guard commissioned two large polar icebreakers, *Polar Star* and *Polar Sea*, that have unique dual propulsion plants. A diesel-electric plant is rated at 18,000shp, while three gas turbines can generate 60,000shp. Although plagued with some early problems with their state-of-the-art controllable-pitch propellers, the *Polar* class icebreakers have proven to be highly effective ships. They have operated in Alaska, around Greenland, through the Northwest Passage, and in McMurdo Sound, Antarctica, on annual resupply missions.

The table of typical icebreakers (page 165) includes a wide variety of vessels used for polar and sub-Arctic operations. Significantly, this list also represents a diversity of national interests – each country having very specific requirements for highly capable icebreaking ships. These requirements have driven a technological 'revolution' in the specialised fields of icebreaker design and construction.

Advanced icebreaking carriers

Since 1978 the icebreaking cargo vessel *Arctic* (a combination bulk/oil carrier) has set many precedents for commercial ship operations in the Canadian Arctic. It was built in 1978 as a bulk carrier, but was converted to a bulk/oil carrier in 1986. It was able to trade further north in Canadian waters than any vessel up to then and also was able to load cargo at the Panarctic oil facility at Cameron Island. A joint federal government/industry consortium, Canarctic Shipping Co Ltd, has operated the 725ft (221m) and 26,440 dwt ship primarily between the Arctic and European ports. Designed to Class 2 and later Class 4 standards of CASPPR (the Canadian Arctic Shipping Pollution Prevention Regulations), *Arctic* has a double hull throughout the length of its cargo spaces and engine room. The ship's structure

has been engineered to withstand both unusual global and local impacts associated with ice-breaking. *Arctic* has operated at a continuous 8kts in ice nearly 1m thick.

Arctic has pioneered the use of advanced ice navigation systems, the state-of-the-art technology for the 1990s. The ship has a 'shipboard Ice Navigation Support System' which receives, stores and displays a variety of environmental information. Real-time satellite imagery and airborne radar imagery are integrated with traditional navigation data (gyro, radar, satellite navigation fixes). This system has allowed the ship to navigate unassisted through ice-covered waters in much of the Canadian Arctic.

During the 1980s Soviet shipyards constructed four advanced LASH (lighter aboard ship) vessels for Arctic operations. Three ships of the *Aleksey Kosygin* class (37,464 grt) were of geared-diesel design, while the fourth, *Sevmorput* (38,226 grt), was nuclear-powered. These icebreaking barge carriers were built to be able to support remote Arctic communities that lacked adequate port facilities. *Sevmorput* was designed to operate unassisted in 1m thick ice and is capable of carrying either 1300 TEUs or 74 lighters (or barges). While there is great potential for adapting LASH technology to polar operations, the first three years of *Sevmorput*'s service have not proven economically viable. However, a smaller icebreaking class,

Three icebreaking ship additions to the Soviet polar fleet during the late 1980s. Vitus Bering *is a shallow-draught, multi-purpose Arctic cargo ship commissioned in 1986. Built in the USSR, the ship has a tonnage of 10,800 dwt.* Taymyr *is a shallow-draught, nuclear polar icebreaker designed for icebreaking operations near the mouths of the Siberian rivers.* Akademik Fedorov *built in Finland in 1987 is an Antarctic logistics and research ship.*

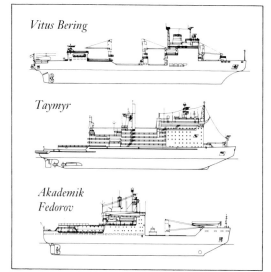

the *Vitus Bering* class multi-purpose supply vessels, have been adapted to Arctic service. These designated SA-10 Arctic freighters have a relatively shallow draught (29ft) and employ embarked helicopters for the rapid off-loading of their cargoes.

One Baltic class of icebreaking carriers also deserves mention. The four *Lunni* class icebreaking tankers have operated in the Baltic Sea during winter since 1976. Owned by the Finnish oil company Neste Oy, the *Lunni* class tankers (11,290 grt) are designed for unassisted navigation in the most severe of Baltic ice conditions. The ships are rated as conforming to the Finnish-Swedish Ice Class 1A Super and are designed with a double hull. Their 16,420 dwt and 540ft (165m) length make them sizeable vessels for winter navigation. Each of the ships has been highly successful at delivering oil products along the coast of Finland during the three to four month ice season.

Norilsk class icebreaking cargo carriers

One of the most versatile and successful icebreaking classes added to the Russian polar fleet in recent years has been the SA-15 icebreaking cargo or *Norilsk* class. Nineteen of these polar ships were delivered by Finland's Valmet and Wartsila shipyards during 1982–87. The final five ships, on a second order to Valmet, incorporated many improvements developed from an extensive review of the earlier ships' performances. The 570ft (174m) *Norilsk* ships, although primarily Arctic freighters, are highly capable as icebreakers under their own power. With 21,000shp on a single shaft, each ship is able to maintain continuous progress through ice more than 1m thick. The SA-15s performed well in the severe ice conditions of the Chukchi Sea where a large Soviet convoy was trapped during autumn 1983. They have made a number of eastbound transits of the Northern Sea Route during June, which is early for the seasonal navigation of convoys. During October to December 1985 three SA-15s completed late season voyages, periodically being escorted by polar icebreakers, from Vancouver, British Columbia, to Archangel on the White Sea. In the 1989 summer navigation season, SA-15 class ships, under charter to Western shippers, carried cargo along the Northern Sea Route from Germany to Japan. In 1990 the SA-15 *Kola* sailed from Hamburg to Japan along the Northern Sea Route in 19 days and 12 hours, a record carriage of cargo from Europe to Japan across the top of Russia.

These multi-purpose carriers of 19,950 dwt tons are designed for a wide variety of general

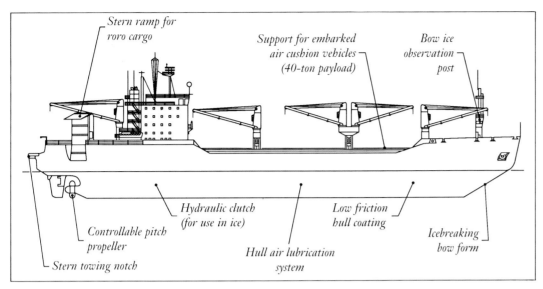

Stern ramp for roro cargo

Support for embarked air cushion vehicles (40-ton payload)

Bow ice observation post

Hydraulic clutch (for use in ice)

Controllable pitch propeller

Low friction hull coating

Icebreaking bow form

Hull air lubrication system

Stern towing notch

SA-15 *Arctic icebreaking cargo carrier* Norilsk *delivered to the USSR in November 1982. Nineteen vessels of this type now sail the Northern Sea Route.* (Wartsila Marine)

cargo including long and heavy loads, pallets, containers, trailers and other vehicles, packaged goods, refrigerated containers, explosives, inflammable liquids and chemicals in packages, coal and bulk ore, ore concentrate in special 10ft containers, grain, and sawn and packaged timber. Unloading can be accomplished on the ice, at the pier, or by using embarked air cushion vehicles. This flexibility is crucial for operating in the remote regions and ports of Siberia. In many respects, most significantly their proven capability for independent navigation through ice fields without icebreaker support, the SA-15s represent a key advancement in Arctic marine transportation. The *Norilsk* class and Canada's *Arctic* are in a real sense the prototypes for future generations of even larger icebreaking freighters.

Technological innovations

Advances in marine technology that are unique solutions for icebreaking ships and have been particularly successful include auxiliary systems for icebreaking, electric power propulsion plants, propeller design and arrangements, and bow form. One challenging aspect for designers has been attempts to reduce friction between the ice and an icebreaker's hull. Most early icebreakers (and many in service today) have an internal heeling system designed to produce a rolling motion of the ship. Not only does this action reduce the friction of ice on the hull, but it can help when the ship becomes

Swedish icebreaker Oden *which reached the North Pole on 7 September 1991 during the International Arctic Ocean Expedition. The ship has a waterflushing system in the bow to reduce friction between the hull and the ice, a side thrust system and heeling capability.* (The Swedish National Maritime Administration)

beset on an ice ridge. Nearly two decades ago low friction hull coatings were developed and applied to icebreakers hulls. Most noteworthy has been an epoxy paint named 'Inerta 160' which has been used on many of the world's icebreakers. The Finnish shipbuilder Wartsila also developed a hull air lubrication system where large volumes of compressed air are pumped through ducts in the icebreaker's hull. The resulting air/water mixture acts as a lubricant reducing the friction of the ice. This system has proven very effective at improving the icebreaking process when thick snow is encountered. Many icebreakers and icebreaking cargo carriers have this so-called 'bubbler system', as well as variations on this technology including the use of water jet nozzles on the stem. Stainless steel has been used on the waterline of a new Baltic icebreaker and one Russian nuclear icebreaker has a heated ice belt, both intended to reduce friction.

The propulsion systems for a majority of icebreakers built during the past thirty years have

been diesel-electric (where generators are normally powered by diesel engines and the electricity produced runs electric motors that turn the shafts). Propeller-ice interaction has always been a concern in icebreaker design, and diesel-electric systems are easily controlled and have proven highly reliable. The earlier power plants had direct current generators and motors (a DC-DC arrangement). However, total ship's power was limited by the size of the DC motors. The advent of modern semiconductors allowed the development of alternating current generators, and since the mid-1970s, icebreakers have used an AC-DC combination of components. Today, with solid state electronics and through the use of frequency converters, a number of recent icebreakers have AC-AC plants. All future diesel-electric plants will be of this type, as the AC motors allow for much higher power levels, and the new plants are highly efficient and more easily maintained.

More icebreaking ships today are using geared-diesel power systems with controllable-pitch (CP) propellers. The *Norilsk* class has a single, large CP propeller, as does *Sevmorput*. The German polar research ship *Polarstern* has a twin, CP arrangement with nozzles to shroud each propeller. Shrouded propellers were also used aboard a number of the offshore support icebreakers developed in the late 1970s for operation in the Canadian Beaufort Sea. As indicated in the table of typical ships, most of the largest polar icebreakers have been designed with a triple-screw arrangement. This has been the norm so as to distribute their very high

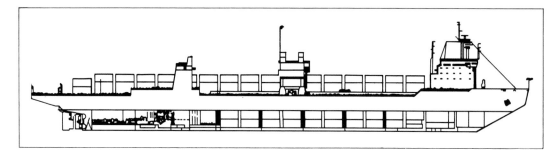

Profile of the world's first nuclear icebreaking LASH (lighter aboard ship) vessel. The Russian Sevmorput *(of 62,000 tons) can carry 74 lighters (barges) or more than 1300 containers to Arctic ports.*

power and also to provide some back-up if one or two propellers are damaged while operating in heavily compacted ice of the Arctic Ocean.

There has been a wide diversity in the bow forms of icebreakers since the late 1960s. Most early icebreakers had rounded bows with straight stems that were angled to the ice at 30 degrees or more. The 'White' bow on the icebreaking tanker *Manhattan* (116,508 dwt) was a notable departure from this tradition with its concave stem line. The bows of the two US *Polar* class icebreakers were of similar design. A trend since the 1970s for most new icebreaker designs has been to reduce this stem angle to the ice. Ice model tests in large tanks and full scale trials during the past two decades have shown that perhaps no single bow form is clearly superior in all conditions. Spoon-shaped bows (usually with a water lubrication system), flat bows with hull chines, and other innovative designs have proven effective for specific icebreaking missions. A recent technical development, the German Thyssen-Waas bow, presents a flat, sled-like surface to the ice where reamers along the sides break the ice in shear. The track produced in level ice is quite smooth and clear. Most of the larger Antarctic icebreaking ships have more traditional or conventional bows to maximise seakeeping characteristics and minimise the open water resistance of the hull. Thus, while there are many effective icebreaking bow and hull forms available, operational requirements must dictate the selection for a specific environment.

The future

Several factors point to an increase in the number of icebreakers, icebreaking carriers and polar research vessels that will be operating in the Arctic and Antarctic into the next century. The level of winter operations in such ice-covered waters as the Baltic and St Lawrence River should also experience steady growth if today's world-wide recession abates and international shipping increases. Projected scientific research in both polar regions will require polar icebreakers and icebreaking support ships to traverse ever higher latitudes. Increased propulsive power and enhanced endurance will be the key requirements for conducting effective environmental monitoring by ship in remote polar areas. In the future the use of modern remote sensing technologies (in particular the radar imagers aboard the European ERS-1 and Canadian Radarsat satellites) will greatly enhance the available ice information for improved navigation.

There is increased interest in the early 1990s in making the Northern Sea Route a profitably and truly international waterway. Using this waterway, shortening of the shipping route from Europe to the Far East is technically feasible. However, due to the extreme ice conditions in the Laptev and East Siberian Seas, it may not be possible to extend the navigation season for convoys beyond five to six months, despite the presence of the Russian nuclear icebreaker fleet. The SA-15 carriers and possibly new variants of larger icebreaking container ships (owned by Western companies) may sail unassisted along the entire length of the Northern Sea Route in the late 1990s.

In many respects the future of Arctic marine transportation rests with the pace of non-renewable resource development in the Canadian Arctic and Russian North. In Canada 200,000 dwt icebreaking oil tankers and icebreaking lng carriers have been on the drawing boards of designers for more than a decade. An improved world market for oil and gas might stimulate exploration and development of fields in the Canadian Beaufort, Barents and Kara seas. Although the economics is understood for using such large ships for transporting hydrocarbon cargoes out of the Arctic Ocean, safety and technological concerns remain unresolved. Future Arctic commercial shipping is clearly feasible as evidenced by current systems, but it must be developed with strict ship standards and comprehensive management regimes for the protection of the marine environment.

Captain Lawson W Brigham

Commercial icebreaking supply vessel Robert LeMeur *designed for operations in the Canadian Beaufort Sea; built in Vancouver 1982. (Canadian Marine Drilling Limited)*

Ocean and salvage tugs

The use of tugs in ports and port approaches can be traced back to the early nineteenth century, but dedicated ocean and salvage tugs on the other hand have not been around for nearly so long. Certainly in the twentieth century the leading owner and operator of ocean and salvage tugs has been L Smit & Co's Internationale Sleepdienst, now part of Smit International, of Rotterdam.

As early as 1892 Netherlands owners took delivery of two ocean-going tugs, *Noordzee* (228 grt) and *Oostzee* (233 grt), both of 750hp, with a length of 40.94m. Before the turn of the century several more large tugs were built including *Oceaan* (1895, 399 grt, 1200hp), and *Roode Zee* and *Zwarte Zee* (1898, 540 grt, 1500hp), and it was about then that Dutch ocean tug operators gained their leading position in long-distance towage, a position retained until relatively recently. From 1900 several more large tugs were introduced, and by the beginning of the First World War the Dutch fleet had increased substantially, the largest being the second *Zwarte Zee*, built in 1906 of 605 grt and 1500hp.

However, the first tugs intended for ocean and deepsea rescue were only placed on station in 1923–24, these being at the Hook of Holland, Rotterdam and Vlissingen, to cover the Netherlands and Belgian coasts, North Sea and English Channel. A major departure was the stationing at the Azores of an ocean salvage tug in 1924, this having been made feasible by the introduction of radio transmitters on board. Smit had in 1923 merged with International Towing Co to form an enlarged entity, and resulting in a fleet of several sea- and ocean-going tugs.

Prior to this tugs were only placed near ports and known danger points, but with the establishment of permanent salvage stations, the numbers of such vessels involved grew in what was becoming a very lucrative business, being close to areas where strandings, collisions and adverse weather were common. The stations increased in number and included the Dardanelles, Malacca Strait, Cape Town, the North Sea, the English Channel approaches, northwest Spain, and Gibraltar.

The 9000bhp ocean-going salvage tug Koyo Maru *was built in 1968 for Nippon Salvage Co of Tokyo.* Koyo Maru *is a well-equipped vessel with three workboats and much tween deck salvage store space, and carries the necessary underwater welding and cutting gear, diving apparatus and numerous pumps, ground tackle, etc.* (Nippon Salvage).

The vast majority of salvage operations were carried out on the basis of 'No cure, no pay'. The award was based on the residual value of what was salvaged so everything depended on success; tug owners invested large sums of money in ordering purpose built and dedicated salvage vessels. The tugs became ever more sophisticated and better equipped, to the point where they carried everything that was considered necessary for a successful salvage operation. A typical dedicated salvage tug carried a mountain of equipment with which to tackle most salvage operations. Equipment included items such as: diving equipment; assorted electric and diesel pumps; portable generators and cables; portable air compressor, pressure value and hoses; steel plate, welding and cutting gear; both wooden and inflatable workboats; beach gear etc.

Both major wars took their toll of tugs; indeed the Hong Kong-based firm of Moller lost its entire fleet due to the Japanese. Britain's leading ocean-going tug owner Overseas Towage & Salvage had its new *Neptunia* (798 grt) stationed at Falmouth under Admiralty orders in September 1939. In the middle of that month *Neptunia* was sunk by a German U-boat. At 2000ihp she was the most powerful tug under the British flag.

During the Second World War the majority of large tugs did not have engines exceeding 3000bhp, with a bollard pull of about 30 tons. One notable exception was the Smit-owned *Zwarte Zee*, the third to bear this name, which was built in 1933 and of 4200bhp. Apart from being the first motor vessel owned by Smit's, she was also the world's most powerful tug. She lasted well into postwar years, and was in fact renamed *Ierse Zee* in 1962 so that the name *Zwarte Zee* could be used on a vessel then being built.

In the 1960s the size of vessels started to increase rapidly. Oil tankers of 30,000 tons that once were considered supertankers were dwarfed. This meant that if they were to hand-

le these vessels tugs had to increase in power. Steam had almost disappeared and by the end of the decade tugs were being built with in excess of 13,000bhp and with a bollard pull of 150 tons. In the 1970s the change continued with numerous large salvage tugs being built, some with up to 19,200bhp and bollard pull of 200 tons, but the tide was already starting to turn.

The end of the dedicated salvage tug

Worries about strandings, collisions and pollution were being raised more and more frequently. By the late 1970s with better and wider use of radar and sophisticated navigational equipment, together with the introduction of traffic separation schemes in congested waters the number of vessels colliding and stranding started to decrease. This coupled with the increase in size, reliability and consequent reduction in the number of ships meant that keeping tugs on salvage station became no longer economically viable. Today, apart from the isolated occasion or where governments fund the operation (such as on the northwest French coast), the practice of keeping tugs on salvage station has to all intents and purposes ceased.

The fall in the number of salvage operations and the high cost of keeping expensive tugs on station meant that tug owners found that they had no option but to seek other bread and butter work for their salvage vessels. Many of the larger tugs were used for towing heavy oilfield structures and rigs, but generally this phase was short lived. Heavy lift vessels capable of carrying rigs were built, which could transport their cargo over long distances more quickly and safely than could be achieved by towing. In addition the need to have multi-purpose tugs capable of transporting equipment and handling anchors as opposed to dedicated towing vessels meant that the salvage tug which could only tow was outliving its purpose. Some of the

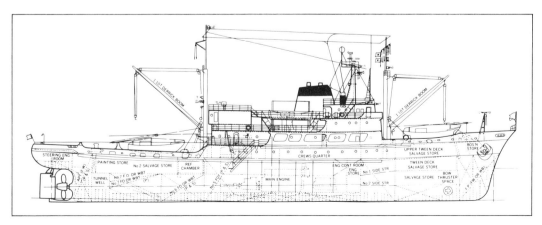

The Norwegian-owned Orla *was a typical ocean-going anchor-handling offshore tug of the 1970s. With a useful 8000bhp and bollard pull rating of 90 tons,* Orla *and scores of other similar vessels provide the bulk of towage services for the offshore industry and have displaced in this role large numbers of conventional deep-sea tugs.* (FotoFlite)

larger tugs were modified to handle anchors but were never able to really compete with the new purpose built supply and anchor handling vessels.

The rapid development of the offshore oil fields meant that a large number of supply vessels with high horsepower were built for laying anchors, towing rigs and servicing platforms. When the downturn in the offshore oil industry came, the supply boat owners entered the tug market and consequently these vessels are now being used in commercial towing and salvage operations on a regular basis. So that they could service offshore platforms and rigs, most offshore supply/anchor handling vessels were designed to be highly manoeuvrable. Most had side thrusters and variable pitch propellers. They also had a large clear deck for anchor handling and cargo storage. High capacity fire monitors were fitted on many. These advantages mean that in many ways they are ideal for use as work-bases in salvage operations. Many of the old salvage tugs were single screw and not fitted with side thrusters. They often needed their own assisting tug when working in restricted areas. Few salvage tugs have been built in recent years and the number of such vessels is falling continuously. Unless some solution to their loss of profitability is found, it seems likely that they will disappear altogether within the next decade.

The Russian tug SB 131 *is one of two vessels claimed, according to their 25,000bhp rating, to be the most powerful tugs ever built. They were built by Hollming Ltd, of Rauma, Finland, and have fire-fighting and salvage capabilities.* (Hollming Ltd)

In 1963, the Netherlands ocean and salvage tug fleet numbered at least thirty-one vessels, in 1975 it was twenty-seven, in 1986 it had risen to thirty-five, but in early 1992 had fallen sharply to twenty-one. A similar trend has been noted in other leading maritime nations; in 1963 the UK had six large tugs, in 1975 it was eight, in 1986 eleven, and early 1992 this had fallen to seven. For Germany, in which the largest ocean and salvage tug operator is Bugsier, of Hamburg, the 1963 figure was six vessels, and was sixteen, fourteen and nine in 1975, 1986 and 1992 respectively. In the mid-1970s, however, the USSR had a fleet of about fifty ocean and salvage tugs, all of which were relatively modern, having entered service in the 1950s, '60s and '70s. The majority are still in existence, although several have been used mainly in naval roles.

The use of offshore supply vessels, brought other problems and thus more change. Supply vessels do not normally carry any significant salvage equipment and if it is needed it must be brought in. The major salvors still keep a substantial amount of equipment on stand-by for use in salvage operations but again the economics of keeping and maintaining high capital cost items on stand-by has meant that this stock is also running down rapidly. Fortunately as one stock is run down other sources emerge. Most, but not all, equipment can be obtained in a relatively short time from shore based plant hire firms and flown to the casualty. If one piece of equipment is not readily available others usually are, and improvisation has and will always play a large part in salvage. In addition, many items of equipment developed for the oil industry can be used or modified for use in salvage operations and are often available.

When operating away from their home base and equipment source the major salvage companies, in order to keep costs down, have when it was at all possible relied on hiring equipment and labour locally. In recent years this practice has become even more pronounced and there are emerging salvage companies which do not own any equipment and which rely on hiring plant when it is needed.

One exception to the general rule in the demise of the dedicated salvage tug is the recent introduction of two large 25,000bhp salvage tugs built in Finland for the now defunct USSR. Probably the greatest change in this tug is the provision of fuel and stores for the helicopter. The vessels, on the strength of their main engine output, are claimed to be the most powerful tugs ever built. There are four HFO diesels each of 4500kW. Two CP propellers in fixed nozzles are driven by the main engines via two reduction gears.

The tugs are identical and have bollard pull ahead of 250 tonnes, and a speed of 18kts without tow.

For rescue work the tug has systems for supplying halon, extinguishing powder and foam, fresh water, fuel and pressure air and floating cables for AC and DC. There is a cargo transfer system for dry cargo up to 200kg. The capacity of the portable hydraulic and electric pump equipment is 2000cu m per hour. For rescuing people there are rescue nets and a rescue cage which are operated by the vessel's cranes. For underwater work there is heavy and light diving equipment for two divers. The equipment allows diving to the depth of 60m. The diver's tools include among others' hydraulic hand tools and welding and flame-cutting equipment. The tug also has a fixed

The Smit tug Smit Rotterdam *(2273 grt) towing the rig* Key Biscayne. *When completed in 1975,* Smit Rotterdam *and the sister-ship* Smit London *were the most powerful tugs afloat, at 22,000ihp (13,500bhp). Built at the 'De Merwede' shipyard in Hardinxveld, these vessels' salvage pumps have a capacity of 1800 tons/hour and they also have a substantial fire-fighting capability. Their twin towing winches each have 1300m of 9in towing wire.* (Smit International)

decompression chamber and a portable one-man decompression chamber.

Four water/foam guns for fire-fighting are installed on top of the navigation house and mast. At fire-fighting situations the tug is protected by a water curtain system. The total capacity of the fire-fighting pumps is 2000cu m per hour and they are connected to main engine gears. The vessel has also three portable fire pumps. The towing winches are midships on the main deck in the towing winch room. The vessel has two main towing winches – traction winches of 150 tonnes. The static brake power is 400 tonnes and the dynamic brake power 190 tonnes. The storage winches for cables and spare cables are in the same space, waterfall type installation. Between the traction winches there is one reel type towing winch of 60 tonnes, with static brake power of 150 tonnes. When towing heavy objects both traction winches operate synchronously.

All towing, working and mooring winches, as well as capstans, operate with 40–60 bar low pressure hydraulics. The hydraulic system is divided into three sections. This makes the towing and deck machinery very reliable, service free and silent.

The towing winches are controlled from the control room on the aft navigation deck, also the propulsion units can be controlled from the towing control room. The main towing cables and spare cables, totalling four, are 79mm diameter, length 1500m, with a breaking strength of 400 tonnes. The diameter of the cable for the 60 tonnes winch for towing smaller objects is 64mm, length 1500m. The vessel has pennants and hawsers for every towing line and a wide selection of connection elements and connecting chains. The total length of the cables and wires is about 14km.

Jim Kearon

Typical research and survey vessels since 1960

Ship (Type of research)	Flag	Built	By	GRT DWT	Length (oa) × breadth × depth × draught Feet–Inches Metres	Handling gear	Engines	Speed	Remarks
BEAUPORT (Hydrographic)	Can	1960	G T Davie & Sons, Lauzon, PQ	813 107	167–6 × 35–8 × 16–8 × 9–1 *51.06 × 10.85 × 5.06 × 2.76*	Crane 1 × 8 tons	2 Canadian Locomotive/ Fairbanks, Morse diesels, 1280bhp; 2 shafts (shafts driven at dead slow by 2 electric motors)	11kts	5 pass, 1 hold, 1 hatch
DISCOVERY (Oceanographic)	UK	1962	Hall Russell, Aberdeen	2321	261–3 × 46–1 × 25–8 × 15–7 *79.63 × 14.05 × 7.83 × 4.74*	Cranes 2 × 2.5 tons	3 Ruston & Hornsby diesels, 3645bhp driving 3 generators each 610kW connected to electric motor 2040shp; 1 shaft	12kts	
ERNST HAECKEL (Fisheries)	DDR	1963	Mathias-Thesen, Wismar	1351 638	222–1 × 38–9 × 27–11 × 16–1 *67.7 × 11.82 × 8.51 × 4.9*	Derricks 2 × 3 tons	2 Goerlitzer diesels, 1420bhp; 1 shaft	12kts	1 hold, 1 hatch
CHALLENGER (Fisheries, hydrographic)	UK	1973	James Lamont & Co, Port Glasgow	988 489	178–5 × 37–1 × 16–6 × 13–3 *54.39 × 11.31 × 5.03 × 4.04*	Gantries 1 × 15 tons, 1 × 8 tons; crane 1 × 8 tons	1 Peter Brotherhood steam turbine 1050shp; 1 shaft (later converted to diesel-electric)	10kts	19 crew, 14 scientists
HAKUREI MARU NO 2 (Oceanographic, hydrographic, geophysical)	Jap	1980	Mitsubishi HI, Shimonoseki	2111 1478	291–6 × 45–4 × 18–1 × 17–10 *88.85 × 13.82 × 5.52 × 5.43*	—	1 Daihatsu diesel, 4200bhp; 2 shafts	12kts	

Ship (Type of research)	Flag	Built	By	GRT DWT	Length (oa) × breadth × depth × draught Feet–Inches Metres	Handling gear	Engines	Speed	Remarks
MITRA (Hydrographic)	Ne	1982	Scheeps Damen, Bergum	869 —	184–8 × 37–10 × 14–10 × 11–5 56.27 × 11.54 × 4.53 × 3.5	—	3 Stork-Werkspoor diesels, 1425bhp; 2 shafts	—	
POLARSTERN (Oceanographic, weather)	WG	1982	Howaldstwerke-Deutsche Werft, Kiel	10,878 4400	385–8 × 84–4 × 44–8 × 34–5 117.56 × 25.71 × 13.62 × 10.5	Cranes 2 × — tons	4 KHD diesels, 20,000bhp; 2 shafts	16kts	
POLAR PRINCESS (Seismographic, hydrographic)	Nor	1986	Kleven/Loland, Leirvik	2508 —	227–10(bp) × 46–0 × 25–11 × 18–1 — 69.45(bp) × 14.03 × 7.9 × 5.53		3 BMV Maskin/ Wichmann diesels 4076bhp driving 1610kW generator and 2 × 1210kW generators connected to 2 electric motors each 2040shp; 1 shaft	14kts	
DISCOVERY (Oceanographic)	UK	1992[1]	Rebuilt at Est Navais de Viana do Castelo, Portugal	2450	296–3 × 45–11 × 25–8 × 17–5 90.3 × 14.0 × 7.83 × 5.3	Cranes 1 × 120 tonnes 1 × 70 tonnes, 3 × 30 tonnes	2 Mirrlees-Blackstone diesels each 1400bhp, and 2 each 1020bhp driving generators connected to electric motor 2040shp; 1 shaft	12kts	22 crew, 28 scientists

Notes:
[1] 1962 vessel rebuilt 1991–92.

Typical offshore supply and anchor-handling vessels since 1955

Ship	Flag	Built	By	GRT DWT (Deck cargo tons) Metres	Length (oa) × breadth × depth × draught Feet–Inches Metres	Cargo handling gear	Engines	Speed	Remarks
EBB TIDE	US	1955	Alexander SYs, New Orleans	148	119–0 × 31–0 × 8–0 × — 36.27 × 9.75 × 2.44 × —	—	2 General Motors diesels, 1000 bhp; 2 shafts	10kts	
BAROID HUSTLER	US	1963	American Marine, New Orleans	196 260	123–9 (bp) × 32–0 × 11–9 × 10–3 — 37.72 (bp) × 9.76 × 3.59 × 3.12		2 Caterpillar diesels, 760bhp; 2 shafts	12kts	Supply; deck cargo
ESSEX SHORE	UK	1967	NV Ijsselwerf, Rotterdam	499 807	166–8 × 36–11 × 14–0 × 12–5 50.81 × 11.26 × 4.27 × 3.78	Derrick 1 × 5 tons	2 Blackstone diesels, 2000bhp; 2 shafts	13.5kts	AST; 12 pass, 12 crew
DOGGER SHORE	UK	1974	NV Ijsselwerf, Capelle	898 1083	195–9 × 42–11 × 17–7 × 14–8 59.67 × 13.06 × 5.36 × 4.46	—	2 Allen diesels, 5600bhp (bollard pull 74 tons); 2 shafts	13.5kts	AST; deck cargo, 12 pass
CANMAR SUPPLIER	Can	1975	Allied SBs, N Vancouver	1188 995	207–0 × 45–9 × 18–3 × 14–3 63.10 × 13.95 × 5.57 × 4.34	—	2 Bofors-Nohab diesels, 7040bhp (bollard pull 96 tons); 2 shafts	13kts	AST; deck cargo; 3 liquid cargo tanks
BIEHL TRADER	US	1977	Campbell Industries, San Diego, Ca	1181 2560	209–8 × 43–8 × 20–8 × 17–6 63.91 × 13.31 × 6.3 × 5.34	—	2 De Laval diesels, 7312bhp (bollard pull 91 tons); 2 shafts	14.5kts	AST; deck cargo
NMS 201	Pan	1980	Promet Pvt, Singapore	497 1000 (559)	176–0 × 38–2 × 14–0 × 10–4 53.65 × 11.64 × 4.27 × 3.16	—	2 Caterpillar diesels, 2250bhp; 2 shafts	11kts	Supply; fire-fighting
MISCAROO	Can	1983	Vancouver SYs, Vancouver	3254 1965 (1000)	260–0 × 57–8 × 31–10 × 26–9 79.25 × 17.58 × 9.71 × 8.16	Cranes 2 × 5 tons	4 Wartsila diesels, 14,900bhp, (bollard pull 150 tons); 2 shafts	14.7kts	AST; fire-fighting; 19 crew

Ship	Flag	Built	By	GRT DWT (Deck cargo tons)	Length (oa) × breadth × depth × draught Feet–Inches Metres	Cargo handling gear	Engines	Speed	Remarks
MAERSK MASTER	Dmk	1986	Odense Staals, Lindo	3949 2600 (1200)	269–9 × 61–10 × 32–6 × 22–8 82.23 × 18.85 × 9.91 × 6.9	Crane 1 × 80 tons	3 Krupp MaK diesels 14,900bhp driving 3 generators connected to electric motors and geared to screw shaft (bollard pull 175 tons); 1 shaft	16.75kts	AST; deck cargo; fire-fighting; standby and rescue; 14 crew, 12 pass
FAR SKY	Nor	1991	Sigbjorn Iversen, Flekkefjord	2285 1900	241–5 × 53–10 × 26–3 × 18–4 73.6 × 16.4 × 8.0 × 5.6	—	4 BMV Bergen/ Normo diesels, 14,400bhp; 2 shafts	13kts	AST; deck cargo, oil recovery, standby and rescue

Notes:
AST = anchor-handling/supply/tug.

Typical dredgers in service since 1969

Ship	Flag	Built	By	GRT (Hopper capacity m³)	Length (oa) × breadth × depth × draught Feet–Inches Metres	Dredging gear	Engines	Speed	Remarks
KANDLA	Ind	1962	Verschure & Co, Amsterdam	1254 (800)	249–6 × 39–7 × 16–1 × 13–3 76.05 × 12.07 × 4.91 × 4.07	Hopper bottom doors; 1 sandpump 610bhp	Triple expansion steam, 1220ihp; 2 shafts	8kts	trailing cutter suction type
HEDWIN	UK	1969	Robb Caledon, Leith	666 (590)	157–4 × 39–1 × 15–3 × 13–10 47.96 × 11.92 × 4.65 × 4.22	Hopper bottom doors; 1 crane 7.5 tons capacity, dredging depth 16.7m	1 British Polar diesel, 1260bhp; 1 shaft	9kts	grab type
VOLVOX HOLLANDIA	Ne	1971	Verolme, Heusden	6061 (6008)	360–4 × 62–4 × 32–2 × 28–9 109.84 × 19.0 × 9.81 × 8.77	Hopper bottom doors; twin side arm, dredging depth 32m, 2 sandpumps each 2000bhp	2 Lister Blackstone Mirrlees diesels, 7100bhp; 2 shafts	13.5kts	trailing suction type
WDA RESOLUTION	Aus	1972	NSW Govt Eng, Newcastle, NSW	5427 (4000)	382–4 × 59–4 × 28–3 × 23–2 116.54 × 18.09 × 8.62 × 7.06	Hopper bottom doors; twin side arm, dredging depth 25m, 2 sandpumps each 1620bhp	2 Lister Blackstone Mirrlees diesels, 6200bhp; 2 shafts	12.5kts	trailing suction type
SULAWESI II	Ina	1974	Van der Giessen-de Noord, Krimpen	3699 (2654)	301–10 × 52–9 × 26–3 × 21–0 92.0 × 16.06 × 8.01 × 6.4	Hopper bottom doors; twin side arm, dredging depth 20m, 2 sandpumps each 800bhp	2 Smit-Bolnes diesels, 4320bhp; 2 shafts	11kts	trailing suction type
ARCO THAMES (Dredger/sand carrier)	UK	1974	Appledore SBs, Appledore	2645 (1860)	323–2 × 50–11 × 23–0 × 17–10 98.51 × 15.52 × 7.0 × 5.44	Single side arm, dredging depth 20m, 1 sandpump 1600bhp; mechanical discharge	1 Mirrlees Blackstone diesel, 3400bhp; 1 shaft	12kts	stationary suction type
AL MERBID (Dredger/sand carrier)	Irq	1975	IHC Verschure, Amsterdam	3588 (3000)	295–3 × 53–10 × 24–3 × 20–0 90.0 × 16.4 × 7.4 × 6.1	Twin side arms, dredging depth 27m, 2 sandpumps each 1200bhp; sandpump discharge	2 Atlas MaK diesels, 5500bhp; 2 shafts	12kts	trailing suction type
GAMMA BAY	UK	1981	IHC Smit, Kinderdijk	2877 (2500)	288–9 × 54–6 × 23–0 × 16–7 88.02 × 16.62 × 7.0 × 5.05	Hull hinged centreline – split hull; single side arm, dredging depth 20m, 1 sandpump 1500bhp	2 Bolnes diesels, 5400bhp; 2 shafts	12.75kts	trailing suction type

Ship	Flag	Built	By	GRT (Hopper capacity m³)	Length (oa) × breadth × depth × draught Feet–Inches Metres	Dredging gear	Engines	Speed	Remarks
BARENT ZANEN	Ne	1985	IHC Smit, Kinderdijk	9773 (8000)	429–1 × 77–1 × 32–10 × 28–11 *130.79 × 23.5 × 10.01 × 8.81*	Hopper bottom doors; twin side arms, dredging depth 34–74m, 2 sandpumps each 3086bhp	2 Stork-Werkspoor diesels, 13,800bhp; 2 shafts	15.25kts	trailing suction type
MANZANILLO II	Mex	1988	Ch de l'Atlantique, St Nazaire	5485 (4000)	372–8 × 62–5 × 29–7 × 26–3 *113.59 × 19.03 × 9.02 × 8.0*	Hopper bottom doors; twin side arms, dredging depth 27m	2 Alsthom–Atlantique/Pielstick diesels, 6414bhp; 2 shafts	13.5kts	trailing suction type

Typical cable vessels in service since 1945

Ship	Flag	Built	By	GRT DWT	Length (oa) × breadth × depth × draught Feet–Inches Metres	Cable capacity	Engines	Speed	Remarks
LORD KELVIN	UK	1916	Swan Hunter, Newcastle	2641 3338	333–2 × 41–2 × 25–0 × 22–2 *101.58 × 12.56 × 7.62 × 6.77*	893m³	2 triple expansion 2800ihp; 2 shafts	11kts	4 cable tanks
JOHN W MACKAY	UK	1922	Swan Hunter, Newcastle	4105 5018	361–8 × 48–1 × 35–0 × 26–3 *110.24 × 14.66 × 10.67 × 7.7*	1415m³ (from 1967 1639m³)	2 triple expansion 2800ihp; 2 shafts	11.5kts	4 cable tanks
MONARCH	UK	1946	Swan Hunter, Newcastle	8056 8774	479–9 × 55–8 × 40–0 × 27–10 *146.22 × 16.96 × 12.19 × 8.47*	4811m³	2 triple expansion 4005ihp; 2 shafts	13kts	4 × 41ft diameter cable tanks
CABLE VENTURE (ex-Neptun)	UK	1962	Lübecker Flender-Werke, Lübeck	9019 10,635	498–6 × 61–8 × 42–6 × 29–5 *151.95 × 18.8 × 12.96 × 8.97*	5086m³	4 MAN total 5960bhp/diesel electric; 2 shafts	13kts	
LONG LINES	US	1963	Launched Schlieker, Hamburg; completed Deutsche Werft, Hamburg	11,326 9461	511–6 × 69–10 × 45–6 × 28–10 *155.91 × 21.29 × 13.87 × 8.17*	4420m³	Turbo-electric: 2 General Electric steam turbines 10,000shp, driving 2 generators connected to 2 electric motors each 3850shp	15kts	91 crew
C S IRIS	UK	1976	Robb Caledon, Leith	3874 2151	319–1 × 49–4 × 29–0 × 15–9 *97.26 × 15.04 × 8.84 × 4.8*	772m³	2 British Polar diesels 5200bhp; 1 shaft	14kts	76 crew 10 cable tanks
SIR ERIC SHARP	Bm	1989	Swan Hunter, Wallsend	6141 3523	377–3 × 59–0 × 33–1 × 20–8 *115.6 × 18.0 × 10.1 × 6.3*	1416m³	Diesel-electric: 2 Ruston diesels each 778bhp driving 2 generators linked to 2 electric motors each 2991bhp; 1 shaft	16kts	
DISCOVERY	Bel	1990	Boelwerf, Temse	8248 4645	389–3 × 64–9 × 36–1 × 21–4 *118.65 × 19.73 × 11.0 × 6.51*	1850m³	Diesel-electric: 4 Wartsila diesels each 9718bhp linked to 3 electric motors each 1020shp; 3 shafts	13kts	97 crew
GLOBAL LINK	US	1990	Far East-Levingston, Singapore	13,201 7900	478–0 × 70–10 × — × 26–9 *145.7 × 21.6 × — × 8.2*	3422m³	Diesel-electric; 1 shaft	15kts	126 crew
C S SOVEREIGN	Bm	1991	Van der Giessen-de Noord, Alblasserdam	11,242 3200	417–8 × 68–11 × 42–8 × 23–0 *127.3 × 21.0 × 13.0 × 7.0*	2800m³	Diesel-electric: 3 Stork-Wartsila diesels; 1 × 6933bhp (centre) and 2 × 13,866bhp (wing) connected to electric motors; 1 shaft	14kts	78 crew

Typical icebreakers and icebreaking carriers since 1959

Ship (Class)	Flag	Built	By	GRT	Length (oa) × breadth × depth × draught Feet–Inches Metres	Engines	Speed	Capability	Remarks
LENIN	SU	1959	Baltic SB & Eng Works, Leningrad	13,366	439–7 × 90–7 × 52–11 × 34–1 134.0 × 27.61 × 16.13 × 10.4	2 nuclear reactors (renewed 1972); turbo-electric 4 steam turbines total 44,000shp driving 4 generators connected to 3 electric motors; 3 shafts	18kts	–	Now out of service
MOSKVA (5 in class)	SU	1960	Wartsila-Sandvikens, Helsinki	9427	404–6 × 83.4 × 45–11 × 34–4 123.3 × 25.4 × 14.0 × 10.47	Diesel-electric; 8 Wartsila/Sulzer diesels 26,000bhp driving 8 generators each 2160kW connected to 4 electric motors each 5500shp; 3 shafts	19kts	3.5	
LOUIS S ST LAURENT	Can	1969	Canadian Vickers, Montreal	10,908	366–6 × 80–3 × 43–0 × 29–6 111.72 × 24.46 × 13.11 × 8.99	Turbo-electric; 3 Canadian General Electric steam turbines total 31,500shp geared to 3 generators each 2400kW connected to 3 electric motors each 9000shp; 3 shafts	18kts	4	To be converted to diesel-electic
ARKTIKA (5 in class)	SU	1974	Baltic SB & Eng Works, Leningrad	18,172	435–4 × 91–11 × 56–5 × 30–1 148 × 28.0 × 17.12 × 11.0	2 nuclear reactors; turbo-electric; steam turbines 75,000shp; 3 shafts	18kts	7–8	
YERMAK (3 in class)	SU	1974	Wartsila, Helsinki	12,231	442–5 × 85–6 × 54–10 × 36–0 134.85 × 26.07 × 16.72 × 10.96	Diesel-electric; 9 Wartsila/Sulzer diesels 41,400bhp driving 9 generators each 3080kW connected to 3 electric motors each 12,000shp; 3 shafts	19kts	5	
POLAR STAR (2 in class)	US	1976	Lockheed Shipbuilding, Seattle	13,190 displ	399–0 × 83–6 × — × 33–6 121.7 × 25.45 × — × 10.21	Diesel-electric; 6 Alco diesels 18,000shp and 3 Pratt & Whitney gas turbines total 60,000shp; 3 shafts	18kts	6	Dual propulsion plant with gas turbines for heavy icebreaking or diesel electric for routine operations
KAPITAN SOROKIN (4 in class)	SU	1977	Wartsila, Helsinki	10,609	424–6 × 87–7 × 40–4 × 27–11 129.39 × 26.7 × 12.30 × 8.5	Diesel-electric; 6 Wartsila/Sulzer diesels 28,840bhp driving 6 generators each 3040kW connected to 3 electric motors each 6666shp; 3 shafts	18.75kts	4	
OTSO (2 in class)	Fin	1986	Wartsila, Helsinki	5799	324–10 × 86–10 × 37–1 × 26–3 99.00 × 24.46 × 11.31 × 8.0	Diesel-electric; 4 Wartsila diesels 29,690bhp driving 4 generators each 6032kW connected to 2 electric motors each 10,200shp; 2 shafts	18kts	3–3.5	
HENRY LARSEN (4 in class)	Can	1988	Versatile Pacific SYs, N Vancouver, BC	6166	328–2 × 65–0 × 25–6 × 23–9 100.3 × 19.82 × 8.08 × 7.24	Diesel-electric; 3 Warsila diesels 24,145bhp driving 3 generators each 5000kW connected to 2 electric motors each 8157shp; 2 shafts	13.5kts	3	

Ship (Class)	Flag	Built	By	GRT	Length (oa) × breadth × depth × draught Feet–Inches Metres	Engines	Speed	Capability	Remarks
ODEN	Swe	1989	Gotaverken Arendal, Gothenburg	9438	353–8 × 102–0 × 39–4 × 27–11 107.8 × 31.08 × 12.0 × 8.5	4 Cegielski/Sulzer diesels 15,684bhp; 2 shafts	17kts	4–5	
TAYMYR (2 in class) (2 in class)	SU	1989	Wartsila, Helsinki	20,791	491–1 × 95–10 × 51–5 × 29–6 149.7 × 29.2 × 15.68 × 9.0	Nuclear reactor; steam turbines 44,000shp; 3 shafts	18kts	6	

Notes: [1]Capability is estimated continuous icebreaking in level ice at 3kts (thickness of ice in feet)

Typical ocean and salvage tugs since 1965

Ship (Class)	Flag	Built	By	GRT	Length (oa) × breadth × depth × draught Feet–Inches Metres	Horse power (bollard pull)	Engines	Speed	Remarks
TURMOIL (Bustler class)	UK	1945	Henry Robb, Leith	1136	204–11 × 38–8 × 19–0 × 17–8 62.46 × 11.79 × 5.8 × 5.37	3020bhp (40t)	2 8-cyl British Auxiliaries diesels; 2 shafts	14.5kts	Salvage; range 5000nm
JEAN BART	Fra	1956	At & Ch de France, Dunkirk	638	173–3 × 31–11 × – × 16–5 52.81 × 9.73 × – × 5.0	2500bhp (34t)	2 Werkspoor diesels; 3750ihp; 1 shaft	15kts	Salvage;
ZWARTE ZEE	Ne	1963	J & K Smit, Kinderdijk	1539	254–0 × 42–2 × 22–8 × 20–2 77.44 × 12.86 × 6.91 × 6.15	9000bhp	2 Smit/MAN diesels; 1 shaft	20kts	Salvage; range 14,000nm; pump cap 1300t/hr; 28 crew
OCEANIC	WG	1969	F Schichau, Bremerhaven	2047	286–2 × 48–7 × 23–10 × 20–8 87.23 × 14.80 × 7.27 × 6.31	13,190bhp (170t)	2 Deutz diesels; 2 shafts	20kts	Salvage; range 20,000nm; pump cap 2600t/hr
SMIT ROTTERDAM	Ne	1975	De Merwede, Hardinxveld	2273	245–6 × 51–9 × 25–0 × 22–4 74.83 × 15.78 × 7.6 × 6.81	13,500bhp (176t)	2 Stork-Werkspoor diesels; 2 shafts	16kts	Salvage; range 20,000nm; pump cap 1800t/hr
TANGARA	BZ	1976	Mitsui SB, Tamano	2162	282–2 × 48–0 × 23–8 × 19–8 86.01 × 14.64 × 7.22 × 6.0	12,400bhp (140t)	2 12-cyl Niigata/ Pielstick diesels; 2 shafts	18.5kts	Salvage
S A JOHN ROSS	SA	1976	Brown & Hamer, Durban	2821	310–6 × 52–0 × 28–3 × 24–8 94.65 × 15.85 × 8.62 × 7.52	19,200bhp (205t)	2 Mirrlees Blackstone diesels; 1 shaft	20kts	Salvage; range 20,000nm
DE DA	PRC	1979	IHI, Chita	3356	321–6 × 51–10 × 26–3 × 22–3 98.0 × 15.8 × 8.01 × 6.77	20,800shp (200t)	2 IHI/Pielstick diesels; 2 shafts	20kts	Salvage; range 14,000nm
SALVAGEMAN	UK	1980	Chung Wah SB, Hong Kong	1598	226–7 × 48–9 × 22–4 × 20–2 69.07 × 14.86 × 6.81 × 6.15	11,280bhp (162t)	4 Ruston diesels; 2 shafts	17.5kts	Salvage; range 22,000nm; pump cap 1300t/h
PRESIDENT HUBERT	Bel	1982	Niestern-Sander, Delfzijl	1593	198–4 × 50–4 × 23–1 × 20–6 60.46 × 15.35 × 7.04 × 6.25	12,000bhp (164t)	2 Krupp/MaK diesels; 2 shafts	16kts	
SMIT SINGAPORE	Ne	1984	Niestern-Sander, Delfzijl	2273	245–7 × 51–5 × 25–0 × 22–4 74.86 × 15.68 × 7.62 × 6.8	13,500bhp (188.5t)	2 Stork-Werkspoor diesels; 2 shafts	16kts	Salvage; also 22,000ihp
SB 131	Ru	1989	Hollming, Rauma	4200	322–2 × 64–0 × 29–7 × 23–4 98.02 × 19.51 × 9.02 × 7.1	25,000bhp (250t)	4 Wartsila diesels; 2 shafts	18kts	Salvage

9

Fishing Vessels

IT is commonly held, almost as a truism, that modern fishing vessels in all their variety are, to a greater extent than in any other class of shipping, the outcome of tradition. Indeed fishing tends to be regarded by many not familiar with it as somewhat backward, not least because it remains a hunting activity. In reality the period since 1945 marks a revolution in fishing vessels no less than in other types of shipping. Until the Depression of the 1930s, nearly all major vessel types were directly descended from traditional sailing antecedents to which steam or motor power and other modern developments had been added. From the 1930s onwards, vessel types and technology were largely influenced by specialisation of gears and fish handling. Gear developments have been of primary importance, as in all fisheries the gear comes first – the vessel's immediate purpose is to operate the gear, followed by shipment of the catch ashore.

This chapter accordingly begins with a discussion of the expansion of fishing effort and progressive worldwide enclosure of the shelf seas since the 1930s, highlighting the development pattern of industrial and management regions which have become the framework for the evolution of fisheries throughout the period. This is followed by consideration of basic trends in vessel technology, including hulls, propulsion, gears, fish finding and fish handling and processing aspects. There then follows systematic treatment of the major vessel types defined primarily in terms of gear operation, namely trawlers, seiners, liners, multipurpose vessels and whalers; and secondarily in relation to such factors as the divi-

sion between pelagic and demersal fisheries, range of operation and degree of specialisation. In conclusion, key aspects of industrial and technological developments are briefly summarised in relation to the continued evolution of vessel types, as the next major stage of economic and technological development begins in the course of the 1990s. Throughout there is emphasis upon the major commercial vessel types fishing offshore – the misleadingly termed 'inshore' fisheries of the continental shelf waters and the distant water fisheries conducted at long range from home ports, both in shelf seas and in the deep ocean beyond. The myriad of small boats used in coastal waters' fisheries are not discussed. In these tradition remains very strong in most parts of the world.

The modern fishing industry

Despite its traditional roots in all parts of the world, the modern commercial fishing industry is a relatively recent phenomenon, dating largely from the sequence of developments which commenced in the 1930s, which is when current economic, technological and social patterns of fisheries developments have their origins. Indeed this period is relatively well defined in terms of both regional and global markets and fisheries, which form part of the latest stage in the general long sequence of develop-

ment of the global economy which commenced with the 1930s Depression.

The first feature of this pattern to be noted is the expansion of the world fish catch from the late 1940s onwards at a rapid rate which decreased sharply after 1970, since when there has been a slow upward trend to present levels, and during which period overfishing has become a progressively more serious problem, exacerbated by continuing high levels of investment in catching capacity coupled with technological improvements in both gears and vessels. In the pelagic fisheries there have been some spectacular failures which, despite the difficulties of separating natural fluctuations from overfishing, must be largely ascribed to the fishing industry. These include the fisheries for Peruvian anchovy and North Sea herring, the latter being suspended during 1977–83. Another landmark was the withdrawal of Britain and Norway from whaling in the Southern Ocean in the early 1960s. By the late 1980s severe pressures were also being placed upon some demersal stocks, particularly in the North Atlantic.

The second major aspect of development has been the progressive enclosure of the shelf seas where most inshore fishing effort is concentrated. Until the early 1970s there was continued development of distant water fishing operations by the leading fishing nations, in-

The fish factory/stern trawler Moonzund *was build by VEB Volkswerft Stralsund, East Germany, in 1986, and was the eighteenth of a series of sister-ships built for the Soviet Union. Since the mid 1950s, the Soviet Union has acquired over 600 such vessels, the majority of which remain in service today.* Moonzund *(7765 grt) can carry over 3900cu m of frozen processed fish.* (Volkswerft Stralsund)

cluding the United States, the Soviet bloc, Japan and a number of western European countries. The only exception was whaling, where distant water effort was partly curtailed earlier, as noted above, due to declining stocks. Other key turning points were the extension of fishing limits of countries on the west coast of Latin America in response to the expansion of the United States' tuna fisheries in the eastern Pacific in the 1950s; and the Icelandic fisheries dispute which culminated in the expulsion of UK and West German distant water trawlers from the waters around Iceland. The trend gathered pace in the 1970s, reinforced by the process of negotiation of the Third Law of the Sea Convention concluded at Montego Bay in Jamaica in 1982. Most major fishing countries, together with the European Community declared Exclusive Fishery Zones (EFZs) or Exclusive Economic Zones (EEZs) out to the 200 nautical mile limit. Thus there was a sharp curtailment in the development of distant water fleets, and increasing pressure put on shelf seas as the leading fishing nations concentrated increasingly upon home waters, and there were parallel developments in inshore fleets and gear technology.

The twin processes of development and enclosure have resulted in the emergence of a number of increasingly sharply defined fishery regions in terms of industrial structure, resource availability and management regimes. The first of these is western Europe, centred on the increasingly powerful European Community. Although there are important pelagic fisheries for herring, mackerel, sprats, Norway pout and sardines (in the south), the cornerstone is the major multi-species demersal fisheries. The industrial structure is based mainly on share-owned coastal inshore craft of a wide variety of designs; the company sector has declined markedly with distant water fishing operations, which are of limited importance, and include trawling by Spanish and French vessels in the north, as well as limited tuna fishing in the Atlantic. There are important coastal shell fisheries and extensive investment in finfish and shellfish farming. The inshore fishing regime based on EFZ/EEZ was pioneered by Iceland, but the main thrust of fishery management is now provided by the Common Fisheries Policy (CFP) of the European Community. The only truly supranational management organisation in existence, it was negotiated in its present form between the accession of the UK, Ireland and Denmark in 1973, and 1983, and is undergoing a review of its operation in 1992. Under the CFP, substantial Soviet bloc distant water operations in

western European waters were terminated in the 1970s. The CFP is growing in influence with the expansion of the Common Market itself, with the addition of Greece in 1981, Spain and Portugal in 1986, and East Germany with German reunification in 1990. While fisheries have been a major and, in some cases decisive influence in keeping the Scandinavian countries outside the EC (particularly the non-entry of the Faroes and the withdrawal of Greenland), it is likely that the leading Scandinavian fishing nations will join in the course of the 1990s. Major management issues include effort limitation, overfishing, and allocation among states. Important trends in response to the management situation have been the development of large, multi-purpose inshore vessels, and ever increasing sophistication of gears, including the introduction of purse seining principally by the Norwegians in the 1960s, and a range of light trawl gears partly replacing seine nets for demersal fishing.

The second fisheries region is North America, consisting of Canada and the United States. The latter pioneered integrated regional fisheries management in the establishment of eight regional fisheries councils in the 1976 Fisheries Conservation and Management Act. Canada introduced more integrated approaches for the predominant Atlantic fisheries following the 1982 Kirby report. On the east coast there are important lobster, herring and demersal fisheries in the north, and menhaden and distant water shrimp fisheries in the south. On the west coast, ground fisheries are relatively less important, with salmon fisheries in the north and distant water tuna fisheries in the south and Pacific islands. The new management regime has restricted the distant water

Fletcher Fishing Ltd, New Zealand, in 1982 purchased two Hull freezer trawlers, one of which, Arctic Buccaneer, *(1660 grt) was renamed* Otago Buccaneer. *Destined for service out of Dunedin, this vessel was a unit of a once large fleet operated by Boyd Line Ltd.* (FotoFlite)

fleets of both western and eastern Europe in the Atlantic, and the Japanese in the Pacific, with limited entry agreements covering much reduced distant water fishing effort by other nations.

The third fisheries region is Japan and east Asia, particularly the Republic of Korea and Taiwan. Japan has been the world's leading fishing nation throughout the period, with important coastal, inshore shelf and distant water fisheries. Because of the narrowness of the shelf, the pelagic fisheries are particularly important, including Japanese sardine. All the countries involved rely to a substantial extent on distant water fisheries, including tuna fisheries in the tropical Pacific, Alaska pollack, squid and (in the case of Japan) limited amounts of whaling. This pattern of distant water fisheries has led to the conclusion of various agreements in the 1970s and 1980s, mainly with developing countries for joint ventures and other arrangements to gain access to resources.

The fourth region is the former Soviet Union and eastern Europe. Because of the limited nature of available resources in home waters, much of which are ice covered, these countries have relied upon distant water fisheries and, since exclusion from western European waters in the 1970s, 'klondyking' operations for herring caught mainly in UK waters in which large factory ships buy and process herring and mackerel from local fleets and ship it to their home markets. There is strong emphasis on the use of mother ships with fleets of trawlers in both the Atlantic and Pacific fisheries, because of the great distances involved. Until very recently the entire industry was virtually unique in being state-owned and centrally planned. Perhaps even more than in the Japanese case, this industry has relied upon negotiated agreements and joint venture operations to maintain distant water fisheries. A notable recent enterprise has been krill fishing in the Southern Ocean, while limited amounts of whaling for the Japanese market was also carried on until the 1980s. The precipitate decline of Soviet influence has already led to the incorporation of eastern Germany into the main European sphere of influence, where the other eastern European countries are likely to follow, leaving Russia as a separate fishing region.

The fifth and final fisheries region is the developing world, which is mainly tropical or sub-tropical. Traditional subsistence fisheries remain the basis of the industry, being usually coastal in nature, with larger vessel operations being mainly carried out by distant water vessels, including the east Asian and former Soviet bloc countries in particular, although American tuna and sometimes shrimp fisheries are also notable in this regard. Resources are frequently limited in biomass terms, but with great species diversity. Apart from technology transfer, joint venture and licensing agreements, management is focused upon the fisheries commission system operated through the Food and Agriculture Organization (FAO) of the United nations, through which the scientific and management expertise of the North can be transferred to the South.

Fishing vessel technology

Fishing vessel technology is influenced not only by the technology of vessel operation itself, but also by gear developments on the one hand, and processing and marketing influences on the other. In many ways the central theme in all these developments since the 1930s and especially since 1945 has been the diversification of gears, vessel designs and in processing and marketing of fish products.

Vessel technology may be considered under the headings of hull, propulsion, fish finding, gear handling, and fish handling and processing. In the matter of hull design and layout, the basic pattern of wheelhouse/casing with crew accommodation and engine room aft is a direct descendant from the days of sail. The forward casing design gained markedly in importance in the 1950s with the advent of the diesel stern trawler, and has been adapted to varying degrees, especially in small coastal craft. It has the advantages of more deck space and fish hold/processing space, as well as enhanced deck safety due to the shelter provided by the casing, although safety has been improved in many traditional designs by installation of a whaleback or even a full length shelter deck. As engine power has increased, hull designs have gradually moved away from their sailing vessel antecedents with traditional emphasis on seakindliness and low resistance going through the water, to greater emphasis upon carrying capacity, and thus greater displacement and gross tonnages in relation to length. Wood has remained the principal choice of material for coastal and inshore vessels, but steel is virtually universal for larger inshore and distant water craft. The use of other materials, such as fibre glass and ferro-concrete has been largely experimental and very limited for the sizes of vessels discussed here.

It is remarkable the extent to which sail persisted in the evolution of modern commercial fishing craft, being common until the 1920s and even into the 1930s. Steam power was first

The demersal pair trawler Guide Us *(built 1973; 25 tons), based at Pittenweem, Fifeshire, Scotland, and one of a type which dramatically decreased in numbers from about 1975.* Guide Us *(KY 340; KY = Kirkaldy) is typical of this type of vessel, and has a 270bhp diesel engine and carries a crew of 5. The vessel is 55.2ft in overall length. Pittenweem is a small, but busy, port which in 1992 has a substantial fishing fleet.* (A Denholm)

applied to distant water vessels: the whalers of the 1860s, bottom otter trawlers of the 1880s, and herring drifters in the 1890s, for example. In the modern era marine propulsion for all classes of craft from the 1940s has been the purpose-built marine diesel engine, though many smaller high speed engines since the 1960s have been derived from designs for lorries and buses. Since the 1950s these have been coupled to various combinations of variable pitch propellers and/or reduction gears to give the low speed pulling power necessary both for towing gear and operating hydraulic equipment such as power blocks in purse-seining.

Until the 1960s, the majority of inshore and distant water vessels were purpose-built for specific gears and fisheries, be these trawlers, seiners or liners. These vessel types continue to be developed, but have been joined, particularly in western Europe, by a class of multipurpose inshore boats which use a variety of gears. The most important gear innovations include the development of the purse-seine in the 1930s for fishing herring on the west coast of Canada, which reached its apogee in the Scandinavian herring fisheries in the 1960s and early 1970s, and continued use in the Pacific tuna fisheries. A second important development has been the advent of a large variety of light trawls to supplement the seine net designs in demersal fisheries, especially in Europe; net drums have replaced coiling for warps in this field. Also important has been the introduction of the large pelagic trawl, extensively used by

the Soviet bloc countries from the 1950s. The continued development of the bottom otter trawl and pelagic trawl was a factor in the emergence of the distant water stern trawler in the 1950s, where this design now predominates. In static gear the most notable developments include long lines which can be baited and hauled automatically, in use for a limited amount of demersal fishing in the North Atlantic. The Pacific tuna fisheries are notable for the development of both very long lines, and very long monofilament gill drift nets. Underlying all the gear developments since the 1950s has been the replacement of traditional materials such as cotton and sisal with artificial fibres for net meshes, lines and ropes.

The period since the 1930s is also readily definable by the advent of advanced technology in fish finding and position-fixing, beginning with the echo-sounder, and Decca and Loran radio-navigation systems in the 1940s and 1950s, which gradually replaced traditional methods of locating grounds using crossbearings and dead-reckoning in inshore fishing. In the 1960s sonar and radar were adopted, and it is likely that the use of the satellite based Global Positioning System (GPS) will eventually supersede radionavigation technology. These developments have led to a high degree of electronic sophistication in the wheelhouse, which in larger vessels is now normally equipped with echosounder, sonar, Decca/Loran, radar and GPS, as well as ship-to-shore radio.

The most important development in fish handling and processing since the 1940s has been the gradual replacement of fresh by frozen fish in the major demersal fish markets worldwide. In distant water operations this has led to the installation of freezing and sometimes processing equipment on board. For near water operations gutting machines have made considerable headway for landing fish which is further processed and frozen on landing. Refrigerated seawater tanks have been introduced for maintaining the freshness of whole fish until landed. A particularly important develoment has been the advent of reduction to meal and oil for production of animal feed, which has been the prime objective of a number of major pelagic fisheries, notably in the North Sea and off the west coast of Latin America. About onethird of the world catch is now used in this way, and it has been a major factor in increasing capacity of vessels and adoption of large pelagic trawls and purse seiners. Bulk fish handling, rather than attention to quality is the prime objective, with large clear holds, and pumping or brailing of fish into and out of the hold.

The general arrangement of the pioneer fish factory stern trawler Fairtry, *built by John Lewis & Son Ltd, Aberdeen, in 1954, for Fresh Frozen Foods Ltd, a subsidiary of Christian Salvesen & Co, Leith. The Soviet Union soon adapted the concept for its own needs; this led to the construction of what was to become the world's largest fleet of factory trawlers. The knowledge and experience gained in the operation of* Fairtry *led to the building of* Fairtry II *and* Fairtry III *(1959).*

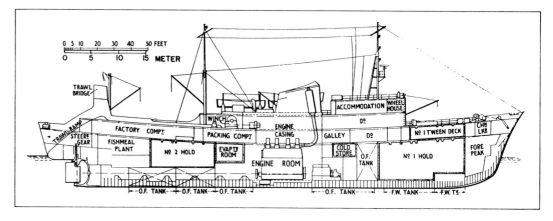

Trawlers

The antecedent of the modern trawler was the sailing trawler of the second half of the nineteenth century, operating light beam trawls in the shallow waters of the southern North Sea, for example. Steam power was applied first to trawling – rather than to any other type of fishing – in the 1880s, whaling excepted. It had the attraction of providing greater and more consistent power supply for dragging trawl gears over the seabed, and was associated not only with the advent of heavier beam trawling gear, but also with the development of the more flexible bottom otter trawl. Diesel engines were introduced in the late 1940s, since when the continued development of power has been associated with increases in both size and sophistication of gear, together with increasing specialisation of trawl types (both heavy and light) to suit particular fisheries. The principal modern trawls and trawler types are now beam and otter trawls and trawlers for demersal fishing; and pelagic trawls and trawlers for midwater fishing, which have been extensively developed since the 1940s, notably by the Soviet Union and Japan. The use of the latter has also been adopted in pair trawling, which enables smaller vessels to be used. Apart from the northeast Atlantic, the other major trawling regions are the northwest Atlantic coast of North America, and the northern Pacific, with limited amounts of trawling off the coast of southern Africa, south east Australia and New Zealand.

From its early history onwards trawling has tended to be a distant water activity, using large specialised vessels, with western Europe being the primary centre of innovation and development of bottom trawling (notably Britain,

West Germany, France and Spain), and the Soviet Union and Japan for pelagic trawling, while the United States has been home to the development of shrimp trawlers on a large scale. By the 1930s a huge fleet of steam trawlers existed in a number of northwest European countries, of which those of England and Scotland were pre-eminent. These were conventional 'side' trawlers with gallows placed fore and aft on the starboard side. Casing and engine room were aft, with the trawl winch in front of the wheelhouse. These vessels were steel built and were from 40m to 55m in length, and lasted in considerable numbers until the 1950s.

By the 1950s two new trends became apparent. First the steam otter trawlers were replaced by diesel trawlers which, while retaining the casing aft and side gallows configuration were of different hull design. These included both middle water vessels for fishing the nearer grounds around the British Isles and Faroes particularly, and larger distant water vessels up to 60m in length for fishing in Arctic waters, including the White Sea, Barents Sea, around Bear Island, Iceland and the Davis Strait.

The second development applied initially mainly to the distant water fleet, and was the introduction of the stern trawler, with casing forward and a single set of gallows aft, placed across the stern. The first of these vessels, notably *Fairtry* built in 1954 were over 2000 grt, and were equipped with freezing and processing capacity. The latter was associated with the

rapidly increasing importance of the frozen fish market from the 1950s onwards. It is possible to produce 'sea fresh' fish products by immediate freezing at sea, rather than using lengthy storage on ice, when a limited amount of deterioration takes place. The modern trawlers which succeeded the *Fairtry* experiment in Britain were smaller and less elaborate. Good examples included *Junella* built in 1962 as Britain's first full whole-fish freezer stern trawler, and *C S Forrester* which was built as a wet fish stern trawler in 1969, her catch being stored on ice; this ship was the first British deep sea trawler to install a Type 28 Shetland gutting machine.

Fairtry was built by John Lewis of Aberdeen for Christian Salvesen of Leith, at one time famous as a whaling company, and was followed in 1959 by two successors, *Fairtry II* and *III*, which incorporated improvements based on experience with the first ship. While the British – and others – progressed, the Soviet Union developed a large proportion of the freezer and factory trawler fleet in the 1960s. First came the *Pushkin* class ship, which was 84.5m in length. Twenty-four were built in West Germany between 1954 and 1957, and were followed by the longer *Mayokovski* class, built in the USSR, and the Polish B15 class. By 1970 there were around 900 freezer-trawlers and factory trawlers over 1000grt, including 400 belonging to the USSR, 175 to Japan, 75 to Spain, 50 to West Germany, 40 to France and 40 to Britain. By the late 1960s and early

The first Soviet fish factory stern trawlers were the Pushkin *class built during 1954–57 in West Germany and having a remarkable resemblance in size and appearance to* Fairtry. *The* Pushkin *class eventually numbered twenty-four vessels, including a slightly later improved version, but the early vessels were about 2370 grt, 85.2ft in length and could process 1491cu m of fish at the rate of 20 tons a day, and which was carried in five insulated holds. The success of these vessels brought about the construction of two large series of vessels in the USSR and Poland.*

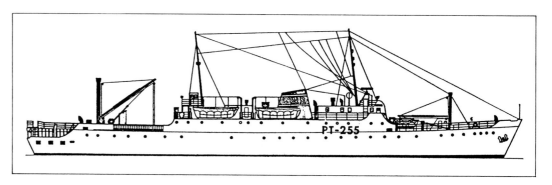

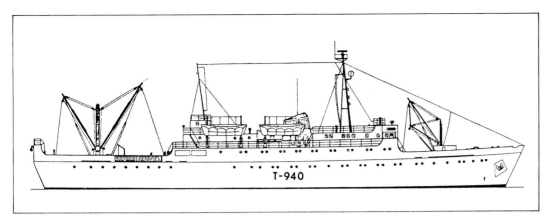

T-940

Profile of the USSR-built Mayakovski *class fish factory stern trawler (3170 grt), which became the most numerous of Soviet vessels of this type. Although the processing rate, 30 tons per day, was not a great deal better than the earlier* Pushkin *class vessels, they went to fishing grounds, including those in the south Atlantic, which had not been heavily fished up to then. As a result their catch performance was high and the decision to build these vessels in large numbers was proved to be justified.*

'70s, this type of vessel had reached a peak of development in the Soviet *Natalia Kovshova*, 128m in length and 8425grt. Built in 1965 by Ateliers et Chantiers de Nantes as the world's largest stern trawler, she was equipped as a factory ship, and was joined in 1966 by her two sister-ships, *Maria Polivanova* and *Anatoly Khalin*. Also notable were the large Japanese trawlers built in the early 1970s for the pollack fishery, typified by the 111.45m, 5295grt *Tenyo Maru*.

The advent of 200-mile limits has largely curtailed bottom otter trawling activities in the North Atlantic. Most of the distant waters vessels have been scrapped or sold off for other uses, including conversion to survey vessels for both oil and gas and oceanographic surveys, or transferred in a few cases to other parts of the world as trawlers. In a few cases, such as around the Falklands, east European vessels have continued to operate under licensing arrangements. However, a modern middle water version of the stern trawler, 30–40m long, has also been developed, notably in Britain, for operation in home waters within the new limits, in the course of the 1970s. More importantly, a generation of light trawl gears has been developed since 1970 which can be used by larger

classes of seine netters and multi-purpose vessels discussed below. Thus the purpose-built bottom otter trawlers in both distant and middle water versions has become of limited significance.

In contrast to the bottom otter trawler, the beam trawler has retained an important role, especially in the southern waters around the British Isles and in the southern North Sea, where it remains an important means of catching groundfish. Beam trawling has experienced a similar scaling up of gear in both size and weight, with a corresponding increase in the size and sophistication of vessels. The Dutch, Belgians and to some extent French, have been the main developers of these gears and vessels, which also exist to some extent in two sizes, although the distances to grounds are much less on the whole than in the cases of either bottom otter or pelagic trawlers. Similar developments in propulsion and hull design have occurred since the 1950s. A typical example of a modern Netherlands beam trawler, is *Marrie Jacob*, launched in 1987. The vessel is just over 40m in length, with a beam of 9m and a depth of 5.10m. The main engine is 2000bhp and speed is 13 knots.

Pelagic trawling for herring by the Germans

dates back to the 1930s. It modern development commenced in the 1950s, and it has been extensively employed for most of the major pelagic species, including herring, capelin and mackerel in the North Atlantic, Alaska pollack in the North Pacific, shrimps in the west central Atlantic, and krill in the Southern Ocean. The majority of pelagic trawlers have originated during the era of the stern trawler. Leading examples have been the Soviet trawlers operating in the North Atlantic, Japanese trawlers in the North Pacific, US shrimp trawlers working in the western tropical Atlantic. Also of interest have been Russian krill trawlers operating in the Southern Ocean in the 1980s. With the exception of the shrimp trawlers, some of the fleets have been operated in conjunction with mother ships equipped as floating factories for first-stage processing of catches. This is especially necessary for oily pelagic species, and above all for krill, which deteriorate in a matter of hours after being caught.

It should be pointed out that the largest trawlers are often capable of using either pelagic or bottom trawls, although the quantity and shoaling nature of common commercial pelagic species are such that these tend to require the greatest carrying capacity. The Japanese were building large distant water factory trawlers by the early 1960s. The sheer capacity of a modern pelagic trawler can be illustrated by *Franziska*, owned in the Netherlands and launched in 1989 as the world's largest fishing trawler. This ship, together with *Zeeland* was the first in the 10,000bhp class, with loading capacities of up to 5000 tonnes each. Each vessel lands the equivalent of forty drift netters of the post-Second World War period. These forty drift netters would have been manned by

DANISH SEAFOOD

When delivered to Danish owners in 1985 Ocean Prawns *(3090 grt) was regarded as the world's largest and best equipped prawn trawler. Built in Norway, the £9m vessel was completed in nine months from passing of final design to delivery. It operates mainly in areas such as the Barents Sea and has therefore been strengthened for navigation in ice and has an icebreaking bow. It has a hold capacity of 1670cu m.* (Langsten Group)

The 1990-built Glenrose 1 *is a typical modern British stern trawler. Based in Hull, and owned by Onward Fishing Co Ltd, she is 554 grt and has an insulated hold capacity of 360cu m. The vessel is driven by a 1725 bhp Ruston diesel.* Glenrose 1 *was built by Cochrane Shipbuilders at Selby, a member of the Howard Smith (UK) Ltd group. (Cochrane Shipbuilders)*

around 600 crew, shooting 120km of drift nets. The new trawlers each have a crew of forty, and a one-mile (1880m) circumference single boat pelagic trawl.

The sophistication of the modern pelagic trawler is illustrated by *Ocean Prawns* launched in 1985 for Danish owners, when it was probably the largest and best equipped prawn trawler in the world, with the hull strengthened for working in heavy ice in areas such as the Barents Sea or Davis Strait. This vessel is 74m in length and powered by a 4080bhp (3000kW) main engine. There are four shrimp trawls equipped with sensors which make it possible to monitor the spread, headline height and contents of the cod end of the net. The ship is equipped with four horizontal place freezers and two blast freezers; the processing deck is largely automated, with four sorting machines to grade the shrimp for the various markets. The shrimp then pass to lines for cooking, drying and individual freezing before being packed into five kilogram cartons. Some of the latest ships, such as the Canadian *Atlantic Champion* (2336 grt) launched in 1988, are equipped for handling both prawns and groundfish.

Seiners

In contrast to trawling, commercial seining has developed from small scale coastal and inshore fishing, although in the end it has come to have a very similar geographical distribution, with centres of development in the northeast Atlantic and northwest Pacific. As in the case of trawling, both demersal and pelagic seining occur, with the initial emphasis on the former, particularly in northwest Europe.

The initial development of modern demersal seining was located in Denmark, and grew in the second half of the nineteenth century from beach seining for plaice in the Limfjord in response to declining catches from the shore. This is the so-called anchor dragging method which involves shooting the warps and net, anchoring the boat and winching the net aboard. The operation may be repeated several times from the same anchoring position to cover specific areas of ground. It is a method suited to shallow waters with sandy or muddy bottom and relatively few obstructions, which is the case around the Danish islands and in much of the southern North Sea where this method of operation still prevails. The fishing vessels remain of conventional casing aft design, mainly of wood and 20–27m in length.

The Scottish fly dragging method developed from the 1930s as a replacement for the inshore small and to some extent long (or great) line fishing. In contrast to the Danish seine, the requirement was for a gear which could be operated in deeper water on relatively restricted patches of sandy bottom surrounded by rocky or hard bottom in conditions of appreciable tidal currents varying in direction and strength according to the state of the tide. Although the net is shot in a similar manner, retrieval is by simultaneous towing and hauling, rather than by anchoring. The main species caught are demersal round fish such as haddock and cod, rather than mainly flat fish.

The development of the Scottish seine netter was more complex than its Danish counterpart. Although a class of small purpose-built boats came into being from the 1930s onwards, the main phase of development was associated with 20–25m dual purpose boats designed for the herring drift net fishing in summer, and seine netting for the rest of the year. The first of these were Motor Fishing Vessels (MFVs) built by the Admiralty in the Second World War for their own use, but designed to be used as fishing boats after the War. These were followed by conventional wooden boats of casing aft designs, generally powered by 114bhp or 152bhp Gardner diesels, and most remained in use until the 1960s or beyond. From the 1960s onwards, when the drift net fishing was replaced by purse seining (see below), the relatively light seine net was replaced to a substantial but not complete extent by a generation of light trawl gears which could be used more flexibly in relation to bottom conditions;

Development of Scottish seine net vessels 1927–77, showing the advances in size and design during this period.

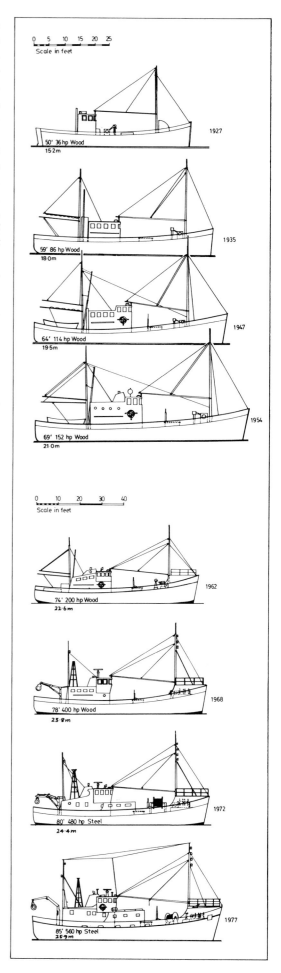

by the 1980s rock hopper trawls had been designed which could be used on hard bottom. The new generation of boats came into being in the 1960s, capable of using both seine nets and light trawl gears. These were larger (25–30m), many being of steel construction, but generally retaining the casing aft design, with addition of a whaleback and/or shelter deck, and with conventional coiling of warps being gradually replaced by the use of net drums. Engine power was from two to six times the old dual purpose boats.

The Japanese tow dragging method was independently developed for use in the much deeper waters around Japan, where the continental shelf is much narrower, and slopes steeply away to the deep ocean. The nets are closed entirely by towing in this situation, with much longer warp lengths in use. The Japanese seine netter is typically around 30m in length, steel built and with the wheelhouse slightly forward of amidships.

The pelagic seine fisheries were developed around the modern purse seine, which originated in the British Columbia herring fisheries in the 1930s. The purse seine came into extensive use in the course of the 1960s in two contrasting situations. One was the pelagic fisheries of the North Atlantic, and the other the pelagic fisheries of the tropical Pacific.

In the North Atlantic, the direction of development was governed by the expansion of the North Sea herring fisheries, led by the Norwegians, followed to relatively limited extents by the Danes, Icelanders, Faroese, Scots and Irish. The herring purse seiner was in essence a purpose-built craft, complete with power block and dory, and ample hold space for the catch, which was often used for reduction to meal and oil, and could thus be handled in bulk. Construction is of steel, with lengths in the 30–60m range, powered by 800–2000bhp diesels. The net is set with the aid of the eight metre, 150–200bhp dory, which tows it into a circle preparatory to pursing. These vessels were cut greatly in number with the collapse and subsequent closure of the North Sea herring fishing in the course of the 1970s, but remain important as the principal means of catching herring and mackerel in the North Atlantic. The use of small mesh nets enables catching of sprats. The latest larger vessels are equipped with freezers, designed to handle herring, mackerel and capelin in vertical free-

A typical tuna purse seiner, of about 1400 grt and 68m in length overall. This type has a tuna processing plant and refrigerated holds, a speed of about 16kts and carries a crew of 22.

zers, and herring in retail packs, as in the case of the Norwegian vessel *Harjan* built in the early 1980s. The North American purse seiner is of similar dimensions to its European counterpart, but generally has a casing forward design, rather than casing aft.

Since the exclusion of Soviet and eastern European vessels from EC waters in the mid-1970s, an extensive klondyking operation has developed for herring caught in the waters around the British Isles. These vessels consist of a mixture of trawlers, factory trawlers and factory ships which buy and load herring and mackerel from the local boats at major landing ports such as Lerwick and Ullapool, and process and ship the fish directly to eastern European markets.

Small mesh purse netting operations have also been developed for smaller species, including sprats and Norway pout, mainly for the Danish industrial fishing in the North Sea. However, the most important of these has undoubtedly been the Peruvian anchovy fishery which expanded and slumped at the same time as the North Sea herring fishing, to a substantial extent for the same reason of overfishing.

The other major tropical purse net fishing is that for tuna in the Pacific, carried on by the United States and Mexico in particular for the large North American market. Tuna clippers are ocean-going craft, typically with a casing forward design, which have used a variety of gears, notably long lines before the advent of the purse seine, and other gears remain in use by the Americans, Japanese and others (see below). A particular problem with this fishing using purse seines has been the catching of large numbers of dolphins. The first generation of these dates from the 1960s. In the late 1980s a larger class of vessel has been introduced, around 100m in length, which is more

economical to run than the previous generation, with improved fish handling facilities. An example is *Albacora* launched in 1990 as the world's largest tuna purse seiner. This ship is 105m in length, 2640 grt, powered by a 7000bhp main engine, and equipped with extensive freezing capacity. An indication of the complexity and demands of the freezing equipment and other requirements of a large distant water vessel such as this can be gained from the specification for auxiliary engines: eight diesels in all, respectively 4×590bhp, 3×820bhp, and 1×300bhp.

Liners

In traditional fisheries world-wide lines, static nets, traps and other static gears have been and remain universal, being operated both from the shore and from boats. In the modern context of overfishing and consequent conservation priorities, line fishing is seen as an important means of conservation as, compared to moving nets, it is highly selective. The economics of fisheries have been and remain, however, such that line fishing is practicable only for relatively large and valuable demersal and pelagic species. The numbers of commercial line fishing vessels are thus relatively restricted, being found mainly in northwest Europe and Japan. There are two major classes of vessel involved, namely, static long liners on the one hand, and a variety of mobile line vessels on the other.

Long liners in northwest Europe tend to be purpose built for distant water demersal fisheries for cod, ling and tusk, principally by the Norwegians for the northern North Atlantic. The intensive labour of clearing, baiting, laying and hauling lines has been increasingly automated using autoline systems for baiting and laying, and line haulers for hauling. A re-

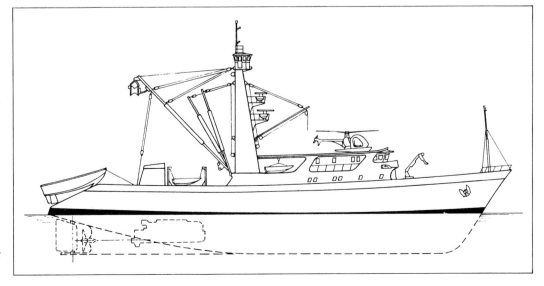

cent example of an autoliner is the 41m Norwegian *Førde Junior* launched in 1987, which is equipped with a Mustad autoliner system with 143,000 hooks, a line hauler and a bait cutter.

The other major type of long liner is the tuna long liner of the Pacific, which are mainly American and Japanese. These vessels operate fleets of lines from 100km to 130km in length at depths of 100–140 fathoms. Such vessels are in the order of 70m in length and around 1300 grt, with a casing aft design.

The Pacific is also the primary location for mobile line fishing. Japanese pole and line vessels are common in the bonito fishing of the western Pacific. These vessels have an external gangway constructed outside the topsides above the waterline on both sides, upon which individual fishermen stand while fishing. The boats steam ahead at the speed of the moving tuna shoal while fishing. Boats tends to be conventional casing aft design, up to 40m in length. Some are combination long line and pole and line boats.

Trolling is mainly used in the coastal salmon fisheries of the northeast Pacific, and consists of steaming at the speed of the swimming salmon using sets of lines trailing astern. Vessels are usually relatively small (10–15m in length), with casing forward.

Finally should be mentioned handlining where the lines are manually operated vertically from a stationary boat. This type of fishing was adopted widely in the nineteenth-century smack cod fisheries based particularly on the Humber and Shetland, and operating around Shetland, the Faroes, Rockall and Iceland. By far the best known, however, is the traditional Portuguese Grand Banks fishery, which uses a mother ship and dories, with most of the fishing taking place from the latter.

Multipurpose vessels

Even in traditional fisheries, boats have commonly been designed for use with a single gear. In the nineteenth-century commercial fisheries of parts of northwest Europe it was not uncommon for fishermen to possess at least two boats, one for the summer herring fishing and another for demersal fishing for the rest of the year. For reasons outlined in the conclusion, there is still a key role to be played by single purpose vessels in a number of circumstances, particularly for demersal trawlers and tuna fishing vessels. However, since the 1960s the economics and technology of inshore, shelf fishing have been such as to encourage increasing adoption of multipurpose vessels which can be fully employed all year round using a variety of gears in different seasonal fisheries in a number of separate regions or locations. In addition, of course, the wide variety of small coastal fishing boats used for shell and line fishing have been and remain flexible in terms of the number of different fisheries which they can be used for.

Among larger craft, the Scottish dual purpose seine/drift netter already discussed was an important early example of multipurpose design. Since the 1960s the main thrust in multi purpose developments has been in the north Atlantic, especially in northwest Europe. These boats are now commonly equipped to use a range of demersal and pelagic trawl gears and purse seines. Boats are mainly of casing aft design, steel built, with trawl winches, gallows and power block, from 20–40m in length and 500–1500bhp. A variety of detailed combinations exist, such as the trawling/long lining combination typified by the 25m French *Le Ressac*, which has a full shelter deck, net drums and lining equipment.

Whalers

Of all the fisheries in the contemporary period under review, the whale fisheries have been most severely curtailed. None the less whaling vessels were an important group until the 1960s, and a small number of Russian and Japanese vessels have continued to operate worldwide until the imposition of the International Whaling Commission (IWC) moratorium. There are three principal types of vessel involved, namely, the shore-based whaler, the conventional whale catcher, and the factory ship.

The shore-based whaler has been largely confined to the North Atlantic, and was also mainly Norwegian. These vessels in the postwar period were mainly of traditional Norwegian regional designs related to specific stretches of coast, wooden built, with a harpoon gun mounted on the bow and a crows nest on the main mast. Some were small – under 20m – and were joined by larger, modern steel built craft in the 1950s.

The whale catchers were trawler-sized ocean-going craft developed in the prewar period for use in the Southern Ocean. Until the introduction of the factory ship in 1925, these operated from shore bases, mainly in South Georgia, where both Britain and Norway had bases. These vessels continued to be used in conjunction with factory ships, and were commonly 45–60m long, steel built with the casing aft and connected to the harpoon gun on the forecastle by a catwalk.

The factory ship was introduced in 1925 in the Southern Ocean fishery in order to extend the range of operations beyond that which was possible using the shore bases alone. These were vessels which were purpose built, with all the processing machinery and storage capacity necessary for the processing and shipping of the largest blue and sperm whales into meat, blubber and oil.

The whale factory ship Southern Harvester *(15,088 grt) was one of the last of a once substantial UK whaling fleet. She was built by Furness Shipbuilding, Haverton Hill, in 1946. Before the Second World War the UK whaling fleet was not only the largest, but also had the highest production, ahead of Norway. Since the War, the fleets were under the control of UK, Norwegian, Japanese, Russian, Argentinian, Greek, Netherlands and South African interests. In 1992 Japan and Russia still had substantial whaling fleets, though not in service as such.* (R W Jordan)

Conclusion

In conclusion it is worth making two points about respectively, industrial and technological developments; and their implications for continued evolution of fishing vessel types in the inshore and distant water categories, as distinct from small coastal boats which are not generally discussed as these are beyond the scope of this book.

Broadly speaking there are two basic sets of circumstances which will be influential in future development of fishing vessel designs. The first concerns the demersal fisheries on the continental shelves, where the continuing emphasis will be to build up home water fisheries. Here an important requirement is for multipurpose craft, which for the most part will continue to be owned by the fishermen with or without shore owners on a share system or, if individual transferable quotas become the norm, by companies which may include fishermen among the shareholders. Both casing aft and casing forward designs will continue, together with both wood and steel construction, according to local requirements. There will remain scope for some seiner, trawler and liner designs as well, especially in areas with large scale specialised fisheries, such as northwest Europe.

The second set of circumstances relates to both shelf and deep ocean pelagic fisheries, where the pelagic trawl and purse seine will remain the most efficient methods of operation. There will continue to be room here both for single purpose designs, and dual purpose seiner/trawlers. If the balance between industrial fishing and fishing for human consumption changes it is reasonable to expect that the larger vessels in these classes will have freezing and processing capacity on board. Alternatively, dedicated factory ships will be necessary.

Finally, it is likely that as the 1990s give way to the next century, emphasis may to some extent shift from fishing gear and vessel design to modes of operation. This will include comprehensive vessel licensing systems, which will become more or less universal for all vessel sizes and types. For larger vessels, sophisticated fish finding equipment will continue to be developed, while the scope of operation of on board computer systems may be extended to show information on markets, the state of stocks and grounds, and perhaps ultimately to computer-assisted control of gear and vessel handling techniques.

Dr Hance Smith

Note
The author is indebted to Dr Helen J Pickering for picture research for this chapter.

Large trawlers and factory vessels since 1954

Ship (Class)	Flag	Built	By	GRT	Length (oa) × breadth × depth × draught Feet–Inches Metres	Freezer capacity	Engines	Speed	Remarks
FAIRTRY	UK	1954	J Lewis & Sons, Aberdeen	2605	280–7 × 44–7 × 24–0 × 22–9 *85.51 × 13.58 × 7.31 × 6.93*	45,885cu ft	1 J Lewis diesel, 1950bhp; 1 shaft	12.75kts	Stern trawler, fish factory
TENYO MARU	Jap	1971	Hayahikane SB, Shimonoseki	4239	365–8 × 55–11 × 36–8 × 23–0 *111.46 × 17.05 × 11.16 × 7.02*	3 hold; 4822dwt	1 Kobe Hatsudoki diesel, 5700bhp; 1 shaft	14kts	Stern trawler; fish factory; pollack
PUNG YANG	Kor	1972	Hayashikane SB, Nagasaki	3527	313–8 × 49–6 × 32–2 × 20–0 *95.61 × 15.09 × 9.81 × 6.1*	3197cu m	1 Kobe Hatsudoki diesel; 4500bhp; 1 shaft	13.5kts	Stern trawler, fish factory
CERNELLO	Sp	1974	Juliana Gijonesa, Gijon	1480	259–2 × 43–5 × 27–3 × 17–9 *79.0 × 13.24 × 8.31 × 5.4*	1626dwt	1 Barreras/Deutz diesel, 3000bhp; 1 shaft	15.75kts	Stern trawler, fish factory
OCEAN PRAWNS	Nor	1985	Tangen Verft, Kragero (hull only)	3090	244–1 × 51–2 × 29–6 × 20–4 *74.4 × 15.6 × 9.0 × 6.2*	1670cu m 1744 dwt	1 Wartsila diesel, 4075bhp; 1 shaft	15kts	prawn/ shrimp stern trawl; processing
HARJAN	Nor	1985	Sigbjorn Iversen, Flekkefjord	999	172–9 × 37–9 × 26–3 × 21–4 *52.66 × 11.51 × 8.01 × 6.50*	900cu m	1 KHD diesel, 2725bhp; 1 shaft	15.5kts	Side trawl purse seiner; fish factory
MOONZUND	SU	1986	Volkswerft, Stralsund	7765	396–0 × 62–5 × 40–2 × 21–0 *120.71 × 19.03 × 12.25 × 6.4*	3900cu m	2 Karl Liebknecht diesels, 7200bhp; 1 shaft	14.9kts	Stern trawler, fish factory
ATLANTIC CHAMPION	Can	1988	Tangen Verft, Kragero (hull only)	233	206–8 × 47–0 × 29–2 × – *63.0 × 14.33 × 8.89 × –*	1200cu m	1 Caterpillar diesel, 4000bhp; 1 shaft	15kts	Shrimp/ prawn/ ground fish stern trawl; fish factory
FRANZISKA	Ne	1989	Yssel-Vliet, Capelle	7135	390–6 × 63–6 × 37–9 × 24–9 *119.0 × 19.35 × 11.51 × 7.55*	8400cu m	1 KHD diesel, 9520bhp; 1 shaft	16kts	Stern trawler, processing

Ship (Class)	Flag	Built	By	GRT	Length (oa) × breadth × depth × draught Feet–Inches Metres	Freezer capacity	Engines	Speed	Remarks
ALBACORA	Sp	1990	J Barreras, Vigo	2058	344–5 × 55–1 × 33–6 × 24–0 105.0 × 16.8 × 10.2 × 7.3	1886cu m; wet fish cap 3000cu m	1 Krupp MaK diesel, 8160bhp; 1 shaft	17.2kts	Tuna purse seiner
ACAMAR (B671 type)	Pol	1990	Stocznia Gdanska, Gdansk	3708	308–5 × 51–4 × 31–10 × 18–4 94.01 × 15.65 × 9.71 × 5.6	1500cu m	1 Cegielski/B & W diesel, 4930bhp; 1 shaft	15kts	Stern trawler, fish factory; class 1990–92

Typical whale factory vessels

Ship	Flag	Built	By	GRT	Length (oa) × breadth × depth × draught Feet–Inches Metres	Tanks; capacity	Engines	Speed	Remarks
UNITAS	Ger	1937	Deutsche Schiff, Bremerhaven	27,059	621–0 × 80–2 × 67–0 × 40–0 189.29 × 24.44 × 20.43 × 12.91	46 tanks; 29,645cu m	2 triple expansion with LP turbines DR geared and hydraulic coupling	11.5kts	Converted to fish factory 1957
SOUTHERN HARVESTER	UK	1946	Furness SB, Haverton Hill	15,088	556–0 × 74–5 × 57–0 × 34–6 169.5 × 22.68 × 17.37 × 10.51		1 NEME triple expansion, 7300ihp; 1 shaft	12kts	
WILLEM BARENDSZ	Ne	1955	Wilton-Fijenoord, Schiedam	26,839	677–5 × 90–6 × 62–4 × 35–2 206.48 × 27.59 × 19.0 × 10.73		2 Wilton-Fijenoord diesels, 10,500bhp; 2 shafts	13kts	Converted to fish factory 1967
KOSMOS III	Nor	1947	Gotaverken, Gothenburg	23,107	638–6 × 78–2 × 58–0 × 35–7 194.62 × 23.83 × 17.68 × 10.84	44 tanks; insulated 4340cu m, oil 20,010cu m	1 Gotaverken diesel, 6750bhp; 1 shaft	12.5kts	
SOVIETSKAYA ROSSIYA	SU	1961	Nosenko SY, Nikolayev	33,154	713–0 × 91–8 × 62–5 × 35–7 217.33 × 27.94 × 19.05 × 10.85	36 tanks; insulated 3980cu m, oil 21,652	2 B&W diesels, 15,000bhp; 2 shafts	16kts	

Typical whalers (whale catchers)

Ship (Class)	Flag	Built	By	GRT	Length (oa) × breadth × depth × draught Feet–Inches Metres	Engines	Speed	Remarks
SOUTHERN SPRAY	UK	1925	Smith's Dock Co, Middlesbrough	319	137–0 × 26–3 × 13–5 × – 41.76 × 8.0 × 4.11 × –	1 Smith's Dock triple expansion, 1200ihp; 1 shaft	12kts	
SOUTHERN WILCOX	UK	1945	Smith's Dock Co, Middlesbrough	427	158–6 × 27–7 × 15–6 × 14–5 48.32 × 8.41 × 4.73 × 4.4	1 Smith's Dock triple expansion, 1850ihp; 1 shaft	14kts	
POL XIV	Nor	1950	Fredrikstad MV, Fredriksstad	617	168–7 × 26–8 × 20–1 × 18–7 51.39 × 9.05 × 6.13 × 5.67			
MIRNYY (Mirnyy class; 160 vessels)	SU	1956	61 Kommunar SY, Nikolayev	718	208–7 × 31–2 × 17–11 × 14–9 63.58 × 9.5 × 5.47 × 4.49	Diesel-electric; 4 diesel driving 4 generators connected to 1 electric motor; 1 shaft	17.5kts	Class built 1956–64
KOS 55	Nor	1964	Hayashikane SB, Shimonoskei	729	224–4 × 32–8 × 16–11 × 13–6 68.38 × 9.96 × 5.16 × 4.13	1 Hayashikane diesel, 3600bhp; 1 shaft	16kts	
SHONAN MARU	Jap	1972	Hitachi Zosen, Mukaishima	916	231–5 × 33–7 × 17–1 × 15–6 70.54 × 10.24 × 5.21 × 4.73	1 Hitachi/B & W diesel, 5500bhp; 1 shaft	15kts	

10

Modern Merchant Ship Navigation

SINCE the Second World War there has been an enormous increase in the number and variety of navigational systems available to merchant ships. Before the Second World War the basic navigational equipment on a ship consisted of a compass to give directions relative to north, log (mileometer/speedometer) to give the distance travelled by the ship, lead and line for water-depth measurement, charts showing minimum (lowest low water) depths of water, coastal features, navigation lights, buoyage, etc, lists of lights giving descriptions of lighthouses, tide tables for determining heights of tides at various places and times, and sailing directions (pilot books) giving local information on hazards, currents, weather, and details of coastlines, ports and their approaches. Additionally, for ocean navigation, a sextant (for angular measurement), a chronometer (for accurate time measurement), a nautical almanac (for determining the celestial positions of the sun, moon, planets and stars at specific times) and nautical mathematical tables were the principal instruments used for fixing a ship's position.

Apart from radio direction finding, the only ways of determining a ship's position in poor visibility were crude dead-reckoning and depth-sounding methods. Dead-reckoning (deduced by reckoning) is a method of estimating a ship's position by noting the distance travelled by the ship along the various tracks it has followed since the last known (fixed) position of the vessel – this is a notoriously inaccurate method because of the difficulty of making allowances for the variable effects of wind, currents and tidal streams on the vessel's speed and direction of travel. The depth-sounding method of fixing position consists of measuring the depths of water at intervals and applying tidal height corrections to these in order to determine the contour of the sea-bed which has been followed by the ship, and then trying to match that contour to the

one of the many contours indicated by the depths shown on the chart. This again is generally a crude and inaccurate method of position-fixing, even when combined with the dead-reckoning method. The radio direction finding method was, and still is, only available in relatively few areas, and in the case of radio direction finding apparatus carried in a ship is only reliable at distances of up to about 20 miles from a radio beacon. It has been possible to obtain fairly accurate radio bearings up to ranges of about 200 miles by the use of shore-based radio direction finding apparatus observing radio transmissions from the ship concerned. The shore-station and ship need to communicate with each other by radio in order to organise the observation of the radiobearing of the ship, and then for the bearing to be transmitted to the ship. There are very few of these shore-stations and they are very rarely used nowadays, usually only for helping to locate distressed vessels.

In summary therefore we can see that before the Second World War the navigational services given to a ship from the shore were those for providing and maintaining lights, buoys, radio beacons, shore-based radio direction

finding stations, and the various relatively simple shipborne equipment; and those services providing up-to-date hydrographic publications.

Nowadays, in addition to the basic equipment and systems outlined above, systems which are available to merchant ships include shipborne radar, sonar (mainly for depth sounding and speed measurement), Consol, Loran, Decca Navigator, Omega Navigation, Transit Satellite Navigation, Global Positioning System (GPS) Satellite Navigation, and Ship's Inertial Navigation System (SINS). The development of very high frequency (VHF) radio-telephony has also permitted navigational information derived from shore-based surveillance radar, and other sophisticated ship-monitoring systems, to be readily communicated to ships, individually or generally, within a limited local area. Apart from shipborne radar, usual merchant ship sonar, and SINS, all the systems in the latter list require shore-stations of generally highly sophisticated design, and requiring highly expert attention. SINS, however, cannot be regarded as being truly independent as it suffers from cumulative errors and so requires frequent checking and

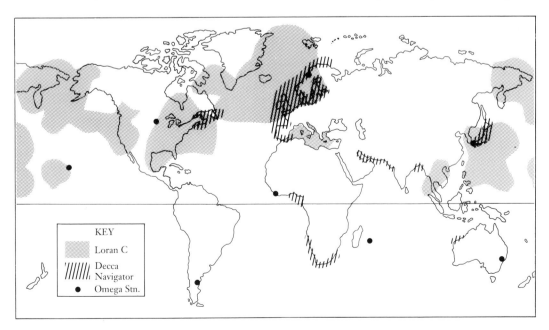

Figure 1: Areas covered by Decca Navigator and Loran C, and positions of Omega stations as at 1983.

KEY

- Loran C
- Decca Navigator
- Omega Stn.

re-setting by reference to other aids – for this reason, and because SINS is relatively expensive, it is not generally carried in merchant ships, and is therefore not described here.

Shipborne marine radar is usually effective as a navigational aid for distances of up to about 10 to 60 miles off-shore, depending upon the nature of the coast and/or the ship, as explained below. Radar (radio detection and ranging) uses the co-called echo-ranging principle. It is comprised basically of a radio transmitter, a receiver, a directional aerial (scanner) and a display which is actually an electronic clock. The transmitter produces short pulses of very short radio waves (microwaves) which travel in nearly straight lines much like light waves. The radar scanner directs these radio pulses in specific directions and collects reflections (echoes) of these pulses which are returned towards the scanner. The scanner then feeds the echoes to the receiver for amplification and the time difference between transmission and reception is measured by the radar display. As the speed of travel of the radio waves is fairly constant, the measured time differences are in direct proportion to the distances of the reflecting objects from the ship. As the scanner is unidirectional, the direction of a returning echo is measured in addition to its range, thus directions (bearings) and ranges of objects in the vicinity of the ship are portrayed on the radar display. The maximum ranges at which objects are detected depends on the power output of the transmitter, the heights of the radar scanner and of the objects, and upon the shape, texture and electromagnetic characteristics of the objects. Thus low-lying and sloping sandy shores are detected at

much smaller ranges than shore-lines comprised of high steep cliffs, and small wooden craft at much smaller ranges than large steel ships. Specially designed radar reflectors are mounted on some navigational buoys and beacons to increase their range of detection by radar, and Racons (radar responder beacons) are similarly used to help both in the detection and identification of important navigational marks such as lightvessels which might otherwise be confused with ships at anchor when detected by radar.

Rain droplets and sea waves can also be detected by radar, and there can be multiple reflections of the transmitted pulses which create false echoes which, like the rain and sea-wave echoes, can cause some difficulty in interpreting a radar display. Shipborne radar, therefore, although a highly valued navigational and collision avoidance aid, should be used in conjunction with all the other available aids. For collision avoidance, in particular, it was soon found that radar information could be misleading unless careful radar plotting methods were used. Manual radar plotting proved to be tedious and time-consuming; however the advent of the electronic computer has enabled ARPAs (automatic radar plotting aids) to be developed and these are now installed in most merchant ships.

Sonar (sound navigation ranging) is used in various forms. The most used form is in the shape of the echo-sounder for measuring depth of water. The echo-ranging principle is used but in this case high frequency sound waves (ultrasonic waves) are used. Transducers for converting electrical energy into sound energy, and vice-versa, are installed at the bottom of

the ship's hull and these transmit and receive ultrasonic waves to and from the sea-bed. Like radar the time difference measured between transmission and reception represents the distance of the reflecting object, in this case the sea-bed, from the ship. This is a much quicker and more convenient method of sounding than using a lead and line, and most merchant ships are provided with it.

Sonar in another form is used for ship's speed measurement. In this case the transducers direct ultrasonic waves in four fairly narrow beams which slant forward, aftward, and to each side of the vessel. In this case the doppler shift, ie the difference between the frequencies of the transmitted and received waves, in each beam is measured. The doppler shift is in direct proportion to the ship's speed, and the vectorial summation of the doppler shifts in the four beams enables both the fore-and-aft and the thwartship (sideways) components of the ship's speed to be found. In relatively shallow waters so-called bottom-lock sonar-doppler is used, ie the four beams impinge on the sea-bed and therefore the ship's speed is given in relation to the ground (sea-bed).

In relatively deep-water, where the transmitted power of the ultrasonic waves is inadequate to produce detectable sea-bed echoes, sea-lock or water-lock sonar-doppler is used, ie echoes which are returned from the sea-mass itself are compared with the transmitted waves to find the ship's speed relative to the sea. Shipborne sonar-doppler is not very commonly carried by merchant ships although some larger vessels have been fitted with the equipment in order especially to help them judge their ground speed when approaching jetties.

Another method of monitoring the speed of approach to a jetty has been to use a form of sonar-doppler installed on the jetty itself. In this system transducers are mounted at each end of the jetty, on the jetty piles below water-level, and their ultrasonic beams are directed horizontally and perpendicular to the line of the jetty, ie towards the underwater side of a ship which is being pushed sideways towards

Modern navigation has become very precise with satellite coverage. Satellites are used also for related services to shipping. The INMARSAT system, for example, provides telephone, telex, weather data and safety and distress facilities. It is also developing position determination techniques. This map shows the coverage of the global system of INMARSAT-C, and the satellite relative positions: AOR(E) = Atlantic Ocean Region (East); AOR(W) = Atlantic Ocean Region (West); IOR = Indian Ocean Region; POR = Pacific Ocean Region. (INMARSAT)

the jetty. In this case the sonar-doppler measures the distances of the forward and after parts of the ship from the jetty in addition to the speeds of the forward and after parts of the ship towards the jetty. This information is shown graphically to the ship with the aid of electric lights mounted on a large display board on the jetty. Two sets of red, amber and green lights are used to show whether the speeds of the respective ends of the ship are too fast, a little too fast, or safe; and two bars of light of variable length are used to represent the distances of each end of the ship from the jetty. The main object of the bars of light is for the ship to judge whether or not it is parallel to the jetty. This combined information therefore helps the ship to direct its tugs to keep her parallel to the jetty and approaching it at a safe speed so she may land gently against the jetty without either demolishing it or damaging herself.

Consol, Loran, Decca Navigator, Omega Navigation and Transit Satellite Navigation systems are all basically so-called hyperbolic navigation systems. A hyperbola is the locus of point which moves in such a way that the difference in the distances, from that point to two fixed points, remains constant. In other words a hyperbola is a line of a shape that the difference in distances from two fixed points to any point on that line is constant. Thus if a radio transmitter is placed at each of the two fixed points, and these two transmitters transmit signal pulses simultaneously then, because the speed of radio waves is relatively constant, the difference in time between the arrival of these two signals at a receiver will represent difference of distances and will therefore indicate a particular hyperbola (or position line) on which the receiver is situated. If another pair of transmitting stations is observed in the same way, a second hyperbolic position line can be obtained, and the intersection of two or more such hyperbolic position lines will fix the receiver's (ship's) position. In fact there can be ambiguity between two hyperbolae if it is not known which of the two signal pulses from a pair of stations arrives first. In the case of the Decca Navigator and Omega systems the transmitters transmit continuously and the difference in the phase of the signals is measured at the receiver. This means that there is a whole family of hyperbolae, upon any one of which the ship might be situated. These ambiguities of the various hyperbolic systems can, however, usually be resolved easily, and reliable positions (fixes) obtained.

Consol is the most primitive and least accurate of these hyperbolic systems; it is provided

in very few areas and appears not to be much used nowadays.

The areas covered by Loran and Decca Navigator systems are indicated approximately on the map in Figure 1. The areas covered by Loran C and Decca Navigator may be increased during the next few years though it is possible that the satellite navigation systems may eventually make both of these systems redundant. The latest version of Loran (Long Range Navigation) is known as Loran C, and this has replaced the earlier version known as Loran A. Loran C and Decca Navigator have similar accuracies but Loran C can cover a wider area with fewer shore stations. (Loran C accuracy: 50ft to 1500ft to a range of about 800 or 1000nm from the transmitters. Decca Navigator accuracy: 0.2 to 2.0nm to a range of about 240 miles from the transmitters.)

The Omega Navigation System and the Transit Satellite Navigation System each give global coverage.

The Omega provides continuous position-fixing with an accuracy of plus or minus one or two nautical miles anywhere on the earth's surface. The positions of Omega transmitting stations are shown in Figure 1. Global coverage is achieved by these ground stations transmitting very low frequency (VLF) radio waves which cannot penetrate the earth's ionosphere to escape into space, and therefore spread outwards from their respective stations in the duct formed between the ionosphere and the earth's surface.

The Transit Satellite Navigation System consists of usually about five operational satellites following relatively low-lying (600nm high) polar orbits. The satellites are tracked and provided with orbital information by ground stations in the United States. Each satellite commences transmitting information describing its orbital parameters exactly every two minutes: that is, precisely at 0000, 0002, 0004, 0006, etc. A special receiver and computer on a ship can detect and de-code these signals which give the spatial position of the satellite at the beginning of each transmission. Any difference between the actual frequency transmitted and the received transmission (that is, the doppler shift) is also measured. This doppler shift is used to find the difference in distances between the ship and the positions of the satellite at the commencement of two successive transmissions and thereby a hyperbolic position line can be derived. By continuing to observe the satellite in this way every two minutes for as long as possible, as it proceeds along its orbit in the vicinity of the ship, a number of hyberbolic position-lines can be obtained, and

the point where these intersect represents the position of the vessel. Owing to the spacing and the low-level of the orbits of these satellites, and the rotation of the earth under them, they cannot be observed continuously, but accurate fixes can be obtained over a period of a few minutes every hour or two. The accuracy is about 0.25nm world-wide except for small areas near the geographical poles.

More accurate global positioning systems using satellites in high orbits (20,200km above the earth's surface) have been developed and are already in considerable use although the planned systems are not yet fully operational. The systems have been developed by the United States and the Soviet Union. The American system is known as GPS (Global Positioning System), and the Soviet Union system is known as GLONASS. Each system is planned to give continuous highly accurate position-fixing, in three dimensions, worldwide. These systems are already proving to be highly accurate and reliable with the existing satellites of the two systems, though at present (1992) there can be some occasions in the day when insufficient satellites are available above the observer's horizon to give him an accurate fix. Positional accuracy of standard GPS is in the order of twenty-five to one hundred metres, but a differential form of GPS, provided for certain local areas, can give an accuracy in the order of five metres, or even better.

The GPS system uses ranging methods for position fixing, rather than hyperbolic methods. The satellites transmit coded signals at known precise times. The user's receiver has a highly accurate clock to determine the times of receipt of these signals. Thus the time taken for the signals to travel from a satellite to the receiver is determined, and therefore the distance or range of the satellite can be calculated. Signals from the satellites also give their ephemerides from which each satellite's position in space at any instant can be determined. The observer is clearly on the surface of an imaginary sphere with the satellite at its centre and its radius equal to the distance of the satellite at its centre and its radius equal to the distance of the satellite from the observer. By observing three satellites simultaneously the intersection of the three imaginary spheres with the surface of the earth determines the latitude and longitude of an observer on the surface of the earth. By observing four satellites simultaneously a three-dimensional fix can be obtained, that is, latitude, longitude and altitude above the earth's surface. By observing the doppler shift of the satellite transmissions it

With one-man bridge operation becoming more common in the 1990s, manufacturers of bridge equipment, through the use of modern technology, are having to provide systems which combine utmost sophistication with the highest reliability. An example of such developments is an integrated bridge system developed by leading manufacturer Kelvin Hughes, a subsidiary of Smiths Industries plc. In a compact area this system includes an electronic chart work station, navigation display, navigation monitor, and ship control, vessel monitoring, and communications work stations, radar, plotter, and other units. (Kelvin Hughes)

is also possible to determine the observer's velocity – the accuracy of the speed component being within about one tenth of a metre per second. All the satellites are monitored and controlled from land stations to ensure that their data transmissions are correct in content and accurately timed.

In addition to the various individual systems described above, there are various computer-controlled hybrid navigation systems available, for example, Transit Navigation receivers combined with either Omega Navigation receivers or SINS, are available. These hybrid systems provide continuous world-wide position-fixing of higher accuracy than can be obtained by using their component systems separately.

So-called shipborne integrated navigation systems have also been developed. These extend the hybrid principle by further utilisation of computers to filter and combine the data obtained from several basic navigation systems and instruments in order to derive the statistically most likely position of a vessel.

Apart from the above-mentioned systems developed for general ship navigation, very high accuracy derivatives of some of these systems (Decca Hi Fix, and various differential systems) and specialised range-range radio systems and laser systems, are used by some hydrographic surveyors, civil engineers, dredgers, etc – such systems are often portable and are usually for exclusive use.

The development of the navigational chart in recent years should also be mentioned. The work of the International Hydrographic Bureau has been successful in ensuring that charts produced by the hydrographic organisations world-wide use standard symbols and abbreviations which has made the use of charts provided by different agencies much easier. However the need to carry many additional charts, to show the lattice grids (hyperbolic lines) of the various hyperbolic systems, has increased the difficulty in the up-keep of charts on ships, especially on those ships which trade

world-wide. This problem has been alleviated to a certain extent by the development of hyperbolic system receivers which incorporate a computer to give position information in latitude and longitude format instead of the raw hyperbolic grid data. Another notable development which is in progress is that of the electronic chart which is stored on computer disc and displayed on a television type monitor. Electronic charts could be more versatile than paper charts and are expected to alleviate the storage, retrieval and correction problems which exist with paper charts.

Finally, in this discussion of merchant ship navigational aids, it must not be overlooked that navigational lights, lightvessels and navigational buoys are still fundamental, and often essential, for safe navigation, particularly for making landfall, coastal navigation, marking marine traffic separation schemes, and for high accuracy pilotage in narrow waters. Furthermore, information published and broadcast on weather conditions and on ice and other navigational hazards can also be vital for the safe and economic navigation of a ship. Dedicated equipment for the broadcast and reception of such information is yet another development in merchant ship navigation which has occurred in recent years. More is said on the topic of weather routeing in the section on marine traffic control.

Modern ship's bridge design

In the days of sail the normal conning position was at the stern of a vessel on the open quarter-deck where the tiller or helm was situated with a simple linkage system to the rudder, and

where the set of the sails could be easily observed, though the view ahead was largely obstructed and separate look-outs needed to be posted forward and aloft. With the development of steam power and improved mechanical steering gear, the conning position was moved to near midships. A position about a third of the ship's length from forward was generally preferred as this is near to the turning-point of the ship when the rudder is applied, also it is the more comfortable position on the ship when the ship is rolling and pitching is heavy weather, and with much less propeller vibration there than exists near the stern. The conning position was also raised, usually on top of an accommodation block, and a small wheelhouse and chartroom provided to give protection from the weather, and a walkway going across the ship from side-to-side, sometimes extending slightly over each side of the ship to form so-called bridge wings from where a pilot could con the ship more easily when bringing her alongside a jetty. Another reason for choosing the midship position for the conning position was that it made voice communications to the engine-room easier. The midship position of the main engine was dictated by stability trim requirements, that is, to help to keep the ship on an even keel in ballast conditions. In the case of early oil tanker design, however, the engine-room was put at the stern of the ship in order to segregate it more easily from the volatile cargo and thereby reduce the risk of explosion. The ballast trim problem did not exist in oil tankers because of their versatility in water ballasting. The bridge structures on these earlier tankers, nevertheless, were kept amidships in the preferred conning

The bridge of the Ditlev Lauritzen, *a 14,406 grt reefer that can be manned by a total crew of only six, although usually operated by nine.* (The Motor Ship)

position especially as, by that time, communication systems from the bridge to the engine-room had been improved by the development of the mechanical engine-room telegraph and the telephone. However, in the 1950s it was found that a number of explosions occurred owing to the collection of oil cargo fumes under the midship bridge structures, so it was decided to design and build oil tankers with all their accommodation, including the bridge platform, at the stern. A vessel with this design is also cheaper to construct, and this economic factor led to designers of other types of cargo vessels, especially dry bulk carriers and container vessels, to adopt the same all aft accommodation, bridge and engine-room configuration. The trim problems of such ships was overcome by improved water ballasting arrangements, and the navigating officers had to adapt to cope with the lack of the advantages of the midship conning position described above. Incidentally, a few oil tankers which are used frequently to load oil at single point moorings

Details of the bridge layout of the Ditlev Lauritzen. (The Motor Ship)

have a secondary bridge conning position right at the bow of the vessel for use when making fast to such moorings. Passenger ships, including ferries, in order to keep a clear view ahead, generally have their bridges forward of the main accommodation structure, which extends over most of the length of the ship. Some ferries, which frequently need to navigate stern-first when berthing, have a secondary bridge conning position at the after end of the main accommodation structure.

As the size of ships grew, the wheelhouse became much larger and could easily house all

the new navigational equipment as it was developed and became available after the Second World War. There were initial problems with reflection of instrument lights in wheelhouse windows causing difficulty in keeping look-out from inside the wheelhouse at night, but this was overcome by slanting the windows from the vertical plane. Initially there was scant attention paid to the placement of instruments for convenience of use, but in recent years the science of ergonomics has been utilised to improve this aspect of ship bridge design, and instruments are being grouped together care-

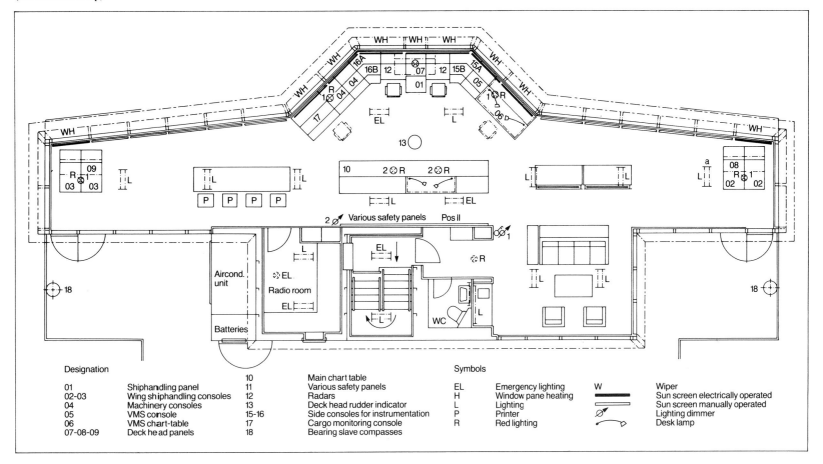

Designation			
01	Shiphandling panel	10	Main chart table
02-03	Wing shiphandling consoles	11	Various safety panels
04	Machinery consoles	13	Radars
05	VMS console	15-16	Deck head rudder indicator
06	VMS chart-table	17	Side consoles for instrumentation
07-08-09	Deck head panels	18	Cargo monitoring console
			Bearing slave compasses

Symbols			
EL	Emergency lighting	W ▬	Wiper
H	Window pane heating	▭	Sun screen electrically operated
L	Lighting	▭	Sun screen manually operated
P	Printer	∅	Lighting dimmer
R	Red lighting		Desk lamp

fully to enable easy observation and operation by a single person. Experiments and developments have been made on the presentation of navigation information from various instruments, and information such as rudder angle, rate of turn, propeller revolutions, propeller pitch, and bow thruster force, on to a single television type display monitor which permits selective viewing of such information and gives warnings of dangerous conditions. This development is capable of being combined with that of the electronic chart described in the section on navigational aids on page 180.

The advent of automatic steering for merchant ships after the Second World War reduced the bridge manning requirements, and in more recent years the introduction of direct control of the main engine propulsion from the bridge, and improved engine design, has enabled reduction of engine-room manning, with some ships even having engine-rooms completely unmanned at night. Bridge watch officers generally prefer having direct control of the propulsion rather than having to rely on engine-room staff responding to commands given via an engine-room telegraph – such an indirect control system inevitably has response delay.

As an example of the exterior and interior appearance of a modern ship's bridge the refrigerated container ship *Ditlev Lauritzen* has been chosen. This vessel has an overall length of 538ft, a summer loaded draught of 33ft, and a service speed of 19kts. This relatively large and complex vessel can be operated by a crew of just six persons, although in practice a crew of nine is used. Notice that the bridge equipment has a console for cargo management in addition to consoles for management of navigation, machinery, etc, ie virtually all the ship's functions can be monitored, and many can be controlled, by a fully integrated ship's bridge control system.

Marine traffic control

Before the Second World War the scope of marine traffic control was very limited and consisted basically of International Regulations for Preventing Collisions at Sea, some prohibited areas established by some states for military purposes, a North Atlantic Track Agreement, which was a form of traffic separation adopted voluntarily by the large passenger ship companies; and limited direct scheduling control, mainly by means of visual signals, of ships within, and while entering and leaving, ports and canals.

Since the Second World War, with the de-

Figure 2: Various classes of Marine Traffic Control (MTC).

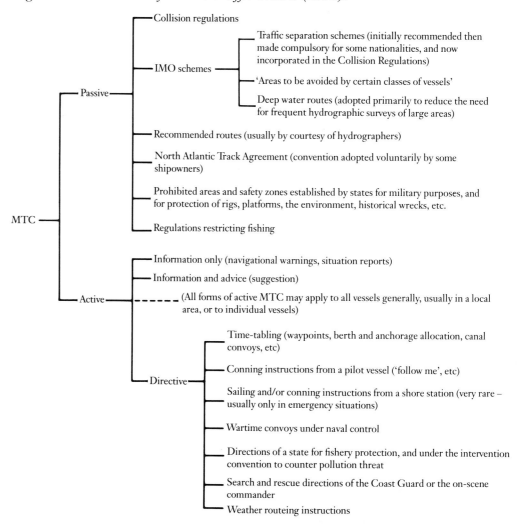

velopment of much improved communications, especially VHF radio-telephony, shore radar surveillance, and improved meteorological services, it has been possible to develop much more extended active marine traffic control from the shore. With the advent of satellite communication and navigation systems it is technologically feasible for there to be global active marine traffic control, though there are many social, commercial and political impediments to such development. The work of IMO (International Maritime Organization) has, however, very much extended and improved the methods of passive marine traffic control, especially in the form of marine traffic separation schemes which have generally been highly successful in reducing collisions in certain local areas such as the Dover Strait.

Figure 2 gives an outline of the existing system of both passive and active marine traffic control. Active marine traffic control is defined here as meaning any pragmatic involvement in the navigation of ships by a person not on board such ships. It embraces, but is not limited to, the activity referred to as vessel traffic

services. Passive marine traffic control is accomplished by ships conforming with regulations or agreements which do not require any pragmatic involvement of persons not on the ships concerned. Passive methods are generally applied to the open sea and most coastal sea areas, whereas active methods are usually confined to narrow waters, port areas and canals and their approaches. An exception is weather routeing which is a voluntary form of active control which is applied to ships on the open sea.

The most common type of active marine traffic control is procedural control, ie scheduling or timetabling of ship movements, anchoring, berthing, etc. An example of an area where strict procedural control is used is in the Suez Canal, in which there are few places where ships can pass each other, and where, therefore, a convoy system is used, with the ships in each convoy entering the canal with intervals of about ten minutes between each ship, and with convoy speeds in the order of about 12kph. The ships are carefully monitored in their progress through the canal by signal sta-

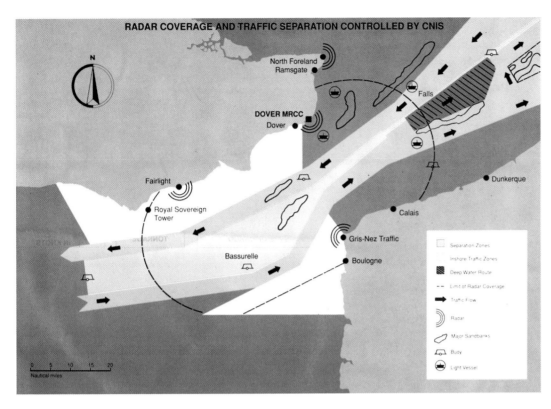

RADAR COVERAGE AND TRAFFIC SEPARATION CONTROLLED BY CNIS

The traffic separation system operating in the Dover Strait is controlled by HM Coastguard from Langdon Battery Centre near Dover. The Coastguard provides the Channel Navigation Information Service (CNIS), which includes a 24-hour radio safety service for all shipping in the area. This service gives warnings of navigational difficulties and unfavourable conditions likely to be encountered in the Strait, which is the world's busiest international waterway. There has not been a major collision in the area since 1979. Before 1969 an average of 30 collisions a year were recorded. (Crown Copyright)

tions placed about ten kilometres apart throughout the length of the canal. Another example of where active marine traffic control is used is in the River Thames and its estuary where marine traffic is closely monitored by a combination of a procedural reporting system and radar surveillance using several remote radar scanner sites from which radar signals are relayed to the central control station. Here again procedural methods of control are used to modify marine traffic flow when required to avoid congestion and to give channel priority to certain vessels on safety grounds. This modern method of marine traffic control enables marine traffic to keep flowing in the Thames in poor visibility conditions which formerly caused nearly all shipping movements to be halted. Many ports are now provided with similar systems of marine traffic control.

Ocean passages are often planned on the basis of ocean passage climatic charts which describe seasonal weather, ice regions and ocean currents, and recommend routes to be followed to try to avoid heavy weather, ice and freezing conditions, and thereby to make reas-

onably safe and quick voyages. Nevertheless, weather systems can vary considerably about the so-called normal climatic conditions and climatic routeing has been shown to be not so reliable as pragmatic weather routeing based on modern weather forecasting. Numerical methods of forecasting developed by the United Kingdom Meteorological Office now produce reasonably accurate forecasts for periods ahead of four or five days, whereas a few years ago a similar reliability extended for

just twenty-four hours ahead. This improvement in forecasting has enabled pragmatic weather routeing to be much more successful. There are various specialist public and private organisations which offer weather routeing services on a commercial basis. As mentioned above, ships often carry special radio receivers which permit them to receive weather and sea wave charts and therefore enable shipmasters to employ pragmatic weather routeing themselves rather than just climatic routeing. However, the meteorological data transmitted to ships is still much less than that which is available to the specialist weather routeing meteorologists ashore, so weather routeing from a land station is likely to be more successful.

In weather routeing, as with all other forms of marine traffic control, the shipmaster remains responsible for his ship and is always the ultimate arbiter for the actions it takes.

A G Corbet

The control room of the Port of London's Thames Navigation Service, Gravesend, which monitors and controls vessel movements in the River Thames from its middle reaches to the estuary limits. This vessel monitoring system has been supplied by leading Norwegian manufacturer Norcontrol, which has provided such equipment to customers worldwide. (Norcontrol)

11

Modern Merchant Ship Propulsion

THE evolution of merchant ship propulsion systems follows, to the limit which technology will allow, the directions laid down by the maritime transportation industry. These directions and the objectives they dictate are normally based on economics. An examination of the path followed since the 1950s shows an upward curve of progress punctuated by an occasional radical alteration in course due to economically driven changes in development objectives.

During the Second World War, demands were abnormal and considerations such as production times or availability of materials overshadowed cost. Following the War, while the industry caught its collective breath, it was the world economy which dictated the continued use and adaptation of existing power plants. Reciprocating steam, steam turbine and diesel engines continued in service for several decades. Occasionally these hastily produced power plants outlived the ships they drove and were married to hulls designed for postwar demands.

These propulsion systems of the Second World War serve as a starting point for this study of modern ship propulsion systems.

Engine manufacturers and their engineers have many objectives in their effort to produce the 'best' system. However, what they produce must compete in the race for selection with the systems developed by others. Therefore, the situation in the shipping world often amplifies one particular objective into dominance and it becomes the focus of this competition.

Up until the oil embargo of 1973–74 there was a continuing demand for faster and bigger ships which translated, for the propulsion system, to more and more power. The cost of good quality fuel when compared with capital investment, maintenance, and labour costs,

constituted a relatively insignificant fraction of operating cost. The competition for dominance between steam turbine and diesel engine was tilting towards the former. The largest boilers ever used on a ship powered the 33kt, 880ft SL7 design containership (see Chapter 4), and this seemed to be a precursor of future demand. Between 1968 and 1973, steam turbine orders increased from about one fourth to about one third of the large engine orders. The argument that the diesel could not compete with the turbine for the increasing power requirements was regularly heard.

With the sudden embargo-produced increase in the price of oil by a factor of six, fuel cost became more than significant, it became dominant. Minimising fuel consumption became the main objective, the primary concern for competition.

The operators reduced speed and new slow speed injection nozzles were incorporated to reduce fuel consumption. Engine suppliers concluded that fuel cost would never return to pre-embargo levels and it became clear that future orders for propulsion systems would be heavily based on low specific fuel oil consumption (SFOC). Economics demanded that reduced fuel consumption become the leading objective. The diesel engine, with its intermittent high temperature combustion, is well suited to high thermal efficiencies and so the diesel engine became the choice of the maritime industry.

The race for control of large ship propulsion, until recently so promising for the steam turbine, became a race for lower SFOC among diesel engine manufacturers. Rarely has a design objective been so singular and so emphatic. At the beginning of this race SFOC for the large low speed diesel was around 210 grams per kilowatt hour (g/kW/h). Since there is only so much energy which exists in a gram of fuel, there exists a lower practical limiting value which the optimum design can only approach. During the early stages, quantum reductions in consumption were possible and

The engine room of Lady Cecilia *(364 grt), one of a class of five 52-tonnes bollard pull tugs operated by Humber Tugs Ltd, Grimsby, serving the Humber area. This vessel is equipped with two Ruston 6RK270 engines, producing a combined output of 4750bhp at 1000 rpm (Ruston Diesels)*

were achieved. However, as the lower limit was approached, only marginal improvements remained possible. We have reached the point where other negative factors may rule against making small reductions in SFOC. In this period, during which the various manufacturers of low speed diesels strove toward the optimum in fuel consumption, there were technically only a few areas where change could take place. It is therefore not surprising that production differences between various manufacturers decreased and they approached great similarity. In fact, the number of distinct manufacturer designs available reduced to three: MAN-B&W, Sulzer and Mitsubishi, and in truth the operating engineer who is intimate with one will not be a stranger to the others. Consequently it would be presumptuous and unfair to declare a winner. One and then another would be first to capitalise on an area for improvement and in each case the others would quickly follow suit.

It is therefore unnecessary to follow changes and improvements of each manufacturer through this development. Though they may not have reached the same point, they have reached the same small area. Another factor which precludes calling a winner in this race is the progress made with the geared medium speed diesel engine. It is not to be ignored when considering winners. Medium speed development will be discussed after we follow the development steps of the large low speed 'cathedral' direct drive diesel engine.

The two-stroke marine diesel engine

During the early 1950s practical turbocharging came of age. This resulted in an immediate increase in engine power of between one third and two thirds over the same engine without turbocharging. It should be noted that providing effective turbocharging for a two-stroke engine was an order of magnitude more technically demanding than providing it for a four-stroke engine.

Satisfactory operation with heavier, cheaper fuels was achieved in the mid 1950s. High alkaline cylinder lubricants which could neutralise the highly acidic combustion products of the heavy fuels were developed, and this resulted in acceptable wear rates. Welding techniques, developed back in the 1940s, were applied to frames and bedplates, giving considerable weight and cost savings.

At the end of the 1950s, through the 1960s, and until 1973, the maximum combustion pressure was kept fairly constant at about eighty bars. Manufacturers made larger diameter cylinders, increased rigidity, simplified and reduced fabrication costs, improved service life, and simplified overhaul procedures. Specifically, they improved liner, valve, and piston design, facilitating cooling and extending service life. They designed for increasing the interval between overhauls, and for reducing production costs. They strained to increase engine outputs to the limit. Generally speaking, they strove to compete with the steam turbine.

Then came the oil embargo of 1973. The quantity of fuel oil consumed for propulsion of a ship had not controlled operations nor had it been a primary consideration influencing design. The dramatic increase in cost caused operators and designers to rearrange priorities and to minimise the cost of fuel oil.

The cost of fuel oil for a given marine transport operation is influenced by a variety of factors. The task of reducing this cost involves many people and is complex. However, this effort can be examined in a simple logic pattern. To reduce fuel oil cost we can use cheaper oil or use less oil. The former means designing machinery to burn poorer quality oil with similar efficiency of operation and without undue detrimental effects on machinery.

The latter is more involved. We burn fuel oil to produce power, therefore we can use less power or get more power from each gram of fuel. Using less power falls largely to the operations planner who can lower speed and plan passage with due consideration for currents and weather. The naval architect can design the hull to minimise wave resistance, apply coatings for low skin resistance, and design so that the power delivered to the shaft is used as efficiently as possible for propelling the hull. One example is to have large diameter slow turning propellers, but there is much more to this subject. It will be mentioned again later.

Getting the maximum energy from the fuel burned is achieved by having the minimum SFOC for propulsion and for auxiliary power, in combination with waste heat recovery. An attempt is made to extract, for ship needs, as much heat as possible from combustion products before their release to the environment and to use this heat energy as efficiently as possible. It is important to note that economy of operation is measured not just for the main engine but for the entire machinery package.

Currently, main engine thermal efficiencies exceed fifty per cent. To produce electrical power near this high level, generators are driven by the main engine system, using power take off (PTO) systems. Waste heat recovery can bring overall plant thermal efficiency above seventy per cent.

In addition to providing the 'best' engine and associated machinery, the supplier is obligated to turn the shaft at speeds which meet the naval architect's needs for propeller efficiency.

From the time this fuel economy challenge was presented, in 1973, industry progress has been exemplary. What is more, the engine manufacturers made this progress with imagination and innovation, but responsibly, without rash change. In fact, they continued to make strides in areas of reliability, serviceability, and maintainability while optimising SFOC and providing required propeller speeds.

The following changes were especially significant:

Piston stroke was increased giving a higher stroke to bore ratio, decreased SFOC, and lower engine revolutions per minute (rpm) for a given piston speed. The longer stroke allowed for better combustion and scavenging which in turn also reduced SFOC.

The turbocharger, which was relatively late in becoming adaptable to the two-stroke engine, was the real star of development. Change from pulse to constant pressure turbo charging gave reduced SFOC for both long and short stroke engines. It also substantially reduced the thermal load on the engine components which permitted increased cylinder output and a still greater reduction in SFOC. The importance of turbo charging has steadily increased. It now more than doubles a naturally aspirated engine's output power. While making this extraordinary improvement in engine performance, the efficiency of the turbocharger itself has increased to the point where only a part of the engine exhaust gas energy is needed to drive it. In this context, the importance of improvements in gas turbine design technology must be recognised. This 'excess' exhaust gas energy is available for auxiliary power or can supplement power to the propeller shaft.

In the period 1976 to 1982, firing pressure was increased in stages from 80 to about 130 bars; pressures as high as 160 bars have been used. Super long stroke engines became common and stroke to bore ratio went up in stages from 2.0 to about 3.8. Spurred by competition from each other, as well as from the medium speed four-stroke engine suppliers, manufacturers have made available a spectrum of engine powers and speeds covering an impressively broad range. They offer cylinder bores from 26cm to over 90cm with rpm from less than sixty to over two hundred. Selection of number of cylinders and adaptability of timing, fuel injection, etc, results in a large win-

One of the four engines installed on the catamaran Hoverspeed Great Britain *(3003 grt), built in 1990 by International Catamarans Tasmania Pty Ltd, Hobart, for Hoverspeed Ltd. The four Ruston 16RK270 diesel engines each develop 4895bhp and provide the vessel with a speed of 35kts.* (Ruston Diesels)

turbine the output of which can be added to main engine crank output or utilised elsewhere.

Propeller and hull improvements

The power delivered from the engine through the shaft is intended to drive the ship hull through the water. But how efficiently power produced by the main engine and delivered through the shaft drives the ship hull through the water is a very complex matter involving diverse actions and interactions. Consequently, there is much potential for innovation.

The bulbous bow is a well known example. The performance of a screw propeller in open water is a complex matter with endless choices including number of blades, fixed or controllable blades, lateral and axial pitch variations, diameter and revolutions per minute. Operating that propeller not in open water but close behind a hull, with the asymmetric flow pattern which the flow around a hull form inherently produces, as well as the pressure interaction between the propeller blades and the hull, give a staggering degree of variability. It also provides enormous potential for design improvement. Ducted nozzle, contra-rotating, overlapping, wheel vanes, and vertical axis propellers, as well as asymmetric rudders, and ship sterns which are not symmetric about the ship centreline are examples of areas which can produce increased speed for a given power delivered into the water.

dow of performance for each engine. This gives the buyer a variety of engine choices at his required speed and power.

The four-stroke medium speed diesel engine

As previously mentioned, the race for acceptance among diesel engine types was not limited to the direct drive slow speed diesel. However, with regard to SFOC the geared medium speed main engines were left behind for at least a decade. They never were out of the running, just behind.

A range of engines presented in 1984 by Pielstick included increased stroke and reduced SFOC. Whether they have caught or even passed the two-stroke in certain areas is a pointless argument to pursue. The geared four-stroke and the direct drive two-stroke propulsion engines can be provided with comparable SFOC values. Their differences, many of which are so fundamental that the ship designer should consider them carefully before completing design, are real and considerable. Surely these factors overshadow any fuel consumption advantage that either might argue. Which type is better constitutes an argument which will continue to be debated. The statement that difference of opinion puts the spice in the race is certainly true here. It is safe to judge that both types are improving steadily. It may not be as safe to give the opinion that one might best consider two-stroke engines where very large power is required. Where design space and clearances are a problem for the de-

signer, on a roro for example, four-stroke engines may have the edge. It is not wise to register absolute preference criteria for one type or another because each is attacking the strongholds of the other.

For example, medium speed four-stroke proponents are claiming real gains in long term reliability. High power applications are in operation. The 130,000hp diesel-electric plant using nine 9L58/64 engines to replace the boilers and steam turbines on *Queen Elizabeth 2* is one prominent example. By contrast, a 250 rpm simplified, economy designed two-stroke engine (B&Ws S26MC) came on the market in 1987.

Two major improvements

Though machinery system design improvements have been mentioned collectively under waste heat recovery, two items require additional comment. Taking electrical power from main propulsion engines offers more than improved fuel economy. Included improvements are lower acquisition cost, reduced weight, noise reduction, reduced maintenance, and space saving.

The exhaust gas power turbine is a pure benefit of design improvement. Improved engine efficiency has substantially reduced available exhaust gas energy. As the main engine itself becomes more efficient, the waste heat energy which is available for use is reduced. However, turbocharger efficiency has been so radically increased that even this remaining waste heat is much more than is needed to drive it. The remaining surplus drives a gas

The future in marine propulsion

There will be continuing improvement in both the two-stroke and the four-stroke engines in areas of reliability, simplified and reduced maintenance, and reduced overall dimensions. Competition between two- and four-stroke diesel engines will continue. In the area of SFOC it is more likely that improvement will be realised in the overall system than in the engine itself. Significant gains in efficiency are much more likely to occur with changes outside the engine room.

As previously stated, economics will determine the demands which propulsion systems will develop to meet. Continued restriction in oil supply is likely to force the return of coal energy for marine propulsion, especially in those regions which possess an inadequate supply of petroleum and which do have major coal reserves. A return to coal would not require furnace fired boilers. It would be well suited to internal combustion since liquefaction of coal is an existing technology. The conversion of coal into oil or gas calls for adding hydrogen or the removal of excess carbon. During the Second World War, Germany had twelve plants to produce synthetic liquid fuel from coal. The world-wide availability of low cost crude oil starting in the early 1950s removed the demand for these synthetic fuels. Renewed activity returned after the 1973 oil embargo. A great deal of emphasis on research and building of test facilities followed and was accompanied by plans for major production. During the 1980s, reduction in crude prices again resulted in decreased interest and investment in synthetic fuels. However, beginning in about 1983 there have been particularly impressive technological improvements. By 1988 costs had been reduced by sixty per cent and increased efficiency and cost reduction are continuing. While the clean burning synthetic fuels hold great appeal for environmentalists, it will be comparative cost which will bring them into general use, either as low cost crude is used up or as it becomes unavailable at a competitive price for either political or economic reasons.

An insufficient supply of fossil fuels could

force renewed consideration of nuclear power and resurgence of the steam turbine. The public has rejected this system in the past. However, its engineering advantages have resulted in its expanding application in military propulsion. *Savannah*, a nuclear-powered demonstration vessel, pioneered commercial service. Since then the German ship, *Otto Hahn*, and a series of Soviet icebreakers have been isolated, but successful, applications.

This past decade has witnessed a strong return to the use of the earth's wind systems for propulsion of commercial ships. Traditional square rigged sailing ships are in service. However, systems harnessing the force of the wind for assistance of mechanical propulsion have been and will continue to be of dominant interest. These applications, which have been successfully used in coastal and short-sea vessels in Europe and Japan, have now been adopted in a fleet of cruise ships.

Judicious choice of geographical areas and routes have resulted not only in fuel savings which are in excess of 30 per cent, but also in the welcome reduction of noise and vibration. Ship size does not appear to be a hindrance to effective wind assistance.

There is great variety in the approaches used for wind assistance. Included are rotors, wind sails, turbosails and kites. The promise is great. Considerable and diverse design attention has been applied.

There is no shortage of technology that can

and likely will impact the nature of marine propulsion in the next few decades. There are a number of 'ships of the future', such as the BCV 300, which are now in service. The performance of their advanced systems and futuristic arrangements provide material for a steady flow of reports. Information and control systems based on computer and satellite capabilities are heavily relies on. We can also expect high voltage electrical systems. Auxiliary power systems designed for floating frequencies which therefore are well suited to economical drive by the ship's shaft without severe restrictions on the rpm of the prime mover will become common. The Stirling Cycle may find increased application, especially with commercial submersibles. The zero resistance and levitation characteristics of super conductivity, which are currently being used in land transportation and in naval ship propulsion will be widely applied as soon as this new state of matter can be maintained above cryogenic temperatures. Further into the future, as superconductivity takes on its expected role, magnetohydrodynamic propulsion which eliminates the need for shafts or propellers may evolve from the laboratory, not only to propel submarines but also commercial surface craft. The mass production of micro motors could have an impact on power use analogous to that which its cousin the micro circuit has already had on electronics.

There are numerous novel ship types which hold promise for popular common future application. Included are very high speed surface effect ships, small waterplane area twin hull (SWATH) and outrigger configurations. Even the long discussed commercial submarine may be built. Whichever types come into common demand, power systems will be provided and will be steadily improved. Engine manufacturers have earned our confidence in their capability to deliver what is demanded.

The present status of marine propulsion is strong. The future looks challenging and exciting. One thing is certain. If the developments in marine propulsion of the next thirty years match those of the past thirty, they will be thrilling to observe.

Professor Charles E Mathieu

A modern compact diesel engine. The Ruston RK215 medium speed unit is turbocharged and charge cooled and features fuel injectors. It provides a cost-effective high power to weight ratio. It is manufactured as a 6-cylinder in-line or 8-cylinder vee form and at 1000rpm develops 1448bhp (6-cylinder) and 1930bhp (8-cylinder). (Ruston Diesels)

12

The Modern Shipbuilding Industry

SHIPBUILDING, perhaps more than any other industry, has been subject to rapid and major shifts in geographic location in recent years. Western Europe, long the core of the industry, has declined in relation to, first, Japan, and then the newly-industrialised countries such as South Korea, Taiwan, Brazil and more recently the People's Republic of China.

Characteristics of shipbuilding industries

The shipbuilding industry is characterised by a number of features. Firstly, it is essentially an assembly industry which is labour and capital intensive and, being such many of its major costs are outside the industry's direct control. Secondly, precisely because of cost consideration, the industry has gravitated towards the lowest total cost producers. Cost competitiveness has thus largely governed the geographical spread of the industry; third, the dramatic shift in the locations of shipbuilding over the past decade reflects changes of the factors confronting the industry which are affecting the operational efficiency of individual shipyards and diversification of shipbuilding enterprises. Fourth, vessel types have become increasingly specialised to serve specific trades. Also, an increasingly important part of individual yard order books are conversion and upgrading activities. Fifth, widespread productivity gains are being made in the industry, thus counterbalancing reductions in physical capacity. Vessel construction time has been much reduced by planning and the application of computers and prefabrication.

Structure of the world shipbuilding industry

World shipbuilding activity aggregated some 10.91 million grt in 1988. The global annual level varied within the 16–18 million grt range over the whole of the 1981–86 period. To set that level of activity in its proper context, however, the 1988 level represented less than one-third of that witnessed in the mid-1970s, with the volume of new vessel completions reaching a peak of over 34 million grt in 1975,' after continuous growth since the late 1960s.

Following the 1975 peak, the global shipbuilding total suffered annual declines over the second half of the 1970s – by as much as 34 per cent in 1978 – to the extent that by 1980 the overall decline equated to some 62 per cent, or over 21 million grt.

In Japan, new vessel completions have declined in volume from 17 million grt in the mid-1970s to less than 6.0 million grt in 1987 and 4.0 million grt in 1988. In Korea, total new vessel completions increased from just over 1000 grt in 1970 to over 500,000 grt in 1986, and in 1988 reached 3.2 million grt, representing 29 per cent of the global total. In western Europe, taking together West Germany, France, the United Kingdom, Spain and the Netherlands, new building completions declined from almost 7.5 million grt in 1975 to 1.0 million grt – a fall of over 86 per cent.

Shipbuilding facilities and the production process

The merchant ship is the world's largest factory-built product. Even the modest sized 26,000 dwt bulk carrier might typically contain 5000 tons of steel and 2500 tons of other components ranging from the main engine to many thousands of minor items of cabling, pipes, fur-

In the 1970s, the specially-constructed A/S Stord Verft, located at Stord on the west coast of Norway, concentrated on the building of VLCCs. During 1971–74 it built four VLCCs for Hilmar Reksten, of Norway, and in this 1972 photograph Fabian *(285,700 dwt) is fitting out whilst tank sections of the ultimately similar-sized* Julian *are in the building dock. This yard, part of the Aker Group, changed direction with the rapid decline in demand for VLCCs and went on to build specialised equipment and modules for the offshore industry. (Aker Group)*

In the late 1960s the Swedish shipbuilder Gotaverken inaugurated the A/B Gotaverken Arendal shipyard, a few miles from Gothenburg. The yard was designed specially for the construction of VLCCs, built partially under cover. Here, the 1969-built Veni *(227,425 dwt) owned by Norwegian company Peder Smedvig is about to undertake trials, whilst in the building area on the right two identical vessels are emerging from the construction sheds.* (Gotaverken)

niture and fittings. Because of their size and value, virtually all merchant ships are built to order and the construction period is anywhere in the range eighteen months to three years, depending on the ship size and the length of the order book held by the shipbuilders.

Shipbuilding production facilities must accommodate three main operations – the design of the ship, the construction of the steel hull and the outfitting of the hull with machinery, equipment, services and furnishings. These operations are not necessarily sequential and there is considerable overlap. The eight manufacturing stages are:

Design

The design, estimate, building strategy and production plans are produced by shipyard staff, initially in outline and then gradually developed in greater detail involving the production of working drawings and parts lists. Computer graphic equipment is now widely used in ship design to speed up this process and create better and more accurate information. Materials are then ordered. Developing comprehensive and accurate information at an early stage in the design programme is one of the most crucial areas for high productivity and product quality in modern shipbuilding.

The steel stockyard

The steel is ordered at an early stage in the planning of the vessel and when it arrives it is stored in the steel stockyard. The two principal steel components used in ship manufacture are plates and rolled sections, (used primarily to stiffen the plates). A modern stockyard is laid out in an orderly manner and materials are retrieved using an overhead gantry crane.

Steel shotblast plant

Steel plates and sections are retrieved from the steel stockyard and processed through the steel shotblast plant. This involves rolling plates and straightening sections to ensure that they are true, followed by shotblasting to remove rust and priming to protect the plate from further rusting and provide a foundation for paint.

Plate and stiffener preparation

The primed steel plates are cut to the precise required size using profile burning machines. Any plates that do not need cutting are transferred to the flame planer to have their rough edges removed and create the proper edge profile for welding. If required, they are bent to shape using a six hundred-ton press. Framing members are prepared from steel sections, cut to size and then bent to shape using a frame-bending machine. By this process, the many thousands of steel components for constructing the ship's hull are prepared, cut to size and numbered in accordance with the drawings. In practice, this is a flow process with a steady stream of components moving through the steel preparation bays.

Assembly

The next stage is to assemble the steel components into the 'building blocks' from which the ship will be constructed in the dock. Shaped steel is formed into 'minor assemblies', typically weighing less than half a ton. The larger plates that make up most of the hull are transferred to the panel assembly line where framing members are welded in place to form 'panel assemblies'. Finally, the minor assemblies and the sub and panel assemblies are welded together into major three-dimensional (block)

assemblies using various types of welding equipment.

Pre-outfitting

The hull must be fitted with tens of thousands of 'outfit' items such as pipes, electrical cables, switchboards, furnishings and machinery. During the various stages of assembling steelwork, advance fitting-out is undertaken. This involves the installation of as much pipework and equipment as is possible at this stage in production. To achieve high levels of advanced fitting-out requires large amounts of information, accuracy and organisation.

Assembly on berth

Finally, prefabricated sections of the ship, together with those items already installed, are lifted into the assembly dock where they are carefully aligned, then welded into position. Installations such as pipe runs are also linked up.

Fitting-out

When the hull is complete, the dock is flooded and the vessel is floated across the building dock to a fitting-out berth where the fitting-out of the ship is completed, except for those few items such as upper masts that cannot be fitted until the vessel is floated out to the riverside quay for final fitting out, and for systems commissioning to ensure that on-board systems are operating correctly, and basin (or dock) trials of the main engines.

The production process is thus essentially one of assembly, and few of the individual tasks require sophisticated technical skills. The skill comes in planning and implementing the tens of thousands of operations that contribute to the production of a merchant ship – materials must be ordered and arrive on time; steel parts, fabrication and pipework must fit accurately without the need for rework. All of this requires considerable effort at the design and planning stage along with a production capability to manage material handling and production planning.

Major advances in shipbuilding techniques have also been seen in the introduction of pal-

The hull shop of a modern shipyard. At the Hyundai shipyard at Ulsan, South Korea, one of the hull workshops has a total area of 127,754sq m and includes steel cutting, sub-assembly and panel line areas. All hull sections are cut, welded and partially assembled here prior to transportation to the building docks for final assembly. (Hyundai)

to CAM. On the other hand, advanced shipyards have been developing modelling systems for ship's structure analysis which will be the processor for a finite element method (FEM) analysis system. One of the world's leading shipyards, Hyundai Heavy Industries Co Ltd (HHI) has used the well-known *Autocon* interactive system for some years, with its suites of programmes including *Autodef*, *Autodraw* and *Autonest*, being developed by the yard. *Autocon* provides a fully integrated system for hull structure design, including lines fairing, structural drawings, nesting plans and working drawings among other print-outs.

The future would seem to lie with those who are able to develop ship designs to meet changing commercial needs; this will necessarily depend upon an increased use of computers in design and in manufacture, as well as in the management of sales, finances and operations.

A recent accelerating trend has been the grouping of shipyards, making possible a sophisticated central planning facility with immediate links with the customers, building sites, suppliers and ancillary services. Co-operation is expected to develop further across industries, such as between steel producers and shipbuilders, thus making the introduction of modern methods affordable. Shipbuilders need to respond to the operational needs of their customers in an increasingly complex environment of hull structural designs where higher

lets for material handling and the extensive pre-outfitting and painting of assemblies before installation in the ship. The application of all of these techniques may take only half the man-hours required by more traditional methods to build the same ship. It will be appreciated from this that as with ship design and operations, shipbuilding techniques at yards have undergone a revolution, and this continues.

The technological revolution in shipyards

Today, shipbuilding is achieving an integrated flow of information throughout the building process. Computer-aided manufacture (CAM), already in use in shipbuilding in some areas, is coming more into its own. Centrally generated data may be fed into controller and microsystems which control the machines used, for

instance, in cutting and punching, or in weighing and testing and in more complex tasks.

The important role computers have to play in management information must also be mentioned. Development and introduction of these systems in shipbuilding is proving costly but is leading to greater economies and tighter control of production.

Not all successful shipyards have been at the forefront of the design revolution. Some yards in Japan and elsewhere have relied upon the production of a standard and proven design and a good work-force without much recourse

Hyundai Heavy Industries Co Ltd's shipyard at Ulsan, South Korea, is an example of efficient production-line shipbuilding. At this yard it has been known for as many as thirty vessels to be in the course of construction simultaneously, from keel-laying to final stages of fitting-out. The yard, totally new in the mid-1970s and which produces all types of merchant ships, has six large and one small building dock. The largest, No 3, is 600m × 92m and is theoretically able to accommodate the building of a 1,000,000-tonner. (Hyundai)

tensile steels are more frequently required, calling in turn for minimum steel weight on economic grounds.

There is also a wide range of both specialisation and sophistication in shipbuilding today; some yards build nuclear submarines; some complex passenger ships; others relatively straightforward tankers or bulkers. In the future, shipyards might be expected to specialise even more, or to find a specific niche in the market. The development is somewhat along the lines of the car industry, where the customer has a range of standard models to choose from with a choice of extras, or the alternative of something more special.

Standard ships

From the foregoing, it will be appreciated that the shipyard process innovations based on computers, welding and prefabrication methods are attuned to the mass production of ships. It is, in turn, through series production of a few basic designs that economies of scale are most telling.

In order to fully benefit from such process innovations, standard ships are now the main products. Apart from economising on design costs, standard ships allow production economies in four areas:

1. The mass production of standard components built into the ship. Items such as winches, pumps, fans, electrical motors, controllers, switchboards, valves, heat exchange units, boilers and hatch covers all become interchangeable parts which can be produced for stock rather than purpose-built.

2. Labour-saving will flow from the reduction in the large variety of components and fittings which hitherto are manufactured to separate specifications.

3. The standardisation of hull structure allows for simplification in the steel assembly and fabrication process. The interchangeable nature of modules and sections reduces the need for skilled workers in the production trades and also simplifies the trades required in ship repair.

4. Standard ships utilise the same propulsion unit and so economies of scale can be realised in manufacture of marine engines. As with components and hull structure, interchangeable parts for the marine engineering element assist in installation at the shipyard and reduce the maintenance costs to the shipowner.

A range of standard cargo ships is regularly updated in line with shipping market trends. The current list of standard types selected from a leading shipbuilding yard would be summarised as follows: 42,000 dwt bulker; 68,000 dwt bulker; 150,000 dwt bulker; 95,000 dwt OBO carrier; 168,000 dwt OBO carrier; 105,000 dwt tanker; 115,000 dwt tanker; 254,000 dwt tanker; 281,000 dwt tanker; 40,000 dwt products carrier; 1900 TEU containership; 2700 TEU containership; 62,000 dwt liquefied natural gas (lng) carrier.

Ship finance and prices

There is no doubt that the shipping industry and the newbuilding sector in particular, needs massive capital. Newbuildings have traditionally been financed through a mixture of private and government funding. Government assistance has been provided through the medium of shipbuilding credits, either in the form of help to the yard which then offers benefits to the purchaser, or directly to the purchaser himself in the form of a favourable loan.

There are several kinds of financing for new shipbuilding. In most instances, loans broadly follow the directive of OECD in the terms offered, with 80 per cent of the purchase price covered by the loan which is taken out for eight and a half years at an annual interest rate of 8 per cent. Finance schemes are either administered through state-controlled banks, for example the export-import banks of the Far East, or through private banks to whom the government in question pays a subsidy as the difference between the fixed rate interest of the loan and the commercial rate. Banks, as well as being involved in newbuilding finance, are very active in the secondhand sector, providing significant amounts of short and medium-term funds.

Table 12/1 shows newbuilding prices for selected years. The overall escalation in shipbuilding prices can be traced to the 25 per cent decrease in global shipping capacity since the 1970s coupled with new orders from shipowners who wish to modernise their vessels and the general improvement in the freight market. Moreover, the prices for newbuildings are expected to remain at this level owing to the long lead time required to add shipbuilding capacity, the continuing expansion of world trade, and pressure from shipowners to upgrade fleets.

Hee Seok Bang

Many builders with yards located on narrow rivers, canals or inland waterways necessarily launch vessels sideways due to restricted space. Here, at Selby, Yorkshire, Cochrane Shipbuilders Ltd launch in 1982 the mini-bulker Norbrit Faith *(2387 dwt). (North British Maritime)*

Table 12/1: Representative Newbuilding Prices, 1980, 1985 and 1987–89 (millions of dollars).

Type and size of vessel	1980	1985	1987	1988	1989	% change 1988/89
30,000 dwt bulk	17	11	13	19	22	16
32,000 dwt tanker	19	18	18	23	27	17
70,000 dwt bulk	24	14	18	24	27	12
80,000 dwt tanker	28	22	24	33	38	15
120,000 dwt bulk	32	27	25	33	42	27
250,000 dwt tanker	75	47	46	63	75	19
125,000m³ lng carrier	200	200	150	150	190	27
75,000m³ lpg carrier	77	44	55	57	68	19
1200 TEU roro	44	28	27	28	32	14
15,000 dwt general cargo ship	14	12	15	17	22	29
2500 TEU full containership	–	26	32	32	41	28

Source: *Shipping Economist* (London), various issues.

13

Ship Registers and the Use of Flags

SHIPS are no different from any other mode of transport in that they must, by law, carry some sort of identifying mark in order to facilitate the safe and orderly conduct of traffic over the ocean. International law and practice demand little more of ships sailing the high seas than that they possess an identifiable nationality.[1] Ships which are unable to demonstrate a national character are, of course, liable to seizure, a principle dating back to the days of rampant piracy.[2]

The ship's flag

A ship's flag denotes the ship's nationality and thus identifies the country in which the ship is registered and the legal regime under which it operates. The types of activities, the standards enforced and the degree of regulation depends on the legal relationship between ships and the state whose flag it flies. No matter where the ship sails, the laws of the country where the ship is registered govern the vessel, the crew, all the ship's internal affairs and also indicates the point of responsibility, of how and where a right can be enforced *vis-à-vis* that ship.

The nineteenth-century treaties of mutual recognition form the basis from which many of the current maritime concepts and principles have grown. It is now a recognised principle of international law that every country or state, whether coastal or land-locked, has the legal right to sail ships under its flag. This right to prescribe conditions for the flying of a maritime flag is considered an exercise of sovereign power and, as such, must be recognised by other states.

Ships have been likened to pieces of floating territory, 'subject to no authority except that of the State whose flag it flies'. This all seems to denote some sort of ambassadorial status for the ship from which one might assume that the state would necessarily take a strong interest in the character of its envoy. Some states, though, have been criticised for not holding their ships to such standards and paying little regard to its actions.

Most shipowners are not bound to register their ships in the country in which they are domiciled – they are free to register their ships under any flag they choose, so long as they meet the registers' criteria for registration. Many shipowners are also free to re-flag ships and thereby register their ships with a different register.

Types of ship registers

All ship registers can be divided into two groups – open registers and closed registers. Any shipowner, regardless of nationality, who wishes to apply for registration and satisfies the necessary conditions can apply for registration with an open registry. Closed registers, on the other hand, restrict registration to nationals of the country.

Within the open registry grouping there are three general categories of registers, which should be viewed with the understanding that a particular nation's flag and registration requirements may share the characteristics of more than one of these categories. On one end of the spectrum are the national registers which treat the shipping company in the same way as any other business in that country. Traditional maritime countries such as France, Japan, and the United States operate national registers and thus use their merchant marines principally for their own domestic needs. These vessels are closely regulated as to safety and environmental standards and are generally owned and manned by citizens of the same country. In the centre of the spectrum are the cross-trading nations such as the United Kingdom, Norway, and Greece, which use their merchant marines primarily to carry cargoes among nations other than their own. These too are usually closely regulated and often owned, managed, and manned by their citizens.

The international open registries are located at the opposite end of the spectrum from the national registries and are operated primarily

1. B A Boczek, *Flags of Convenience. An International Legal Study* (Harvard University Press, 1962), p92.

2. *Ibid*, pp92, 93.

One of the first vessels to join the Luxemburg international ship register was the ore/bulk/oil carrier Vesalius, *built in 1983 for leading Belgian shipowner CMB. In 1991 she changed hands and entered the Luxemburg register, which now has a number of ocean-going carriers. At 135,160 dwt,* Vesalius *has seven holds and seven tanks and is capable of carrying 131,039cu m of oil or 71,650cu m of ore, or 125,671cu m of grain.* (FotoFlite)

by developing countries such as, traditionally, Panama and Liberia, and more recently, for example, Vanuatu. These countries have virtually no import/export needs for most of the shipping registered under their flags, but have been set up with the specific aim of offering foreign shipowners internationally competitive terms, as a means of earning revenue for the flag state. The terms and conditions offered by international registers vary considerably depending on the policy of the country concerned, but all aim to offer terms that are favourable to an international shipowner. For example, ultimate beneficial ownership or control by non-nationals is permitted, little or no tax on income from the ships is levied locally, and manning of the ships by non-nationals is allowed.

The United Kingdom Committee on Shipping provides a more detailed definition of an international open register. The Committee identified six features common to all international open registries:

1. The country of registry allows ownership and/or control of its merchant vessels by non-citizens;

2. Access to the registry is easy. A ship may usually be registered at a consul's office abroad. Equally important, transfer from the registry at the owner's option is not restricted;

3. Taxes on the income from the ships are not levied locally or are low. A registry fee and an annual fee, based on tonnage, are normally the only charges made. A guarantee or acceptable understanding regarding the future freedom from taxation may also be given;

4. The country of registry is a small power with no national requirement under any foreseeable circumstances for all the shipping registered (but receipts from very small charges on a large tonnage may produce a substantial effect on its national income and balance of payments);

5. Manning of ships by non-nationals is freely permitted; and

6. The country of registry has neither the power nor the administrative machinery to effectively impose any government or international regulations; nor has the country the wish or the power to control the companies themselves.[3]

The terms 'international open registers' and 'flag of convenience states' are used interchangeably to refer to ship registers that are described above. It is important to note the difference between flag of convenience states and quasi-flag of convenience states. Quasi-flag of convenience states are very similar to international open registers in that they offer practically the same financial advantages to entrepreneurs but they do not possess all the common characteristics previously noted. Dependency registers (Bermuda–UK) and offshore registers (Kerguelen–France) are considered to be quasi-flag of convenience registers. The difference is that these are national flags and while ships registered in these tax haven states and owned by companies resident there enjoy considerable tax privileges, they are nevertheless subject to the regulations of manning, safety, and certification as prescribed by their countries of origin.

In the case of quasi-flags of convenience, it is less certain than in the case of flags of convenience proper that the country under consideration or the metropolis that it is connected with will not in the long run have 'the wish or the power to control the companies themselves'. It should be pointed out that this is a difference of degree only. As Professor Stanley G Sturmey, a former UNCTAD shipping official notes, 'open registries are simply the most convenient end of the flag of convenience spectrum and there is no sharp cut-off point separating open registries from others'. However, uncertainty due to politico-economic factors seems to be greater under quasi-flags of convenience. Hence the propensity of leading flags-of-convenience entrepreneurs to establish a modern city-state (Monte Carlo, Liechtenstein, etc) where shipping capital would play the dominant politico-economic role.

The procedure for registering a vessel with an international open registry is straightforward. Generally it involves a one-time, initial registration fee and then payment of subsequent annual 'tonnage tax' rates. In exchange, the shipowner is governed by a legal, regulatory and commercial framework specifically designed to accommodate an international shipowner's needs.

These highly competitive international open registries are the product of unbridled, entrepreneurial thinking on the part of these countries. By recognising the desire of shipping enterprises in developed countries to avoid regulations about crew nationality, manning scales, income transfers, and conditions of foreign lending dictated by their national flags, and motivated by a desire to enter the international shipping industry for economic development purposes, these developing countries created shipping registers that are convenient and attractive for foreign owners, capital and crewing.

The coastal and short-sea container vessel Britta II *is beneficially owned by a German firm and placed under Cypriot registration. Amongst others, German owners have favoured 'flagging out' to Cyprus, Singapore and more recently (the 1980s) Antigua. As a result, in the 1990s a very substantial number of short-sea vessels operating in northwest Europe fly the flag of Antigua but will never see their home port.* (Roy Cressey)

The reasons why ships change flags

Throughout history shipowners have taken advantage of flag of convenience services. While this practice is associated with the post-Second World War competitive shipping atmosphere, it has been occurring throughout maritime history wherever shipowners have found it desirable or necessary to evade regulations in their countries of origin. As early as the 1770s shipowners from the Greek island of Hydra carried two sets of all ship papers and documents, one Turkish and one Russian, which were used as the occasion demanded. In times of war, shipowners who were nationals of a warring state often transferred their vessels to a neutral flag to avoid capture. In the early 1920s, Prohibition in the United States made it illegal to serve liquor on board US flag ships. A Panamanian company was formed and two United States passenger ships, *Resolute* and *Reliance*, were, with the full approval of the United States Government, transferred to the company. The ships were then registered with the Panamanian registry, sailed under the Panamanian flag and avoided all the restrictions created by the Prohibition.

Clearly, the shifts of maritime activity from one flag to another do not represent a new phenomenon. But the motivation and reasons for shifting flags has indeed changed over time. In quantitative terms alone, the number of vessels registered under flags of convenience has increased dramatically over time. In the past, the number of vessels registered under foreign

3. *Report of the Committee of Inquiry into Shipping*, chaired by Lord Rochdale (London, May 1970), p51.

There are many nations which have vessels on their ship register which are either beneficially owned elsewhere or the subject of some form of reciprocal arrangement. One is the West African former French territory of Togo which in recent years has had vessels, ultimately owned in Germany and the Netherlands, hoisting its ensign. Wadai, a modern multi-purpose cargo liner operated by DAL Deutsche Afrika-Linien, Hamburg, was put under Togo registration when completed by Warnowwerft, Warnemünde in 1983. (FotoFlite)

flags was not significant on a world-wide basis. Today, the use of international open registers is commonplace and considered by many shipowners as an essential and necessary part of this highly competitive industry.

The entrepreneurs of the last two centuries used the device of the foreign flags simply to ensure the survival of their relatively small shipping firms. It was often a very straightforward matter – if they were unable to register under another flag the business would collapse. While shipping entrepreneurs of today also consider the use of flags of convenience as an issue of necessity, the reasons are more complex and interrelated. Today they must base their decision-making in this respect on such considerations as comparative price and cost relationships, taxation structure, availability of credit facilities, and short-run political developments.

Open registers provide shipowners with many economic opportunities and services closed registers cannot. Confronted with a choice of flags under which a ship can be registered, the shipowner must weigh up the relative advantages and disadvantages of each of the alternatives. Not all registers approach this task in the same way, but they all tend to address the following areas of concern:

Tax: There are generally no taxes on profits or fiscal controls. The only tax is the subscription tax per net registered ton.

Crewing: The shipping company has complete freedom to recruit internationally. There is no requirement to employ high-wage nationals, as either officers or crew. However, regulations regarding crew standards and training may be enforced, depending on the policy of the register.

Company law: As a rule, the shipping company is given considerable freedom over its corporate activities. For example, ownership of the stock in the company need not be disclosed; shares are often in 'bearer' form, which means that they belong to the person who holds them; liability can be limited to a one-ship company; and the company is not required to produce audited accounts. There are generally few

regulations regarding the appointment of directors and the administration of business.

Safety standards: International open registries vary widely in the extent to which they enforce safety standards for the ships on the register. Some enforce high standards, while others leave safety entirely to the shipowner.

Shipowners are attracted to foreign flags because of the economic advantages afforded by lenient tax requirements, relief from the submission of tax returns and flexible insurance, maintenance and repair standards. If one was only to consider crewing requirements, the absence of high crew standards and the consequent operating costs, the use of flags of convenience clearly provides a crucial edge in the highly competitive international shipping industry. As a result of the growth of open registers, a huge market of so called 'crews of convenience' has developed made up of mainly nationals of developing countries.

Shipowners are also motivated by noneconomic considerations to register under foreign flags. History reveals that in times of war, for example, shipowners may be reluctant to be identified with a certain country. It may be necessary for trading vessels to register with particular registers in order to avoid national trade embargoes that are placed on certain countries in the event of a war or other emergency.

While many of the advantages of international open registers to the shipowner are obvious there are additional spin-off benefits. Finance houses are more willing to provide credit facilities, such as capital for fleet expansion, to the shipowner that can boast a high profit earning potential. The very nature of open registers is to provide an environment conducive to increased profit potential by way of freedom from taxation and low operating costs. The shipowner that takes advantage of this opportunity is able to borrow additional

capital which in turn provides the shipowner with a competitive edge which can only lead to increased profits. The benefits that flow from open registers are clearly cumulative in nature.

Rise of open registers

After 1945, the growth of the Panamanian and Liberian open registers exploded. Part of this growth is attributed to the registration of 'Liberty' ships by their new United States shipowners who were anxious to avoid operation under the national flag. This rapid growth, though, caught the attention of European shipowners who then questioned the legitimacy of these registries.

The issue came to a head in 1959 when the first assembly of the newly formed Intergovernmental Maritime Consultative Organization (IMCO) met in London and elected its Maritime Safety Committee (MSC). The terms of the MSC election, as stated in Article 28(a) of the IMCO constitution, required that the eight members of the committee should be the 'largest shipowning nations'. Initially the eight nations elected were the United States, the United Kingdom, Norway, Japan, Italy, Liberia, France, and West Germany. But the United States, India, Liberia (which, at that time, ranked third in world tonnage), and Panama (which then ranked eighth), argued that Liberia and Panama should have been elected instead of France and Germany because they felt the term 'largest shipowning nations' refers to registered tonnage and not beneficially-owned tonnage.

The International Court of Justice was asked to determine whether the election properly followed the terms of the 1948 Convention that established IMCO. The European shipowners argued that for a ship to register in a country there had to be a 'genuine link' between the registration and ownership, and that in the case of international open registry this link did not exist. In a nine to five majority vote, the International Court held, that by not electing Liberia and Panama to the MSC, the IMCO assembly had indeed failed to comply with Article 28(a) of the 1948 Convention. Panama and Liberia were then eligible to be elected members of the maritime Safety Committee as two of the eight largest shipowning nations.

Since the 1950s, the amount of merchant shipping registered under flags of convenience has grown – from about two per cent of total world tonnage in 1947 to forty-two per cent in 1990. The total tonnage under open registries in 1988 amounted to 220.2 million dwt and now exceeds the total tonnage registered in developed countries.[4]

Recent developments

Panama operates the world's largest shipping registry in terms of number of vessels, with more than 12,000, and the second-largest in terms of shipping capacity. According to 1990 figures published by Lloyd's Register of Shipping, the gross tonnage registered with the Liberian register totalled 54.7 million grt, compared to 39.2 million grt registered with the Panamanian register. It is interesting to note that while Panama had experienced a spectacular growth rate – 62 per cent increase in registered tonnage since 1980 – that growth came to an abrupt halt in 1990. In 1990 Panama lost about eight million gross tons. This was due initially to legislation passed by the United States which banned Panamanian-flag ships calling at US ports and then later due to stricter enforcement of regulations by the Panamanian authorities.

The *Journal of Commerce* reported on 17 January 1990, that fifty-four Panamanian vessels had re-flagged, primarily under Vanuatu and Liberian registries, but that a total of 567 ships had requested permission to leave the registry. Liberia experienced a 6.8 million grt increase in 1990 and Vanuatu doubled its registered tonnage to total 2.1 million grt. The Bahamas registry has exhibited a fantastic growth of 15,500 per cent. It has grown from 0.087 million grt in 1980 to 13.6 million grt in 1990.

Clearly, the proportion of tonnage under quasi-flags of convenience and flags of convenience proper that is operated in the tanker, tramp and bulk carrier markets is such that it cannot possibly be ignored either by firms operating tonnage under traditional maritime flags or by the governments of traditional maritime states. And, if the current set of circumstances remain the same, the proportion of flag-of-convenience tonnage in world shipping can only increase in the future.

The open registry controversy

The 1958 *Geneva Convention on the High Seas* (Articles 5, 10 and 12) and, more expansively, the 1982 *United Nations Convention on the Law of the Sea* (Articles 94 and 98) enumerated the administrative, technical, and social matters over which the flag state should exercise effective control. One of the accusations that has been levelled against international open registries is that they do not exercise such control over the vessels they register nor do they stringently enforce international rules and regulations. In fact, they simply enact very liberal registration laws and this has the effect of protecting the identity of the shipowner and operator. Critics of these registries want greater transparency in order to easily trace and identify owners so they can be held responsible for accidents, or breaches of safety or labour laws. The criticisms generally fall into four areas:

1. *Unfair competition.* Some developing countries see the open registry system as a threat to their own merchant marine fleet expansion efforts. They see open registries as unfair competition to their own efforts to foster merchant fleets because they provide developed countries, which already have the competitive advantage of established fleets and established trade routes, with low-wage crews. If open registries were eliminated, the competitive posture of the developing world fleets, in relation to the developed world fleets, would be enhanced because the advantage of low crew costs the developing world fleets have, would balance more evenly with the technological and trade advantages the developed world has.

Others, cognisant of the rapid growth in open registry tonnage, compared this to the quite modest growth rate of the developing country fleets and concluded that there was a causal connection between the two. As a result, they too wanted to see the elimination of open registries.

2. *Labour.* Labour groups such as the International Transport Workers' Federation (ITF) and the International Confederation of Free Trade Unions (ICFTU) are unhesitatingly hostile to the continuance of open registries. They say open registries allow shipowners to escape more stringent union legislation in their home countries and keep costs low by neglecting to provide adequate conditions for their crews.

3. *Oil pollution control.* The 1976 *Argo Merchant* oil spill off New England (1976) and *Amoco Cadiz* oil spill on the French Coast (1978) generated great concern and criticism of the open registry system. While responsibility for oil pumping, leaking, and spilling rests with vessels of all countries, those flying flags of convenience are often seen as presenting the most serious problem because of their relative lack of accountability, and enforcement of international standards. The major flag of convenience countries, although members of the Intergovernmental Maritime Organization (IMO) and often signatory to key IMO conventions dealing with marine pollution and liability and compensation for oil spills, have little motivation to require their registered vessels to comply. If a flag of convenience state were to establish and enforce extensive regulations regarding safety, routeing or timing of particular tanker voyages it would only serve to endanger the register's viability. This scenario was played out in 1990 when Panama lost 8 million gross tons due, in part, to stricter enforcement of regulation. Therefore, since regulation, surveillance, and enforcement measures are delegated to the flag state, some tankers flying flags of convenience can remain outside the scheme set up by IMCO conventions so that their effect is nullified.

4. *Safety.* The problem of safety is similar to the problem of oil pollution control in that it stems from the open registries' apparent inability or unwillingness to provide enforcement mechanisms for safety regulations. Indeed these states have officially acknowledged and accepted the guidelines laid down by various international safety conventions, but these formal requirements can be effective only if the registry administration actively enforces them. Enforcement of these measures is often lacking in the case of flag of convenience countries. A recurrent example is the disregard of crew licensing requirements and their consequences.

Certainly open registries are attacked for protecting unsafe vessels from liability for tanker accidents. But some contend that this attack is not always based on fact but is based on a surge of moral outrage and the attack becomes a crusade:

> But, as too often happens, crusaders in their zeal to rid the world of an evident wrong do not stop to give attention to the determination of the optimum means of attack to be adopted.

4. *Lloyd's Register – Statistical Tables 1990* and United Nations Conference on Trade and Development, *Review of Maritime Transport 1988* (United Nations, New York: TD/B/C.4/3200), p9.

Built in Belgium in 1991 by Fulton Marine, Ruisbroek, Boral Gas is one of only a few vessels registered under the Vanuatu flag which actually trade to that country. Part of the fleet operated by Australian company Boral Gas Ltd, of Sydney, this vessel, with a sister-ship and other vessels, trades in the Australasia/Pacific region carrying cargoes of lpg. (Belgian Shipbuilders Corp)

When the crusading is rampant, the end becomes of secondary importance to the means; those who disagree with the end are regarded as harmless cranks, whereas those who may accept the end but disagree with the means are regarded as traitors, because it is the operation of the crusade, not the objective, which is centre stage. The question as to whether the means adopted will achieve the stated end is taboo.[5]

Nevertheless, while the motivations for characterising open registries as a 'problem' are quite varied, there is a wide range of agreement that they are in fact problematic.

International organisations' response

There are three United Nations agencies within whose jurisdiction the 'problem' of open registries falls: the International Maritime Organization (IMO), the International Labour Organization (ILO), and the Shipping Committee of UNCTAD.

The ILO's principal interest is in maritime labour problems and it has been involved in developing conventions dealing with working conditions on board ocean-going ships, such as vacation, ship pay, pensions and hours of work. Their focus tends to be on very specific issues that are narrow and thus more manageable. As a result, they have not made any moves to deal directly with the broad open registry issue.

The Inter-governmental Maritime Consultative Organization (IMCO) originally was responsible for drafting legislation on matters relating to maritime safety and pollution prevention. IMCO never really made any effort to seize competence over the commercial aspects of seaborne trade. When IMCO was transformed into IMO, several member states felt the organisation should confine itself to techni-

cal matters and not extend its activities to either commercial, economic, or social matters.

IMO membership is comprised of primarily developed free-market countries. They heavily utilise open registries and, as such, label them as 'flags of necessity rather than flags of convenience'.[6] These members do not consider open registries to be in any way a problem. On the contrary, they characterise this facet of shipping as one of the few remaining areas of perfect competition. With these two factors in mind, it is not surprising, even in retrospect, that the IMO did not establish an early framework for controlling the registration of ships, even if it would have ultimately stymied UNCTAD's efforts.

The Shipping Committee of UNCTAD, seeing this jurisdictional gap left open by IMCO and prompted by the Group of 77 concerns regarding the shipping industry, took the initiative and began dealing with relevant problems of a commercial and/or economic nature.[7]

UNCTAD's response

UNCTAD, in response to the developing nations' demands to participate in the transportation of their own trade, developed two international conventions. The Code of Conduct for Liner Conferences[8] was adopted in 1974, and came into force in 1983, and the Convention on Conditions for Registration of Ships,[9] was adopted in February 1986 but is not yet (1992) in force.

The Convention on Conditions for Registration of Ships began as an attempt to phase out open registries and, in the process, to promote the developing countries' fleet of bulk carriers and tankers. But, after seven years of debate, it was concluded that eliminating open registries would not necessarily help many of the Group of 77 (G–77) nations in their efforts to enter the international shipping arena. Thus, the convention that has emerged tries to set minimum conditions and standards that should be applied and observed by states when accepting ships on their register. While the objective sought is good, the document itself has attracted little support.

The Convention addresses five areas of concern: the genuine link; civil and third party responsibility; transparency; labour exploitation; and safety standards. Article I of the Convention defines the objective as being to 'strengthen the genuine link between a state and ships flying its flag, in order to give more effective control of the identification and accountability of shipowners and operators especially in administrative, technical, economic, and social matters'.[10] While other international instruments have required a so called 'genuine link' to exist, the Convention filled a major gap in international maritime law, as the components of the 'genuine link' had never been identified. For the first time an international instrument now exists which defines the elements of the 'genuine link' that should exist between a ship and the state whose flag it flies.

Shannon Bentley

5. S G Sturmey, 'The United Nations Convention on Conditions for Registration of Ships', *Lloyd's Maritime and Commercial Law Quarterly* (Feb 1987), p98.

6. *Tankers and the Flags They Fly*, Exxon Background Series: Public Affairs Dept (June 1979), p3.

7. Wilhelm H Lampe, 'The "New" International Maritime Organization and its Place in Development of International Maritime Law', *Journal of Maritime Law and Commerce*, Vol 14, No 3 (July 1983), p314.

8. TC/CODE/12/Add 1.

9. TD/RS/CONF/22,7.

10. TD/RS/CONF/22,7.

Bibliography

Edited by Robert Gardiner and Roger Jordan from details supplied by the contributors.

Unlike most of the 'History of the Ship' series, this volume deals with the contemporary situation and the very recent past. This is too short a time for a body of historical or general literature to have developed, so the books listed below tend to be professional textbooks and academic studies aimed at what is a dynamic and fast changing industry. Perhaps because few books have attempted to explain the shipping revolution to the layman, modern vessels do not excite the majority of ship enthusiasts, so with the exception of the glamorous types like super-ferries and cruise liners, contemporary ships are not well served by published works on a general interest level. Very few histories of individual shipping companies are listed because although their later chapters may well cover recent developments, in spirit they belong to an earlier period; the most important will be found in the bibliography of the companion volume, *The Golden Age of Shipping*.

After a section of general works, the division of this bibliography follows the chapter order of the book, including the subsections where applicable.

GENERAL

The ongoing business of modern shipping is monitored by several periodical publications which provide the kind of statistical data the industry requires. These include Lloyd's Register's *Statistics*; the publications of the Institute of Statistical Research, Bremen; *Fearnley's World Bulk Trade* and *Fearnley's World Bulk Fleets* (Fearnresearch, Oslo); and papers from the UNCTAD Committee on Shipping.

Analysis of new developments in shipping is well covered by a number of trade magazines like *Seatrade*, *Seaways*, *Fairplay* and *Lloyd's List* (in English); *Journal de la Marine Marchand* (in French); *Hansa* and *Schiff und Hafen* (in German); and *Norwegian Shipping News* published in Oslo. More academic research is carried by the journals of *Maritime Policy and Management* and *Transport Economics and Policy*, while the technical aspects of ship design, construction and engineering are the domain of *The Naval Architect*, *The Motor Ship*, *Shipping World and Shipbuilder* and *Marine Engineering Review*.

For ship data the ultimate source is *Lloyd's Register of Shipping* (annually), but this is beyond the budget of all but companies or the largest libraries. *Jane's Merhant Ships* provided a more accessible source for a few years in the late 1980s but has since ceased publication. On the enthusiast level Ian Allan used

to publish fleet lists in booklet form for many ship types and a combined volume covering ocean-going ships survives (see D HORNSBY below); in some respects these were replaced in the 1980s by the publications of Offerpace Ltd (Grays, Essex) which include individual titles on *Passenger and Cruise Liners*, *Coasters and Short-Sea Vessels* (two vols: UK & Ireland and NW Europe), *Ocean Freighters and Tankers – British Flag*, *Offshore Supply and Support Vessels* and *British Tugs*.

A J AMBROSE, *Jane's Merchant Shipping Review*, Jane's Publishing (London; annually 1983–1985).
A short-lived attempt at a general interest annual review of developments in merchant shipping.

J BES, *Chartering and Shipping Terms*, Barker & Howard (London 1951; 9th edition 1975).

ALAN E BRANCH, *Elements of Shipping*, Chapman & Hall (London 1964; 6th edition 1989).
A comprehensive standard reference book, providing a clear, practical introduction to the complexities of modern shipping.

ALASTAIR D COUPER, *The Geography of Sea Transport*, Hutchinson (London 1972).
Gives an account of the development of routes and cargoes as well as other features of shipping during the early 1970s.

ALASTAIR D COUPER (ed), *The Times Atlas of the Ocean*, Times Books (London 1983).
The section on ocean trade is made particularly accessible by good graphics, maps and statistical tables.

FAIRPLAY PUBLICATIONS, *World Shipping Statistics* (London, annually).
Consists mainly of histograms showing, typically, number and tonnage of: world fleet by flag, and by ship type; main flags by ship type; shipbuilding order book by country of build and date; deliveries by vessel type and date.

FAIRPLAY PUBLICATIONS, *Fairplay World Shipping Directory* (London, annually).
An established yearbook with a comprehensive listing of owners and vessels world-wide and much corporate and service data.

AMBROSE GREENWAY, *Soviet Merchant Ships*, Kenneth Mason (Emsworth; 6th edition 1990).

——, *Comecon Merchant Ships*, Kenneth Mason (Emsworth; 4th edition 1990).
The best available surveys of Soviet and Eastern Bloc shipping in Cold War days and still valuable, although they predate the upheavals of the last few years.

DAVID HORNSBY, *Ocean Ships*, Ian Allan (London; 3rd edition 1986).
The lineal decendant of the many illustrated fleet lists once produced by this publisher for 'ship-spotters'. The larger ships are now gathered together in a single volume.

LANE C KENDALL, *The Business of Shipping*, Cornell Maritime (Centreville, Maryland 1973; 5th edition 1986).
Continuously improved standard work; the three chapters on tramp shipping give evidence of the assistance of Dutch shipping expert J Bes. Also excellent accounts of liner shipping and its management, particularly in the USA.

S A LAWRENCE, *International Sea Transport: The Years Ahead*, Heath (Lexington, Massachusetts 1972).
An unusually thoughtful and well researched analysis of ocean shipping during its peak postwar growth period before the mid-1970s slump. The balance between economics, technology, the regulatory framework and public policy issues is commendable.

JOHN LINGWOOD (ed), *Significant Ships of 1991*, Royal Institute of Naval Architects (London 1992).
Second year of annual review of around fifty of the most interesting new ships of the previous year. Photo, arrangement drawing and description of each ship, drawn from material in the journal *The Naval Architect*. A sister publication is *Significant Small Ships*.

LLOYD'S OF LONDON PRESS LTD, *Lloyd's Maritime Directory* (Colchester, annually).
Latest edition incorporates specifications of 34,000 vessels, including 3000 in the towage, salvage and offshore sectors, and lists of 6000 shipowners, managers, operators, maritime organisations, etc.

MARTIN STOPFORD, *Maritime Economics*, Unwin Hyman (London 1988).
A very good general textbook, well designed to provide an understanding of the various shipping markets.

INTRODUCTION

P M ALDERTON, *Sea Transport*, Thomas Reed (London 1980).
A good basic account of shipping trends in the late 1970s, shipping operations and safety at sea.

EWAN CORLETT, *The Revolution in Merchant Shipping*, Vol 10 in 'The Ship' series, HMSO (London 1981).
Although of smaller compass, this book essentially prefigures *The Shipping Revolution* and deals with the same themes, but with more emphasis on technology than economics.

R HOPE, *A New History of British Shipping*, John Murray (London 1990).
A remarkably good and extensive history, it contains an excellent chapter on the shipping revolution, as well as detailed accounts of what preceded it and what is likely to occur in the future with regard to British shipping.

H S Marcus, *Marine Transport Management*, Croom Helm (London 1987).
Covers some of the effects of technical changes on shipping management and the political dimensions related to it.

B Smith, *Merchant Ship Design since 1945*, Ian Allan (London 1984).
One of the very few attempts to explain to the layman the underlying factors determining the naval architectural development of the modern merchant ship.

S G Sturmey, *British Shipping and World Competition*, Athlone Press (London 1962).
A classic study which focusses on British shipping but has wider implications. It provides an incisive account of shipping as it entered the major period of change.

Modern Tramp Ships, Bulk Carriers and Combination Carriers

H Clarkson & Co Ltd, *The World Tanker and Bulk Carrier Fleets*, Clarkson Research Studies (London, semi-annually).
A regular listing of bulk carriers with relevant data.

Fairplay Publications, *Standard Ship Designs. Vol 4: Bulk Carriers and Tankers* (London 1985).
A review of currently available designs for dry and liquid bulk carriers.

Fearnley's World Bulk Trades, Fearnresearch (Oslo, annually).
A yearly survey of the main bulk commodity movements and an analysis of carrier size.

Fearnley's World Bulk Fleets, Fearnresearch (Oslo, semi-annually).
A listing with data of bulk carriers.

Douglas K Fleming, 'The Independent Transport Carrier in Ocean Tramp Trades', *Economic Geography* 44/1 (January 1968).

Gerald Manners, *The Changing World Market for Iron Ore 1950–1980*, Johns Hopkins University Press (Baltimore, Maryland 1971).
Bulk shipping seen from the perspective of the users, the large commodity-shipping corporations which often encourage industrial services controlled by these same corporations.

B N Metaxas, *The Economics of Tramp Shipping*, Athlone Press (London 1971).

Dan Morgan, *Merchants of Grain*, Viking Press (New York 1979).
Like the Manners book (above), a user's view of one bulk trade.

Erling D Naess, *Autobiography of a Shipping Man*, Seatrade Publications (Colchester 1977).
Fascinating revelation of the ambitions, strategies and career reflections of a very successful entrepreneur who build up what was at one time the world's largest bulk carrier fleet and who was a champion of 'flags of convenience'.

Conventional General Cargo Liners and Refrigerated Ships

Alan E Branch, *The Economics of Shipping Practice and Management*, Chapman & Hall (London 1982).
Several chapters relate to cargo liners, conferences and the container revolution. It also provides a good basic introduction to markets and management practices.

Drewry Ltd, *Reefer Container Market: Progress in the Containerised Transport of Perishable Commodities 1987–2000*, Drewry Shipping Consultants Ltd (London 1990).

Fairplay Publications, *Reefer Ships* (London 1987).
A 'Fairplay' survey of extant refrigerated shipping.

R O Goss, *Studies in Maritime Economics*, Cambridge University Press (Cambridge 1968).
Contains advanced consideration of the regulation of international sea transport, and other essays, at the early stages of the shipping revolution in conventional liner trades.

J C Maillard, 'La Flotte Bananière Français', *Cahiers d'Outre Mer* XXIII/91 (1970).

MERC, *The Market Prospect for Reefer Containers*, Maritime Economic Research Centre (Rotterdam 1990).

W V Packard, *The Ships*, Fairplay Publications (London (1984).
Good descriptions of the characteristic of liner ship designs and details of the basic components of ships.

G Sletmo and E Williams, *Liner Conferences in the Container Age*, Macmillan (London 1981).
Account of the economic changes and policy-making during the period of the shift to containerisation.

Container Shipping

P Carlsson, A Miura and T Ivarsson, 'The Third Generation of Deep Sea Ro-Ros', *Proceedings of the Ro-Ro Conference* (July 1977).

Fairplay Publications, *Standard Ship Designs. Vol 3: Dry Cargo, Container & Ro-Ro Ships* (London 1984).
A review of currently available designs for break-bulk and unitised shipping.

Patrick Finlay, *Jane's Freight Containers*, Jane's Publishing (London, annually).
Yearly reference book to the container industry's ships, equipment and services.

S Gilman, *Ship Choice in the Container Age*, Marine Transport Centre (Liverpool 1980).

B H Koch, 'Ro-Ro on the North Atlantic – the Future Years', *Proceedings of the Ro-Ro Conference* (July 1983).

J Stenberg, 'Deep Sea Ro-Ro Operations and the Future', *Proceedings of the Ro-Ro Conference* (London July 1976).

——, 'Development of the Third Generation ACL Ro-Ros', *Proceedings of the Ro-Ro Conference* (1984).

W Zychski and E Anderson, 'Recent Third Generation Ro-Ros', *Proceedings of the Ro-Ro Conference* (1981).

Oil Tankers, Chemical Carriers and Gas Carriers

BP Statistical Review of World Energy, published by BP (London, annually).
This gives a review of all the trends in oil and in the tanker trades.

H Clarkson & Co Ltd, *The Tanker Register*, Clarkson Research Studies (London, annually).
Published annually, this is a factual list of world tanker fleets giving details of the tankers currently in service.

——, *The Liquid Gas Carriers Register*, Clarkson Research Studies (London, annually).
Like the tanker volume, a yearly listing of gas carriers with their basic data.

Fairplay Publications, *Chemical/Parcel Tankers* (London; 3rd edition 1988).

——, *Product Tankers* (London; 2nd edition 1982).
Two relevant examples of the 'Fairplay' surveys of contemporary shipping types.

Stephen Howarth, *Sea Shell*, Thomas Reed (London 1992).
A history of the Shell tanker fleet under the British flag since 1892 Although devoted to one company, this history depicts the operations of a typical large tanker-owning concern, its personnel and vessels.

William H Mitchell and Leonard Sawyer, *Sailing Ship to Supertanker*, Terence Dalton (Lavenham, Suffolk 1986).
A centenary history of British Esso, with much information on their tanker activities.

Mike Ratcliffe, *Liquid Gold Ships: A History of the Tanker*, Lloyds of London Press (Colchester 1984).
This is a history of the development of the oil tanker from the earliest days until 1984.

Passenger Ships

A. Ferries

Fast Ferry International (edited by A Blunden) is a magazine dedicated to the latest developments in the expanding area of high speed ferry types.

Paul Hynds, *Worldwide High Speed Ferries*, Conway Maritime (London 1992).
A review of the current and projected unconventional ferry types – hydrofoils, hovercraft, twin hulls, wave-piercers etc – in service and on offer from the manufacturers.

Yoshio Ikeda, *Car Ferries of the World 1988*, Y Ikeda (Osaka, Japan 1988).
A world listing of all such vessels over 5000 grt active at December 1987.

RUSSELL PLUMMER, *Superferries*, Patrick Stephens (Wellingborough 1987).
A general survey of the new style ferries that are increasingly common in European waters.

B. CRUISE SHIPS

GARY BANNERMAN, *Cruise Ships: The Inside Story*, Saltaire Publishing (Sidney, BC, Canada 1976).
Although this book is nearly two decades old, it is a must for novice as well as seasoned cruisers.

H L BETH, A HADER, and R KAPPEL, 'Passenger Shipping', in *25 Years of World Shipping*, Fairplay Publications (London 1984).
A chapter in a book that describes the many aspects of shipping since the Second World War. It provides a chronology of the shift from international passenger line traffic to cruise operations by introducing ship names, dimensions and reasons for change.

MARY BOND (ed), *Seatrade Cruise Shipping Report 1989*, The Seatrade Organization (Colchester, annually from 1989).
An annual publication following Seatrade's yearly cruise shipping conference, it is composed of a series of articles, contributed by knowledgeable experts, concerning issues of timely importance.

KLAS BROGREN (ed), *Guide 87*, Plus 2 Ferry-consultation (Halmstad, Norway, annually since 1987).
A publication that contained a series of articles pertaining to the cruise industry.

CENTAUR ASSOCIATES, *An Analysis of the North American Cruise Industry*, Maritime Administration, US Department of Commerce (Washington, DC, 1980).
A dated, but informative, analysis of the North American cruise industry, with particular emphasis on the Alaskan and Hawaiian cruise markets and the potential for the expansion of the US-flag cruise industry.

FAIRPLAY PUBLICATIONS, *Fairplay Cruise Review* (London 1987).
Another compendium on the cruise ship industry. A key contribution is a description of the design and evolution of cruise ships.

LANE C KENDALL, 'Passenger Cruises', in *The Business of Shipping*, Cornell Maritime Press (Centreville, Maryland, 1983).
A chapter in a standard text on shipping. It follows the historical evolution of the cruise ship industry.

ARNOLD KLUDAS, *Great Passenger Ships of the World, Vol 6: 1977–86*, Patrick Stephens (Wellingborough 1986).
The last volume of Kludas' survey of liners over 10,000 tons is necessarily devoted to cruise ships; the earlier volumes, particularly Vol 5 (1951–76), cover earlier liners converted for cruising.

WILLIAM H MILLER, *Cruise Ships*, Conway Maritime Press (London 1988).
A ship-by-ship description of vessels built for, or employed in, cruising since 1945.

DOUGLAS WARD, *Complete Handbook to Cruising*, Berlitz Guides (Lausanne 1989).
Probably the best handbook regarding cruising.

MICHIO YAMADA and YOSHIO IKEDA, *Passenger Ships of the World 90*, Ships and Ports (Osaka, Japan 1990).
Features all large passenger ships extant in 1990.

SHORT-SEA AND COASTAL SHIPPING

KENSO DE JONG and RON TOLLENAAR, *European Coastal Fleets*, Netherlands Maritime Research Institute (Rotterdam 1985).
A research based, statistical study of the European coastal fleets and their employment. For the more technical reader.

K S GARRETT, *Everard of Greenhithe*, World Ship Society (Kendal 1991).
A fascinating history of one of Britain's leading coastal and short-sea ship owning companies with illustrations and details of all their ships from 1892 to the present day.

MAX HEINIMANN and CHRIS CHEETHAM, *Modern Rhine-Sea Ships*, Fairplay Publications (London 1987, revised 1990).
An authoritative and well illustrated study of Rhine-Sea ships with some general chapters of development and use of such vessels and full details of all ships by builder.

DAVID HILLING, *Barge Carrier Systems – Inventory and Prospects*, Benn (London 1978).
A technical study of Barge Carrier Vessels with sections on feeder and short-sea types.

STEIN OVREBO, *Short-Sea and Coastal Tramp Shipping in Europe*, Institute for Shipping Research (Bergen 1969).
Intended as an introduction for novices to the problems of coaster shipping this is a most useful guide to conditions in short-sea trades in the 1960s.

BERNARD McCALL, *Coasters Around Britain* and *Coasters in Focus*, McCall, (Barry 1989 and 1990).
Excellent collections of photographs of the whole range of vessels operating in British coastal and short-sea trades and a useful guide to the character of the many small ports they serve.

DOUGLAS RIDLEY-CHESTERTON and ROY S FENTON, *Gas and Electricity Colliers*, World Ship Society (Kendal 1985).
A comprehensive listing of the fleets of the British gas and electricity companies from the 1850s to the 1980s, together with chronologies of the companies and collier development.

DAVID TINSLEY, *Short-Sea Bulk Carriers*, Fairplay Publications (London 1984).
A comprehensive study of dry cargo shipping in Europe with sections on the trades themselves, the fleets by flag and ship design developments.

ANDREW TRAILL, *Inland Waterways – the Maritime Link*, International Cargo Handling Coordination Association (London 1988).
A technical study of barge-carrier systems, integrated tug-barge systems and low profile vessels in short-sea trades.

SPECIALISED CARGO SHIPS

There is nothing more substantial than the occasional article available on these ships, although some of the more general titles listed earlier are of some relevance.

SERVICE, INDUSTRY AND SUPPORT VESSELS

A. RESEARCH VESSELS

SUSAN SCHLEE, *A History of Oceanography*, Robert Hale (London 1975).
An account of the science of oceanography as it developed in Europe and the US from the mid nineteenth century to the 1960s.

B. SUPPORT TO THE OFFSHORE INDUSTRY

ANON, *Dayton's Guide to Offshore Supply Vessels*, Oilfield Publications (Ledbury, Herefordshire 1987).

CAPTAIN K APPLEBY, *Operating Offshore and Supply Vessels*, The Nautical Institute (London 1984).

CAPTAIN S CHAUDHURI, *The Handling of Offshore Supply Vessels*, The Nautical Institute (London 1987).

H CLARKSON & CO LTD, *Offshore Vessels Register* Clarkson Research Studies (London, annually).
A register of the vast majority of offshore service vessels of all types. In addition to considerable technical detail for each vessel, there is a list of owners and numerous statistical tables.

VIC GIBSON, *Supply Ship Operations*, Butterworth Heinemann (Oxford 1992).

VARIOUS, *Proceedings of the Nautical Institute Seminar 'Offshore Support Services – Initiatives and Developments'*, (London Feb 1992).

CAPTAIN J VENDRELL, *The Oil Rig Moorings Handbook*, Brown, Son and Ferguson (Glasgow 1985).

CAPTAIN M WILLIAMS, J S S DANIEL, and C J PARKER, *Dynamic Positioning Operator Training – Meeting the Need*, The Nautical Institute (London 1984).

C. DREDGERS

Very few general books have been written on the subject of dredgers and dredging but the following textbooks, while overly-technical for most readers, give some indications of development.

R N BRAY, *Dredging: A Handbook for Engineers*, Edward Arnold (London 1979).
This book provides a substantial amount of technical detail; it is well written, with numerous illustrations. An excellent reference book for both engineer and the non-specialist. A second edition is in preparation.

J HUSTON, *Hydraulic Dredging*, Cornell Maritime Press (Centreville, Maryland 1970).
Overall review of dredgers and particularly dredging practice. Examples are mainly from North America.

J B HERBICH, *Coastal and Deep Ocean Dredging*, Gulf Publishing (Houston, Texas 1975).
A comprehensive review (622 pages). A more mathematical treatment of the subject, especially in areas of pump theory, cavitation, gas-bearing materials, dredging methods, and sediment transport.

T M TURNER, *Fundamentals of Hydraulic Dredging*, Cornell Maritime Press (Centreville, Maryland 1984).
An examination of the hydraulic principles in dredging, concentrating particularly on the cutter suction dredger and its machinery.

F J SCHMIDT, *Complete Manual of Dredging*, McGraw-Hill (New York 1989).

D. CABLESHIPS

Apart from a few articles there is little written on contemporary cableships.

E. MODERN ICEBREAKING SHIPS

T ARMSTRONG, 'The northeast passage as a commercial waterway 1879–1979', *Ymer* (Stockholm 1980).

L BRIGHAM, 'New Developments in Soviet Nuclear Arctic Ships', *US Naval Institute Proceedings* 111, No 12 (December 1985).

——, 'Arctic Icebreakers: US, Canadian and Soviet', *Oceanus* 29, No 1 (Spring 1986).

—— (ed), *The Soviet Maritime Arctic*, Belhaven Press (London 1991).

——, 'Soviet Arctic Marine Transportation 1990', *US Naval Institute Proceedings* 117, No 10 (October 1991).

R DICK AND J LAFRAMBOISE, 'An Empirical Review of the Design and Performance of Icebreakers', *Marine Technology* 20, No 2 (April 1989).

V ZAKHARKO, *A Special Mission*, Progress Publishers (Moscow 1981).
A description of the voyage of the icebreaker *Arktika* to the North Pole in 1977.

F. TUGS

M J GASTON, *Tugs and Towing*, Patrick Stephens (Sparkford 1992).
A comprehensive new book offering a world-wide survey of the vessels, techniques and development of the towage business.

J VAN EIJK (ed), *Tugs: 3000hp and over*, Lekko VBS/ITES (Ijmuiden, Netherlands 1986).
Lists over 1700 of the world's more powerful tugs, including considerable detail about each vessel and much corporate data; well illustrated.

FISHING VESSELS

FISHERY INFORMATION, DATA AND STATISTICS SERVICE and FISHERY TECHNOLOGY SERVICE of the FISHERIES DEPARTMENT, FOOD AND AGRICULTURE ORGANISATION OF THE UNITED NATIONS (FAO), *Definition and Classification of Fishing Vessel Types*, Fisheries Technical Paper No 276 (Rome 1985).
Provides a sound compilation of all the major vessel types for the 1980s, and contains a good set of line drawings with related specifications as to vessel size and power.

J A GULLAND, *The Fish Resources of the Ocean* (London 1972).
A detailed account which provides the necessary background to understanding the resource base for the development of fisheries and fishing vessel types in the post-1945 period. The main part of the book is organised by FAO statistical areas.

P HJUL, *The Stern Trawler*, Fishing News Books (London 1972).
Provides a very detailed account of the development of stern trawlers world-wide, amply illustrated by photographs and accounts of specific vessels.

J C SAINSBURY, *Commercial Fishing Methods*, Fishing News Books (Farnham; 2nd edition 1986).
A standard practitioner's text, well illustrated by line drawings and photographs, which covers all the major gears worldwide and relates these at appropriate points to the fishing vessels involved.

D B THOMSON, *Seine Fishing: Bottom Fishing with Rope Warps and Wing Trawls*, Fishing News Books (London, 1981).
The standard work on the operation of seine nets and seine net vessels.

J–O TRAUNG (ed), *Fishing Boats of the World*, Fishing News Books (London, 1955, 1960, 1967).
This large three-volume work consists of numerous papers, which are mainly technical in nature, and cover the design, development and operation of all major vessel types from the 1940s until the 1960s. A standard work, amply illustrated by line drawings and photographs.

A VON BRANDT, *Fish Catching Methods of the World*, Fishing News Books (London; 3rd edition 1984).
This concentrates on the gears and resources which influence fishing vessel design and operation. A standard, comprehensive and well illustrated book, which covers subsistence as well as commercial fishing.

MODERN MERCHANT SHIP NAVIGATION

S F APPLEYARD *et al*, *Marine Electronic Navigation*, Routledge (London; 2nd edition 1988).

W BURGER, *Radar Observer's Handbook*, Brown, Son & Ferguson (Glasgow; 7th edition 1983).

A N COCKCROFT, 'Statistics of Ship Collisions', *Journal of the Royal Institute of Navigation* (31 May 1978).

——, 'Collisions at Sea', *Safety at Sea* (June 1984).

A N COCKCROFT and J N F LAMEIJER, *A Guide to the Collision Avoidance Rules*, Heinemann Newnes (London; 4th edition 1990).

A G CORBET, 'Development of Vessel Traffic Services: Legal Considerations', *Journal of Maritime Policy and Management* 16 (1989).

N HOOKE, *Modern Shipping Disasters 1963–1987*, Lloyds of London Press (Colchester 1988).

C W KOBURGER Jr, *Vessel Traffic Systems*, Cornell maritime Press (Centreville, Maryland 1987).

G J SONNENBERG, *Radar and Electronic Navigation*, Butterworth (London; 6th edition 1988).
Reviews the principal navigation systems from both a theoretical and practical standpoint.

MODERN MERCHANT SHIP PROPULSION

ANON, 'Decision making process for the QEs repowering', *Marine Engineering Review* (March 1986).
An interesting discussion which led to replacing the steam powerplant with four-stroke diesels.

ANON, 'Substantial fuel savings for sail equipped *Usuki Pioneer*', *Marine Engineering Review* (July 1985).
Results from 24,000 dwt bulk/log carrier on Japan to Seattle run. Follows and reinforces substantial savings reported by the first modern sail equipped *Shin Aitoku Maru*.

ANON, 'Eventful year for sail developments', *Maritime Propulsion International* (January 1986).
Refers to Southampton University symposium and includes tradition sail ships, rotors, wing sails, turbosails and kites.

ANON, 'MAN-B&W to dominate', *The Motorship* (March 1990).
Gives statistics on engines built in 1989 and comparison with 1980. lists by manufacturer, number of ships, KW, percentage of total for low speed, medium and high speed and main diesel of all types.

C GALLIN, 'Engine choice for ships of tomorrow', *Marintec Shanghai* (December 1985).
An excellent discussion of progress in design, engine alternatives and economics.

J C KENNY, 'Ship of the future – the BCV 300', *Twelfth international marine propulsion conference*, organised by *The Motorship*, London (March 1990).
Describes the whole ship concept of design. Prototype in service mid 1990, integrates the machinery selection, arrangement, and use with wholeship crew etc.

MAN-B&W, 'The MC engines – an engine programme with innovations', *Ninth International Maritime Propulsion Conference, London (March 1987)*.
An extensive description of the MC engine, engine room optimisation, test results for the 526 MC.

D PARO, 'The CNC ship', *Twelfth International Marine Propulsion Conference* organized by *The Motorship*, (March 1990).
Aspects of ships automation for one-man bridge and the engine builder's role in providing the interface between machinery and the automation system are discussed.

P S PEDERSEN, 'Two-stroke marine diesel engine developments over the past 25 years', *MAN – B&W Publications* (October 1988).
A fine paper on the stages of development from the MAN-B&W point of view for the two-stroke diesel.

K H PAETOW, 'Experiences with SCZ-ships', *Eleventh International Marine Propulsion Conference & Exhibition* (March 1989).
This 'container ship of the future' operation is analyzed. The asymetric stern design and wake distribution nozzles on this class of ships demonstrated the predicted fuel savings. Simplification was the key element in this design.

THE MODERN SHIPBUILDING INDUSTRY

DANIEL TODD, *Industrial Locations: The Case of Global Shipbuilding*, Routledge (London 1991).
A comprehensive account of contemporary shipbuilding worldwide.

SHIP REGISTERS AND THE USE OF FLAGS

B A BOCZEK, *Flags of Convenience. An International Legal Study*, Harvard (Cambridge, Massachusetts 1962).
The primary purpose of this book is to shed some light on the regulation of international competition within the shipping industry with a focus on the international law aspects of this problem. As background to this purely legal analysis the economic, social and political background circumstances surrounding the flags of Panama, Liberia and Honduras are examined.

G S EGIYAN, 'The Principle of Genuine Link and the 1986 UN Convention on the Registration of Ships', *Marine Policy* 12 (July 1988).
This article looks at the details concerning the principle of the genuine link between a ship and the flag state. It discusses this complex issue, the steps taken towards the codification of ship registration and the 1986 *Convention*.

E GOLD, *Maritime Transport: The Evolution of International Maritime Policy and Shipping Law*, D C Heath (Lexington, Massachusetts 1981).
This book examines the various marine law and policy aspects affecting international marine transport. This has been done by tracing the evolution of traditional ocean use and the rules within which it operates from its hazy beginnings to 1981, when the book was published.

HENRY S MARCUS, *Neither Guns, nor Butter: A look at National Maritime Policies*, Grant Publication (Seattle, Washington 1983).
This is a good general survey of the strategies and issues that shape national maritime policies. It provides shipowners with possible strategies for coping with these national issues and policies.It also describes the various national goals and describes the extent to which a merchant marine can help the country achieve those goals. It also identifies the different market characteristics of liner trades and bulk shipping activities.

N P READY, *Ship Registration*, Lloyds of London Press (Colchester 1991).
This provides details of procedures for registration under different types of registers.

Glossary of Terms and Abbreviations

Flag abbreviations used in tables

Alg	Algeria	Fin	Finland	Jap	Japan	Nor	Norway	SL	Sri Lanka
Aus	Australia	Fra	France	Kor	Korea, S	NZ	New Zealand	Sp	Spain
Bbd	Barbados	Ger	Germany	Kuw	Kuwait	Pan	Panama	SU	Soviet Union
Bel	Belgium	Grc	Greece	Leb	Lebanon	Pol	Poland	Swe	Sweden
Bhs	Bahamas	HK	Hong Kong	Lib	Liberia	PRC	People's Republic of	Tur	Turkey
Bm	Bermuda	Ina	Indonesia	Mex	Mexico		China	Twn	Taiwan
BZ	Brazil	Ind	India	Mly	Malaysia	PT	Portugal	UK	United Kingdom
Can	Canada	Irq	Iraq	Mor	Morocco	Ru	Russia	US	United States
DDR	East Germany	Isr	Israel	Ne	Netherlands	SA	South Africa	Ven	Venezuela
Dmk	Denmark	Ita	Italy	NeA	Netherlands Antilles	Sgp	Singapore	WG	West Germany

Compiled by Roger Jordan. This list assumes some knowledge of ships and concentrates on terms unique to this volume.

ABS. American Bureau of Shipping.

ACT. Associated Container Transportation (Australia) Ltd. A London-based container shipping company which owned its first vessels in 1969. It was originally set up by Blue Star Line Ltd, Ellerman Lines Ltd and Port Line Ltd (a Cunard subsidiary). In 1991 it was absorbed into P&O Containers Ltd.

ARPA. Automatic Radar Plotting Aids. Is the automated successor to manual radar plotting and systems are now installed on most new merchant vessels.

articouple. A Japanese pusher tug-barge system introduced in 1972. The tug sits in a relatively shallow notch in the barge stern and is connected rigidly by deck-mounted hydraulic pins which push metal 'shoes' into ratchets on either side of the barge notch. This system has been widely developed and

has applications in northwest Europe and Scandinavia.

BACAT. BArge CATamaran. A barge carrier (*qv*) system based on a catamaran hulled mother ship. The system allowed access to shallower waters but due to labour troubles its development in the UK and Europe was curtailed. The only vessel of the type had limited success as a congestion-beater in the Arabian Gulf.

ballast. Usually water, used to stabilise a vessel not carrying cargo.

barge carrier. The barge carrier was developed in the 1960s, firstly as LASH (Lighter Aboard SHip) as a strategy to maximise the benefits of inland waterways transport and in some areas to avoid port congestion. As originally conceived, barges were lifted on to a mother ship by means of a heavy-lift gantry crane at the stern and then placed on level decks. The barges would be towed by tug to estuarial, river, dock or inland load/discharge locations, and the mother ship's time in port, not at a berth, would be no longer than the time taken to discharge and re-

ceive its cargo of barges. Types included BACAT (*qv*), LASH, Seabee (*qv*) and SPLASH (*qv*).

BCV. Barge Carrier Vessel.

beam trawler. A fishing vessel employing a **beam trawl**, which is a trawl net in which the net is kept open during towing by a beam fitted to the headline.

beneficial ownership. A term applied to ultimate owners of a vessel usually under a flag of convenience. For example, a Greek company may be beneficial owner of a vessel trading under the nominal ownership of a Panamanian company and flying the Liberian flag.

BISCORE. The British Iron & Steel Corporation's ore procurement organisation, responsible for the buying-in of the Corporation's ore requirements and the chartering of vessels.

Blue Riband. Until 1934, when Mr H K Hales presented a fine trophy (the Hales Trophy), the coveted Blue Riband was entirely a nominal title awarded to the passenger ship recording the fastest passage of the North Atlantic.

bulk carrier. A cargo vessel designed for and employed in the carriage of single commodity cargoes in bulk, such as grain, ore, etc.

bunkers. Fuel for a vessel.

C types. C1, C2 and C3 type cargo vessels, with variations, were standard series cargo vessels built in the USA during the Second World War.

C10 type. A series of five containerships built for the Pacific southwest service of American President Lines, and which exceed the limits for vessels using the Panama Canal. The lack of constraints applied to Panamax (*qv*) size vessels allowed greater freedom of design which produced what is widely regarded as the most efficient containerships in service.

CAM. Computer-Aided Manufacture. In use with some shipbuilders where centrally generated data may be fed into systems which control the machines used for cutting, punching, weighing, testing, etc.

Capesize. Describes vessels which are routed via the Cape of Good Hope, being too large for transit through the Suez Canal.

cargo liner. A vessel which operates a regular scheduled service on a fixed route between designated ports and carries many consignments of different commodities. It appeared significantly after the mid nineteenth century when steam propulsion, and the opening of the Suez Canal in 1869, made international scheduled services more possible.

CARPORT. Designed in the USA in 1951 as an economy measure, this was the first tug-barge system, for use between the southern states of the USA and the Caribbean. The tug fitted like a wedge into a notch in the stern of the barge. Due to operational difficulties it was not initially successful, but was later modified under different names and became widely used.

cellular vessels. Purpose-built for the carriage of standard containers and providing a multi-deck capability using the cell guide system for stowing containers on top of each other.

cellular container system. The standardisation of container systems allowing maximum inter-carrier flexibility.

CFP. Common Fisheries Policy of the EEC (*qv*). Considers issues such as effort limitation, overfishing and allocation among member states.

closed register. Restricts registration to nationals of the country concerned.

COB. Container-Oil-Bulk carrier. A concept of the late 1980s, being a specialised carrier for the transportation of roro forest products, containers, and oil products in bottom tanks.

colliers. Carriers of coal cargoes. The term collier is an ancient one and the first recorded shipment of coal from the River Tyne was in about 1340. The first steam collier appeared in 1852. Thames 'down river' colliers, unlike the 'flatiron' (*qv*), traded mainly from the UK northeast coast to the Thames but were restricted to discharge at locations down river of London's low bridges.

Combi coaster. A multi-purpose type of coastal vessel built in series by the Netherlands shipbuilder Damen Shipyards, at Gorinchem.

combined carrier. A term applied to ore/bulk/oil and ore/oil vessels.

conbulker. Developed in the 1970s, is a vessel type which has a combined capability of carrying bulk cargoes in holds and containers in holds and on deck. As economical opportunities for this type are limited, there are only a few vessels in service worldwide.

Consol. An early navigation system, largely superseded by others such as LORAN, Decca Navigator and Omega.

CP propeller. Controllable-pitch propeller.

Danish seine. Fishing method originated in Denmark and suited to shallow waters with sandy or muddy bottom and relatively few obstructions.

Decca Navigator. A co-ordinated navigation system developed in the UK.

demersal fishery. A fishery for fish which feed on the seabed.

derrick. A long spar attached to the foot of a mast or kingpost and used for handling cargo.

displacement. The actual weight of the vessel – the weight of water displaced. When quoted for merchant vessels it is usually the light displacement, ie without cargo.

drift net. A gill net which floats just below the surface and is fastened to the fishing vessel while fishing. Both vessel and gear drift with wind and current while fishing.

deadweight tonnage. A measurement of weight, being the difference between the displacement (*qv*) of the ship when fully laden and empty, ie the actual weight of cargo, fuel, stores, etc, that can be carried.

dwt. Deadweight tons.

econship. A series of twelve large containerships built during 1983–85 for United States Lines with a large container capacity and low operational costs.

EFZ. A 200-mile Exclusive Fishing Zone, first announced by Iceland in 1979.

EEC. European Economic Community, originally loosely referred to as the Common Market.

EEZ. Exclusive Economic Zone. A band 200 nautical miles wide stretching out from the low water line of coastal states, over which those states claim jurisdiction. This covers, among other things, fishing rights in those waters and mineral extraction below it; not all countries exert full EEZ rights, some confining their claims to an EFZ (*qv*) or 200-mile territorial waters.

Empire type vessels. Term applied initially to British cargo vessels of about 10,000 dwt in the Second World War, but later encompassing a wide range of vessels, from passenger liners to tugs. Given names prefixed with *Empire*.

FEM. Finite Element Method.

flag of convenience. A national flag flown by a ship registered in that country to gain financial or legal advantage.

flatiron colliers. Flatiron colliers or 'flatties', were principally employed in carrying coal from the UK northeast coast to gas and electricity works on the River Thames. In order to pass under low bridges they were of low profile, with the minimum of superstructure. The funnel (if any) and masts were telescopic and there were no derricks on board.

float-on/float-off. A cargo handling method relying on the submersion of the mother ship by ballasting.

fly dragging. Seine net fishing method developed mainly in the 1930s in Scotland and which gradually replaced the inshore small and to some extent long line fishing. The gear suits operation in deeper water on relatively restricted patches of sandy bottom surrounded by rocky or hard bottom.

FOC. Flag of convenience.

Fort type. A series of standard construction general cargo vessel of about 10,400 dwt, built in Canada during the Second World War. Given names prefixed with *Fort*.

Fortune Type. A Japanese developed standard type of multi-purpose cargo carrier of the 1970s and of about 20,000 dwt.

FPC. Forest Products Carrier. Designed to carry forest products such as sawn timber and transported in large rectangular units. This type of cargo required large, square, smooth sided holds. FPCs are usually self-sustaining with gantries and cranes for loading and discharge.

Freedom type. A Japanese designed and built 'Liberty replacement' type general cargo vessel with similar general capabilities to the SD–14.

G class. A large series of containerships built in the 1980s for Taiwan shipowner Evergreen Marine Corporation.

GATT. General Agreement on Tariffs and Trade. An international agreement (1947) to promote freer trade through the phased elimination of tariffs, preferences and quotas by its 108 (1991) signatory nations. It is estimated to cover about 90 per cent of international trade.

German Liberty. A German 'Liberty replacement' type designed in the late 1960s.

GLONASS. A global satellite positioning system developed in the USSR.

GPS. Global Positioning System. Developed in the USA.

GRT. Gross Register Tonnage. The internal capacity of a vessel. Although the word ton is used it is not an expression of weight, but of cubic capacity (100 cu ft = 1 ton). Open decks and the like do not form part of a vessel's gross tonnage, although deck cargoes may be carried. It is widely accepted that the origin of the word ton in this context is tun, being a measure of capacity of a certain cask of wine.

handy size. Chartering market term applied to bulk carriers in the 25,000–40,000 dwt range.

ICHCA. International Cargo Handling Co-ordination Association.

IMCO. Inter-governmental Maritime Consultative Organization (1954); the predecessor of IMO (*qv*).

IMO. International Maritime Organization, based in London, is a United Nations agency which provides machinery for co-operation among governments in respect of technical matters concerning international shipping, maritime safety and prevention and control of marine pollution from ships. It also drafts international maritime conventions.

inshore fisheries. The fisheries of the continental shelf waters. A commonly used, but misleading, term which also covers areas often long distances from home ports.

INTERTANKO. International Association of Independent Tanker Owners. A forum for independent (non-oil company) tanker owners and covering about three-quarters of the world fleet falling into this category.

ITB. Integrated Tug-Barge system. *See also* CAR-PORT and tug-barge system.

IWC. International Whaling Commission.

jumboising. Increasing a vessel's cargo or passenger carrying capacity by inserting a new hull section.

klondyking. The practice of buying fish directly from fishing vessels and shipping the cargoes directly to market without landing at an intermediate fishing port.

Ladoga **type vessels.** A series production low-profile type of cargo vessel built in Finland for the USSR from 1972.

LASH. Lighter Aboard SHip. *See under* barge carrier.

Liberty replacement. Term applied to the various general cargo vessels designed in the 1960s specifically to replace the remaining Liberty and similar tonnage vessels dating from the 1940s. Liberty replacements included the SD–14 and Freedom types.

Liberty type. A series production standard type of general cargo vessel of about 7200 grt, of which 2710 were built in the USA during the Second World War.

lift-on/lift-off (lolo). Conventional lifting-on and lifting-off of cargo.

line fishing. A generic term which includes long line, hand line and trolling. Long line fishing involves laying stationary lines on the bottom, mid-water or below the surface and hauling these at intervals. Hand line fishing involves hand-held lines operated at any depth, along a vertical plane. Trolling involves towing relatively short lines just below the surface.

Lloyd's Register of Shipping. The oldest and largest of the ship classification societies. It has its origins with the Lloyd's of London insurance market, but during the 1830s became a separate organisation. The Register Book of Lloyd's Register of Shipping, published annually with monthly supplements, contains details of the majority of commercial vessels over 100 grt, and all vessels with a Lloyd's Register classification. Other classification societies include American Bureau of Shipping (USA), Bureau Veritas (France), Germanischer Lloyd (Germany), Nippon Kaiji Kyokai (Japan), Det Norske Veritas (Norway) and Registro Italiano Navale (Italy).

lng carrier. A carrier of liquefied natural gas – about 80 per cent methane – which is derived from natural gas with most of its impurities removed. It is carried at sea by cooling to a temperature of $-162\,°C$.

LORAN. LOng RAnge Navigation. A co-ordinated navigation system developed in the USA.

lpg carrier. A carrier of liquefied petroleum gasses, the most common being propane and butane. These can only be carried at sea in a liquefied form achieved either by cooling or by pressure.

lumberjack system. A tug-barge system developed for use in the Philippines newspaper industry and introduced in 1974.

MARPOL. The International Convention on Prevention of Pollution from Ships. (1983).

MCC. Medium-sized Crude Carrier. Loosely applied to crude carriers of about 130,000 dwt–170,000 dwt which came into favour following the reopening of the Suez Canal in 1975. The canal was quickly enlarged to take tankers of up to 170,000 dwt. Latterly includes vessels up to 200,000 dwt.

MFV. Motor Fishing Vessel. A class of vessel built for the Admiralty as naval auxiliaries during the Second World War, but designed to be used for commercial fishing after the war.

MIDA. Maritime Industrial Development Area. First emerged in the 1960s in which large scale industrial developments, such as oil refining, iron and steel, power generation, were coupled with dedicated port facilities. The Europoort area close to Rotterdam is a prime example, and other large developments were at Antwerp, Marseilles and Dunkirk and to a lesser extent the Tees and Humber in the UK.

Mini-bulkers. A loosely used term generally describing a bulk carrier engaged in coastal or short-sea trading.

MSC. Maritime Safety Committee. Set up by IMCO (*qv*) and intended to consist of the eight largest maritime nations.

NIC. Newly Industrialised Country.

NRT. Net Register Tonnage. This is gross register tonnage (*qv*) minus the space occupied by crew, engines, navigation equipment, bunkers etc. Broadly speaking, the space available for carriage of cargo or passengers – the earning capacity of the vessel.

OBO. Ore/Bulk/Oil carrier and ore/oil carrier. See combination carrier.

Ocean type. A standard type of general cargo vessel of about 7150 grt and of which 60 were built on the US west coast for Britain during the earlier years of the Second World War.

OCL. Overseas Containers Ltd, London. A British container shipping company which owned its first vessels in 1967. It was originally owned by Peninsular & Oriental Steam Navigation Co (P&O), Ocean Transport & Trading Ltd and British & Commonwealth Shipping Co Ltd, and Furness Withy & Co Ltd. In 1986 ownership passed solely to P&O and the company title was changed to P&O Containers Ltd.

Omega Navigator. A global co-ordinated navigation system.

OPEC. Organization of Petroleum Exporting Countries.

open registry. Is available to any shipowner, regardless of nationality, which can apply for registration subject to satisfying the necessary conditions.

otter trawl. A bag-shaped net in which the net opening is kept open during towing by two otter boards or trawl doors placed on either side and ahead of the net by warps.

Panamax. The maximum size of vessel, by virtue of its breadth, which can transit the Panama Canal.

Park type. A series of standard construction general cargo vessels of about 10,400 dwt, built in Canada during the Second World War. Given names with the suffix *Park*.

PCTC. Pure Car and Truck Carrier. Vessel designed solely for the drive-on/drive-off carriage of cars and trucks; often with roro project cargo capacity.

pelagic fishing. Open sea fishing.

PTO. Power Take Off.

purse seining. A method of encircling fish using a large stationary net drawn together at the bottom by a purse line, while the top of the net in maintained at the surface by a large number of floats.

Racon. RAdar responder beaCON. Device used to help both the detection and identification of important navigational marks such as light vessels, which might otherwise be confused with ships at anchor when detected by radar.

Radar. Said to derive from RADio detection And Ranging. Electro-magnetic device sending out pulses and timing the return of the echo giving location.

reefer (refrigerated) vessels. Vessels in which cargo carrying space is largely or wholly refrigerated.

roro. Vehicular roll-on/roll-off cargo handling method by way of vessels' doors and ramps.

Rudder propellers. An example of this is the Schottel type which takes the form of a conventional propeller which is steerable through 360° in much the same way as an outboard motor. In some applications these units are mounted in the normal position at the stern, and in others, usually as a pair, are mounted under the hull.

SD–14. A standard type of general cargo vessel designed and built in the UK, and under licence in Greece and Brazil, as a 'Liberty replacement'. Originally conceived at 14,200 dwt, on a laden draught of 28ft 6in and with a speed of about 14kts.

Seabee. A barge carrier (*qv*) type designed and built for Lykes Lines, New Orleans, in the 1970s.

seiners. A term applied to fishing vessels which operate purse seines or seine nets (*qv*).

seine net. A bag-shaped net with two wings, made from relatively lightweight mesh, used for fishing on the seabed, by means of towing.

semi-container ship. Vessel with a combined container and break-bulk general cargo capability, seen as a flexible alternative to the cellular system on routes to developing countries.

SFOC. Specific Fuel Oil Consumption.

shelter-deck. A structure above the principal deck; not regarded as part of the enclosed hull for tonnage purposes. Shelter-deck vessels became popular in the 1950s providing owners with a higher cubic capacity on the same gross tonnage.

Single Buoy Mooring (SBM) and **Single Point Mooring (SPM).** Mooring points at the end of a pipeline in deep water some distance from the shore. They were developed to overcome the lack of ports and oil terminals with water deep enough to accommodate tankers in the VLCC and ULCC tonnage range.

SINS. Ship's Inertial Navigation System.

SL7. A series of steam turbine container vessels built for Sea-Land Service Inc in the early 1970s. They had a large container capacity and a service speed of 33kts.

SOLAS. International Convention on Safety of Life at Sea (1980).

sonar. Sound navigation ranging echo-sounder device used for measuring distance from bottom of ship to seabed.

SPLASH. Self-propelled vessels employed in feeder services for LASH (*see* barge carrier) vessels. Introduced between the UK and Middle East in the late 1970s.

spot movement. Chartering of vessels, usually tramps, dictated by immediate availability of cargoes.

stern trawler. A fishing vessel in which the trawl gear is shot over the stern, rather than over the side (**side trawler** or, colloquially, **sidewinder**).

stevedore. A person employed to load or unload ships.

sto-ro. A roll-on stowage method in specialised vessels, accessed by side doors and ramp, with fork lift trucks carrying, on pallets, cargo for the stowage space.

Suezmax. The maximum size of vessel, by virtue of its draught, which can transit the Suez Canal.

Sunderland type. A term loosely describing a type of vessel sought by a British mission to the USA in 1940. Its purpose was arranging the urgent building of cargo steamers and had as its basic plan those of the British steamer *Dorington Court*, built in Sunderland, and of about 10,000 dwt.

SWATH. Small Waterplane Area Twin Hull. Advanced form of catamaran.

T2 type. A US-built standard type tanker (525 were built) from the Second World War. Propelled by turbo-electric machinery, of about 10,400 grt.

TEU. Twenty-foot Equivalent Units. The measurement of standard containers in international shipping. A 40ft container equals 2 TEUs.

tonnage. *See* deadweight, displacement, gross register, net register.

tramp. As distinct from the cargo liner (*qv*), the traditional tramp is a vessel which is built to go anywhere and pick up any type of cargo which is available, often at relatively short notice.

Transit Satellite Navigation. A so-called hyperbolic navigation system using about five operational satellites following relatively low-lying polar orbits.

trawler. Originally a fishing vessel operating a beam or otter trawl. The trawl is often applied generally to vessels operating towed gear, including seine net (*qv*).

tug-barge system. Conceived in the USA as an

economy measure to transport high capacity cargo with the minimum of crewing costs. Used extensively, originally in the US, where units of 40,000 dwt are not uncommon. *See also* CARPORT.

turbocharger. A supercharger consisting of a turbine driven by exhaust gases of an engine.

ULCC. Ultra Large Crude Carrier. A 'development' of the VLCC (*qv*) and first appearing in the 1970s. The term is applied to crude oil tankers of over 300,000 dwt.

UNCTAD. The United National Conference on Trade and Development. Its general objective is the reduction in disparity between rich and poor countries. Amongst the activities of its shipping division has been assistance given to developing nations in achieving more control over the shipping services operating to and from their ports.

VCM. Vinyl Chloride Monomer.

VHF. Very High Frequency radio telephony.

Victory type. A standard series-built general cargo vessel built in the USA during the Second World War. A total of 531 were built , of which 414 were cargo vessels and 117 were a military transport variant. They were about 10,750 dwt and had a speed of 16kts.

VLCC. Very Large Crude Carrier. A breed of crude oil tanker first appearing in the mid-1960s and applied to such vessels of about and over 200,000 dwt.

VLF. Very Low Frequency radio waves.

whaleback. A curved deck placed above the main forecastle deck on certain classes of fishing vessels.

whale catcher. A small hunting vessel equipped with a harpoon gun operated in conjunction with a whale factory ship in the open sea.

Appendix: Types of Vessels

Barge	Semi-submersible pipe-laying barge	Bulk cement carrier	Container/pallet ship	Cement carrier
Accommodation barge	Pipe laying barge	Bulk phosphate carrier	Container/part refrigerated	Dry cargo ship
Log tipping barge	Articulated barge	Bulk carrier ore strengthened	Container/ore carrier	Steel products carrier
Chemical barge		Bulk timber carrier	Container/trailer ship	Pallet ship
Drilling vessel	Bulk carrier	Bulk carrier, self unloading	Container/rail car carrier	Wood-pulp carrier (under 12,000 dwt)
LPG barge	Bulk/Fuel Oil carrier	Bulk vehicle carrier	Dry cargo – beach landing	Part refrigerated vessel
Bulk cement barge	Bulk coal carrier	Bulk wood-pulp carrier	Coal carrier (under 12,000 dwt)	Wood chip carrier (under 12,000 dwt)
Oil barge	Bulk/container carrier	Bulk bauxite carrier	Multi-purpose (container capacity)	Timber carrier (under 12,000 dwt)
Dump barge	Bulk Dolomite Carrier	Bulk slurry carrier	Sand carrier	Phosphates carrier (under 12,000 dwt)
Propelled semi-submersible barge	Bulk salt carrier	Bulk wood-pulp/sulphuric acid carrier	Salt carrier (under 12,000 dwt)	Vehicle carrier
Crane/derrick barge	Bulk fishmeal carrier		Fishmeal carrier (under 12,000 dwt)	Slurry carrier (under 12,000 dwt)
Self unloading barge	Bulk sugar carrier	Container ship	Cargo barge	Bauxite carrier (under 12,000 dwt)
Non-Propelled semi-submersible barge	Bulk wood chip carrier	Container/dock ship	Heavy lift vessel	
Oil storage barge	Bulk limestone carrier	Container Feeder ship	Limestone carrier	Ferry
Vehicle barge	Bulk gypsum carrier	Container/barge carrier	Barge carrier	Container ferry
Work barge	Bulk nickel carrier	ontainer liner	Livestock carrier	Ferry/cargo vessel
	Bulk sulphur carrier	Container (bulk) oil carrier	Cargo liner	Car/passenger/trailer (container) ferry

Harbour ferry
Train/vehicle ferry
Ferry/pallet carrier
Train ferry
Vehicle ferry
Excursion ferry
Lorry ferry

Dredger
Dredger/anti-pollution vessel
Bucket dredger
Cutter suction dredger
Dragger dredger
Gravel dredger
Hopper Suction dredger
Grab dredger
Dipper dredger
Cutter dredger
Sand loading dredger
Tin dredger
Grab/bucket dredger
Training Suction Hopper Dredger
Rock breaking dredger
Suction dredger
Training suction dredger
Suction dredger/waste disposal
Semi-submersible cutter dredger

Icebreaker
Icebreaker-buoy-tender
Icebreaker/lighthouse tender
Icebreaker/research vessel
Salvage vessel
Search and recsue vessel
Fisheries training
Training vessel
Radar training vessel
Sail Training Vessel

Cable ship
Cable ship/icebreaker
Cable repair ship
Product/ore/bulk/oil carrier
Ore/bulk/oil
Oil/bulk/container vessel
Tanker/heavy lift vessel
Ore/oil/slurry carrier
Bulk/oil carrier

Anti-pollution vessel
Buoy tender
Supply/Anchor handling vessel
Oil rig supply vessel
Maintenance Vessel
Tug/anchor handling vessel

Tender
Harbour tender
Passenger tender
Lighthouse tender
Pilot tender
Pipe carrier
Tank cleaning vessel
Offshore supply/tug
Navigational aids vessel

Ore carrier
Ore/oil carrier
Ore carrier (under 12,000 dwt)
Ore/oil carrier (under 12,000 dwt)
Ore/coal carrier
Ore pellet carrier
Oil transfer vessel
Ore carrier, self-unloading
Ore/vehicle carrier

Passenger/container vessel
Passenger/cargo vessel
Passenger liner
Passenger/train/vehicle vessel
Passenger vessel
Passenger/pallet carrier
Passenger/part refrigerated vessel
Cruise liner
Passenger/car carrier
Seismic research
Geophysical research vessel
Fisheries research
Fisheries protection vessel
Research vessel
Polar research vessel
Research and submarine rescue

Oceanographic vessel
Satellite tracking ship
Survey ship
Weather ship
Exhibition vessel
Survey/research vessel

Refrigerated vessel
Refrigerated container vessel
Fruit ship
Fish carrier
Refrigerated meat carrier
Refrigerated pallet vessel
Refrigerated trailer vessel
Polar support/supply vessel
Supply/buoy tender
Coastguard inspection vessel
Spent Nuclear Fuel carrier

Degaussing vessel
Submarine tender
Icebreaking supply ship
Supply ship
eplenishment tanker
Support ship
Patrol vessel
Reefer/supply vessel
Service vessel
Store ship
Logistics vessel
Platform elements carrier

Tanker
Asphalt tanker
Bitumen carrier
Chemical tanker
Acid tanker
Ammonia tanker
Sulphuric acid carrier
LPG carrier
LNG carrier
LPG/ammonia carrier
Solvents carrier
Bunkering tanker
Chlorine tanker
Molasses tanker

Crude oil carrier
Parcels tanker
Chemical/oil tanker
Products tanker
Sulphur tanker
Water tanker
Phosphorous carrier

Vegetable oil tanker
Wine tanker
LPG/chemical tanker
Ethylene tanker
Tank barge
Tug/barge unit
Berthing tug
Tug/Fire float
Harbour tug
Icebreaking tug
Tug/passenger tender
Tug
Pusher tug
Salvage tug
Tractor tug
Waste disposal vessel (liquids)
Incinerator and waste disposal vessel
Deep sea mining vessel
Pile driving vessel
Repair ship
Sludge carrier
Mud carrier
University ship
Diving support ship
Pipe layer
Work ship
Yacht
Self-elevating oil rig
Fixed platform drilling rig
Oil well stimulation vessel
Drilling rig
Oil drilling rig
Emergency support vessel
Semi-submersible oil rig
Work rig

Source: W V Packard, *The Ships*, Fairplay (London 1984).

Index